MOONQUAKE

by
Alan Binder

Dale
I hope you
enjoy this
story

Other books by Alan Binder

NONFICTION

Lunar Prospector: Against All Odds

See excerpt at the end of this book.

Moonquake

Published by Ken Press
Tucson, Arizona USA
(520) 743-3200
Kenpress.com

Copyright ©2008 by Alan Binder

Cover design by Geoff Godwin

ISBN 1-928771-25-4
ISBN 13: 978-1-928771-25-8

PRINTED IN CANADA

For Rebecca and Tom

PREFACE

The impetus for writing this story was the destruction of the Space Shuttle Columbia high in the Earth's atmosphere over Texas in the early morning of February 1, 2003. That morning I was putting the final touches on my book, *Lunar Prospector: Against All Odds*[1], the history of the Lunar Prospector Mission, the lunar orbit mapping mission I defined, developed, and eventually guided to the Moon. The book tells the story of Lunar Prospector from its beginning in late 1988, through the end of its highly successful lunar orbit, mapping mission on July 31, 1999, to the conclusion of its final phase — the numerical reduction and archiving of the data on December 31, 2001. One of the main purposes of the Lunar Prospector book is to show the American taxpayers, who foot the bill for the NASA space program, just how poorly NASA and the big aerospace companies manage and conduct the American space program.

As I watched the TV coverage showing Columbia disintegrating into numerous, meteor-like pieces, I was certain, as was the case in the Challenger disaster 17 years earlier, that 7 astronauts and a Space Shuttle had been sacrificed on the alter of NASA's arrogance, managerial incompetence, and bureaucratic moribund — as the final accident report, which came out seven months later, proved.

As I absorbed the far-reaching impact of the disaster, I realized NASA had handed me a second, and much needed way of exposing its incompetence. As is documented in *Lunar Prospector: Against All Odds*, I demonstrated via Lunar Prospector that space missions can be done "Faster, Better, Cheaper" when a competent scientist, rather than NASA, is in charge. However, Lunar Prospector was an unmanned, lunar orbit mapping mission, not a manned mission, and so its impact was small. Also, the NASA bureaucracy ignored Lunar Prospector's programmatic success, since its

---

Note: [1]Ken Press, (520) 743-3200, ken@kenpress.com. Also see Lunar-research-institute.org, Amazon.com, and bookstores

own efforts to do missions in the "Faster, Better, Cheaper" mode resulted in several costly failures, the most notable being the twin Mars Mission failures in late 1999. NASA was not about to admit that an outsider, and worse, a NASA critic, could do something it could not do.

Though I hope the Lunar Prospector book will have a wide enough readership so my success with the mission will improve the way the US conducts its space program, I realized the morning of the Columbia disaster that a science fiction story, based on solid engineering and solid lunar data, would be a second way for me to expose NASA's ineptness and calloused indifference to the engineering and scientific data that would have prevented the Challenger and the Columbia disasters. I sat down that afternoon and began writing this novel.

In writing this story, I drew on my 43 years of experience as a lunar and planetary scientist, a spacecraft systems engineer, a mission director, and a Lockheed employee at the Johnson Space Center (JSC) doing Manned Lunar Base and Manned Mars Mission design studies. As you, the reader, will see, *Moonquake* is based on A) studies of the Apollo Seismic Network data by Dr. Yosio Nakamura, one of the members of the Apollo Passive Seismic Team, B) my own studies of the stresses that cause the tectonic moonquakes found by Yosio and the thrust fault scarps caused by the moonquakes, and C) both Yosio's and my concerns that we do not know the *lunar seismic risk factor* and that NASA should have long ago set up a global network of seismometers to define it[1, 2].

Further, all the historical events described before May 2004 are real and all the pieces of space hardware — the Delta 4 rockets, Space Planes, Aerobraking Vehicles, Orbit Transfer Vehicles, Lunar Base habitation and laboratory modules, Lunar Rovers, etc. — described are realistic, i.e., they exist or have been designed or have been studied in detail. Similarly, all the

Notes: [1]Appendix 1; [2]Selene, ein Mondlandungsprogramm mit unbemannten Sonden [Selene, a Moon landing program with unmanned probes], Project Leader, Alan Binder, Universität Kiel, Kiel, Germany, 1977

details of the Moon — its surface features, resources, environment, and its tectonic moonquakes — are real. Thus, the story is about a realistic moonquake and its disastrous effects on a fictitious, but realistic crew at a fictitious, but realistic lunar base. Though fiction, this story could happen as written.

Not only are the engineering, lunar science, and story-line realistic, but some of the characters and institutions are real. Both Dr. Yosio Nakamura and I are in the book as ourselves, as are my two Tucson, Arizona, based companies — my science oriented, non-profit, tax-exempt Lunar Research Institute (LRI) and my lunar spacecraft engineering firm, Lunar Exploration Inc (LEI)[1]. The various US and German universities mentioned in the story are also real.

Also, I have named several of the cameo characters in the book after four of my friends and colleagues. They are: John Gruener and David Weaver, the astronauts who fly the rescue mission to save the survivors of the moonquake — in reality, two of my close friends and colleagues from our days back at Lockheed and JSC; Buddy Nelson of *KCBS Radio*, San Francisco, the first reporter to ask a question at the Crew Press Conference — in reality, Buddy Nelson of *KCBS Radio* and the Lockheed PR person who has been totally supportive of my efforts to do the Lunar Prospector Mission and to push for the commercialization of lunar exploration; and Dr. Mark Maxwell, MD, one of two MD's who provide medical advice to the survivors of the moonquake while they are on the Moon waiting to be rescued — in reality, my family physician in Tucson.

In addition to thanking the above friends and colleagues for letting me use their names, I also thank Dr. Maxwell for his patient review of all the medical issues and procedures I describe in the book. However, any medical errors in the book are totally my fault.

I also thank Dr. Taber MacCallum for his knowledgeable discussion of the suitability of a 50/50% mixture of oxygen and nitrogen at 0.3 bars pressure for the Base's atmosphere I use in the book and have long proposed for real lunar bases.

Note: [1]See Lunar-research-institute.org and Lunar-exploration.net

I thank my charming, beautiful, and patient wife, Rebecca, for reading and correcting the manuscript more than once and for dressing the characters in the book, for, like Karl, I have little use for clothes — except to keep warm and out of jail.

I also thank Dr. Joe Staples, Laurie Weaver, Tom Polette, Jason and Nancy Bowels (I had not met Nancy before writing the story, but she is the exact image of Maria in the book), Rick and Joyce Corbell, Chuck Wood, Tad Theno, Richard Godwin, Ken Graun, and Chip Proser for reading the manuscript and giving me their very constructive criticisms.

Finally, I thank Chuck Wood for helping with the lunar illustrations.

I remind the reader that all of the other characters in this book are fictitious, as are all of the events describe after May 2004. Thus, any other similarities to persons, living or dead, or to actual events are purely coincidental.

Finally, I hope you will enjoy the story and will come away with an appreciation of the Moon's beauty and the potential of its resources for the benefit of humanity. I hope to show that we have the capability, knowledge, and much of the hardware needed to build a Lunar Base right now, how such a base could be built and — most importantly — the fact that NASA has failed to provide the nation with a viable space program that has a return on investment and hence, that much of the national space program needs to be put on a commercial basis and taken out of NASA's bungling hands.

Alan Binder, PhD
Lunar Prospector Principle Investigator,
Director, Lunar Research Institute,
CEO, Lunar Exploration Inc.
Tucson, Arizona
April 2004

PROLOG

July 21, 2005, 6:30 PM CDT

Bill Huff, standing in front of his charcoal grill in the backyard of his Nassau Bay, Texas, home, was drenched in sweat from the killer combination of 97% humidity and 39° C temperature, the latter being considerably augmented by the heat from the grill. In addition to the nearly unbearable heat and humidity of a south Houston, July evening, the omnipresent mosquitoes from the swamps and bayous around Clear Lake were eating Bill alive. He was waiting for the Whites from next door, a young couple who had recently joined the Johnson Space Center science staff in Building 31 as post-docs, and his old friend and mentor, George Barker, who lived in nearby Seabrook, to arrive. To the side of the grill was a platter of Texas sized T-bone steaks, just waiting to be thrown on the hot grill.

Finally, Nancy called from the kitchen, where she was busy "fixin' the rest of the fixin's" as they say in that part of Texas, "Bill, George is here and the Whites are coming across the lawn. I'll give them something cool to drink and send George and Sam out to keep you company."

Hearing that, Bill threw the steaks on the hot grill and they immediately began to sizzle. By the time the men had exchanged greetings and had made a few derogatory remarks about the weather, hot grease from the cooking steaks was falling on the glowing embers, creating smoke that helped keep the mosquitoes away.

George opened the conversation to the hot topic of the day, "Well Bill, what do you think of Bush's announcement yesterday in light of the Atlantis disaster? Do you think his scaled down Lunar Base Initiative will fly? You know, President Bush and Congress are mad as hell that NASA lost another Shuttle and crew just 2 years after the Columbia disaster and some on the Hill want to shut NASA down completely."

Since George's well-known contempt for NASA was every bit as great as Bill's, Bill wisely said, "Let's leave that topic until we're in the air-conditioning, away from these damned mosquitoes, and have had our fill of steak. I'd rather talk about the Astros' last game, if we don't and I get caught up in the conversation about NASA, these steaks could get burned to a crisp."

George laughed and nodded and the conversation turned to the Houston baseball team's lousy showing over the entire summer, a topic that itself almost caused the steaks to become charcoal, had it not been for Sam's vigilance.

After a leisurely dinner of salad, steak, and baked potatoes, the group adjourned to the living room, with light, cool drinks in hand, to address Bush's latest proposal to save NASA after its decades long series of disastrous failures. Like many other excellent people who were deeply committed to the American space program, George, Bill, and Nancy had left NASA out of frustration as it continued its downward spiral into incompetence and bureaucratic moribund that started at the end of the Apollo Program.

After they had gotten comfortable, George reopened his favorite topic, bashing NASA, with a few choice comments about NASA's incompetent management. Since Sam and Joyce White were both young and new to NASA, they were quite puzzled at George's caustic attitude. Sam asked, "I don't understand why you think NASA is falling apart. This is a dangerous and difficult business and accidents are bound to happen. I think NASA has accomplished a lot since Apollo and Bush is doing the right thing by having NASA concentrate on a Moon base."

Nancy retorted, "Wait until you've been around NASA as long as we have and then you'll know what's wrong and why the space program has gone nowhere since Apollo."

George opened his mouth to start his usual tirade, but Bill beat him to it, "Before George starts ranting and raving and puts you two completely off being at NASA, I'll give you the short version of George's lecture, or we will be here all night."

George said, "Ok, ok, have it your way, but I reserve the right to correct you when you're being too kind."

Bill laughed and replied, "What, me be too kind to NASA? You've got to be kidding," and Nancy choked on her drink, but nodded vigorously.

As Bill slapped Nancy on her back to help her recover, he said, "If you go back to Apollo, you'd find that the best and the brightest, like old George here, answered the call to put man on the Moon and Congress was more than willing to grant NASA all the money needed to salvage the nation's pride — that is, until the Apollo 1 fire in '67. When Grissom, White, and Chaffee died, the opponents of the program, who had been quiet until then, used their deaths as an excuse to chip away at the program."

George interrupted, "Yeah, I had just joined NASA at Huntsville, where von Braun was developing the Saturn 5 and the program was in turmoil. The public was asking, 'Is going to the Moon worth killing 3 guys? Why in hell are we going there anyway, just to beat the Commies?' The guys I had just started to work with said nobody in NASA, not even at the highest level, had an answer, except, 'Kennedy told us to do it,' and that was no answer at all."

Bill slid back in the driver's seat, "Worse, as soon as Apollo 11 got back to Earth in July of '69, the public asked, 'Ok, we beat the Commies. Why are we wasting money going back to the Moon with more missions?' and NASA didn't have a clue. Your science colleagues tried to come to the rescue with a bunch of scientific reasons, but President Nixon, Congress, and the public had no interest in science. So NASA terminated the program and abandoned the Moon after Apollo 17 in December of '72. And that was the beginning of the decline of NASA."

Nancy broke in, "Bill and George will try to convince you that the termination of Apollo was all due to NASA's stupidity, but there was plenty of stupidity to go around and there were two external factors that helped kill Apollo. You must know, the social unrest caused by the civil rights movement and the growing Vietnam War detracted from the purely politically motivated Apollo program."

George injected, "Damn it Nancy, I've told you enough times, those were side issues. The Apollo fire worried NASA, but after the Apollo 13 accident, NASA management was scared to death about losing a crew in space. They wanted to stop the program while they were still ahead of the game, despite the scientist's pressure to continue and to use the assets — already bought and paid for — to continue exploring the Moon. It just pisses me off that 3 of those 4 remaining Apollo 5's are lawn ornaments at NASA field centers — the one here at JSC, the one at Huntsville, and the one at the Cape. If NASA hadn't chickened out and we had continued with upgraded Saturns, using solid fuel strap-ons, we would have had a base on the Moon by the eighties. But no, NASA was too dumb to press its case with the President, Congress, and the public and we threw away the Saturns, all the rest of the hardware, and all the hard lessons learned and now we're sitting here over thirty years later, getting ready to start all over again. Damn it, that's just bullshit. Pardon my French."

Bill jumped in, "What George says is true enough, but the scientists were to blame, too. Instead of realizing there were political and budgetary issues, the Apollo scientists wanted more and more time between each mission so they could understand the data, study the rocks, and plan each successive mission to maximize the science return.

"An Apollo flew every 2 to 4 months through Apollo 12, but the time between missions increased to 8 months by Apollo 17. The scientists just didn't understand they were cutting their own throats — the high cost of keeping the huge army of mission support people around during those extra 4 to 6 months between each mission was helping to kill the program. Management, which was not interested in science anyway, said, 'To hell with those damned scientists, this is costing too much.' And that was just one more nail in the Apollo coffin.

"If your predecessors had realized, with so many unexplored regions on the Moon, it would have been better to send missions to the Moon as fast as possible, rather than taking forever trying to squeeze the last drop of data from each mission, you guys would have had 4 more missions. So, you see, there was plenty of stupidity to go around, as Nancy said."

Noting that Sam and Joyce were a little overwhelmed by the barrage of negative comments, Nancy asked, "How about dessert? I have a Baskin Robbins ice cream cake. Anyone interested?" She immediately got four positive responses.

Despite Nancy's attempt to give Sam and Joyce a little breathing time, Bill was on automatic pilot and hardly missed a beat, "NASA not only killed Apollo, it also started to commit a slow suicide. As soon as the program was over, many of the German rocket scientists, who had been responsible for the success of the program, were suddenly denounced because they had served Adolf Hitler and were sent back to Germany. Then, a lot of the other top notch engineers and managers were unceremoniously given the boot. Of those left — except slow learners like George here — many saw the handwriting on the wall and quit. As a result, NASA entered the post-Apollo era with second- and third-rate people filling its ranks and it began to decay. Though there were some guys like George, who were too stubborn or too dedicated to leave, and though fools like Nancy and me joined NASA, not knowing what we were getting into, NASA just continued its slow collapse."

George added, with a mixture of pride and sadness, "Yeah, but I was smart enough to eventually get out, as were you guys. You know what I always say, the reason there are so few good people in NASA is — the good people leave, ASAP."

Nancy arrived with a tray full of dishes of ice cream cake, forks, and napkins and everyone dug in. Since George and Bill were busy stuffing ice cream in their mouths, Sam took the opportunity to ask, "What about the Shuttle? It was a brilliant technological achievement, despite the accidents. Don't you think Nixon and NASA were correct in developing it after Apollo was over?"

Nancy, Bill, and George stopped eating for a moment in stark disbelief and George jumped at the bait like a hungry mountain lion. Completely forgetting his ice cream, he answered, "The Shuttle was a good idea, but it was not properly done. In order to get it funded, NASA promised the American taxpayer and Congress that a small Shuttle fleet would dramatically reduce the cost of getting to orbit, there would be a Shuttle flight every 2 weeks, and it would be just like using a commercial airplane. In order to get wide support, NASA tried to make the Shuttle do everything for everyone and ended up satisfying no one.

"When Columbia finally flew in April of '81, it was years behind schedule and cost 40 billion. Only 25 Shuttle missions were launched during the next 5 years. That flight rate was 5 times lower than NASA had promised and the cost per mission was between 500 million and 1 billion dollars. Far from reducing the cost to get to orbit, the Shuttle was the most expensive way to get there. And unlike commercial airplanes, the Shuttles were refurbishable, not reusable. So nothing NASA promised was delivered and the program was so expensive it drained the NASA budget every year."

Nancy added, "It was even worse than that. Since the cost of each mission was a budget buster, NASA didn't have money to buy spare parts. When a Shuttle landed, the ground crews often had to take components out of it and put them in the next one to be launched. But NASA was desperate to keep Shuttles flying as often as possible, so nobody would notice it had failed to deliver anything near what it had promised, and NASA management, hiding behind PR hype, just pushed on.

"And then — and I'll never forget it, I had just joined NASA — on that ice cold day in January of '86 — Challenger was preparing to launch, even though icicles were hanging from the gantry. Any idiot could see it was too cold to launch and it was against NASA's own mission rules to launch at such low temperatures. But NASA had a civilian teacher on board and it needed to get the Challenger launched to keep up appearances. So despite the dire warnings of the Morton Thiokol engineers, NASA's management pressured Morton Thiokol's management to override their engineer's recommendations and give NASA the green light to launch. NASA got its green light and, as you well know, 72 seconds after liftoff and 17 kilometers above the ocean, 1 of the 2 solid fuel booster rockets burned through its casing and Challenger exploded in a fireball."

Though everyone knew the details of the Challenger disaster, Nancy's telling it as she had experienced it, caused everyone to relive that fateful day and they were all silent for a few moments, as their uneaten ice cream melted into puddles.

Bill was the first to recover from their reverie and said angrily, "The disgusting part is, to salvage its own hide, NASA immediately lied, saying the 7 astronauts had not suffered, but had died instantly in the explosion. In reality, the 7 crewmembers were killed only when their intact cabin hit the ocean nearly 3 minutes after the explosion. The fact that the crew was alive during that death plunge came out months later. Challenger, which was caused by the criminal decision of NASA managers to launch, was one giant leap down NASA's road to total failure and I think some of them should have gone to jail."

George nodded and said, "Instead of that, and instead of NASA taking a good look at itself and really paying attention to the Challenger accident report, NASA just swept Challenger under the rug and pushed on with its newest boondoggle — the Space Station. One of NASA's justifications for developing the Shuttle was that it was needed to build a Space Station — NASA has a habit of justifying its current boondoggle by saying the hardware is needed for its next boondoggle. President Reagan bought the idea and announced in January of '84 that NASA would build a Space Station in 5 years for 8 billion. But it wasn't until 15 years and 40 billion dollars later, that the Russians, who NASA had to pay to help build the International Space Station, launched the first component, with another estimated 40 billion to go. Now that's real management."

Nancy broke in, "It was apparent to the three of us by the late eighties that the Space Station was in a downward spiral of increased costs and delays, so we began talking about getting out of NASA. But then, on the 20th anniversary of the Apollo 11 landing on the Moon, the first President Bush announced the Space Exploration Initiative and rekindled our spirits. The SEI was to breathe new life into NASA by putting man back on the Moon permanently and going on to Mars. With a Presidential goal like the 1961 Kennedy proclamation, NASA began planning a Manned Lunar Base/Manned Mars Mission Program. However, NASA's plan was so astronomically costly, Congress did not give it a second thought and, since President Bush thought his job was done once he had made his pontifical pronouncement, the SEI quietly withered away before it even left the paper study phase. That was when we decided to quit NASA."

Joyce interjected, "That's sad. You guys clearly love the space program. You must have hated leaving. Didn't you think there was any way you could have stayed?"

Bill answered in frustration, "Look, not only did we see that NASA was falling apart, so did Congress. Two governmental committees where established, the Stafford and Augustine Committees, to determine what to do about NASA and the future of the space program. Unfortunately, rather than dissolving NASA, which was one option, the Committees recommended that NASA reform itself and commercialize as many aspects of the space program as possible. You can bet the entrenched NASA bureaucracy resisted those suggestions with every bit of energy it could muster."

Nancy added, "But you're right. We didn't want to leave and we did stick it out a couple of years after the SEI was dead."

Bill continued, "Yeah, though the NASA bureaucracy successfully resisted change, Dan Goldin, the NASA Administrator at that time, tried very hard to make the necessary changes. One of his promising and innovative new ideas was the Discovery Program, whose motto was 'Faster, Better, Cheaper' and in which the missions were to be proposed by — and carried out by — the scientists themselves, with financial support from NASA."

George interjected, "Yeah, it was a good program — too bad NASA destroyed it."

Bill, unaffected by George's interruption, rattled on, "At first nobody outside Headquarters knew about the proposed Discovery Program. And totally independent of NASA, a Lockheed scientist, Dr. Alan Binder, who worked on the SEI planning at JSC, and a small group of volunteers decided to do their own lunar orbit, mapping mission he called Lunar Prospector. I heard a talk he gave at JSC and he said, since NASA had abandoned the Moon and since all NASA planetary missions had grown in size to the point were they cost 1 billion dollars or more, there was a desperate need to show that good science could be obtained by small, inexpensive missions and accomplished in a short time. Dr. Binder also said the only way the US was going to have a meaningful space exploration program, which provided a return on investment to the American taxpayer, was to commercialize space exploration and he wanted to demonstrate that lunar missions could be done commercially, without NASA."

Sam said, "Yes, we know about Lunar Prospector, but I didn't know it was started outside NASA. I thought it was a NASA mission from start to finish, though I knew it was selected as NASA's first competitively selected Discovery Mission. I also knew it proved the 'Faster, Better, Cheaper' concept, since the entire mission cost just 65 million dollars, the spacecraft was built in just 22 months, and Binder flew a near perfect, 19 month, orbital mapping mission starting with its launch in January 1998."

George replied, "Yeah, but I'll bet you didn't know Binder proved you could do missions 'Faster, Better, Cheaper', only if — as he emphasized — only if NASA got out of the way. That rankled NASA, but Binder's point was driven home in '99.

"I'm sure you remember NASA lost the 1 billion dollar Mars Observer Mission in '93. The mission was lost because of poor management and poor engineering. What you might not know is NASA tried to do the next two Mars missions, the '99 missions, in the 'Faster, Better, Cheaper' mode. But as you surely know, NASA lost both the Mars Climate Observer and the Mars Polar Lander within 71 days of each other in late '99. Both failures were again due to inexcusably poor engineering and the lack of any real management.

"Mars Climate Observer was lost because Lockheed Martin used English units in its analysis of the tracking data and NASA used metric units — each without the other side knowing it. As a result, the incoming trajectory to Mars was a few tens of kilometers lower than planned and the orbiter burned up in the Martian atmosphere rather than doing an orbit insertion burn. The Mars Polar Lander and its two penetrator probes were lost because they were never properly tested and failed sometime during the Mars atmospheric entry and landing phase.

"The failure of those 2 NASA-run 'Faster, Better, Cheaper' missions, led to a House Committee on Space investigation and to the end of NASA's own attempts to do 'Faster, Better,

Cheaper' missions. Binder testified to the House Committee and said unless NASA was completely reformed, the failures would continue. But the NASA bureaucracy was not willing to reform and Congress was not interested in trying to make it reform — so it was back to business as usual. You ought to read Binder's testimony to the House Committee in the Congressional Record[1] — I have."

Nancy added, "You might also read Dr. Binder's book on his mission if you want to get a detailed account of how it was accomplished and all the problems he had with Lockheed and NASA trying to get it done right. Here, this is Bill's autographed copy of *Lunar Prospector: Against All Odds*[2]," and she handed Sam the book.

Bill said, "Dr. Binder was not alone in his judgment of NASA. Almost everyone outside of NASA, most of whom were ex-NASA employees, like the three of us, were convinced NASA was heading towards more disasters as it continued to resist making any of the changes necessary to get it back on the right track. Unfortunately, we were all correct. The destruction of Columbia and the loss of its crew of 7 during its reentry into the Earth's upper atmosphere over Texas on the morning of February 1, 2003, proved us all too correct.

"I'll never forget those television images of Columbia breaking apart into dozens of meteor-like pieces. Though in my heart, I knew NASA had screwed up again, I hoped against hope that the disaster was just a tragic accident. But as the accident investigation moved forward, it quickly became apparent that NASA management ignored the signs that Columbia had been mortally wounded by insulation falling off the external tank during its launch. The accident was caused by the same combination of NASA arrogance, overconfidence, and incompetence that has plagued the agency since the end of Apollo.

"The worst part is, as the accident committee said, the same management failings that led to the Challenger acci-

---

Notes: [1]See Lunar-research-institute.org; [2]Ken Press, (520) 743-3200, ken@kenpress.com. See Lunar-research-institute.org, Amazon.com, and bookstores

dent, led to Columbia and they feared NASA would again
ignore the need to reform and there would be another
Shuttle disaster for the same reasons. To the many critics of
NASA, the Columbia disaster was the beginning of the last
gasps of NASA — but a giant bureaucracy, even a mortally
wounded one like NASA, dies very slowly."

Sam interrupted, "But as I understand it, President Bush
and Congress took the Columbia disaster to heart and realized that NASA was in big trouble and was leading the space
program nowhere. Isn't that why Bush announced the new
Lunar/Mars Initiative in January 2004, to save NASA and to
give the agency some direction?"

Nancy answered, "Yes, you're right. I'm sure there were
political reasons, too, but I believe he really wanted to save
NASA and the space program. And he seemed to understand
that lunar resources could benefit humanity on Earth and
enable us to push further out into the solar system. He was
also correct in wanting to have the commercial sector do a lot
of the effort for profit, rather than have NASA do it all at taxpayer's expense. However, as you must know, there were a
lot of critics of the new Bush space plan, not only from most
Democrats, but from some Republicans, too. They didn't see
where the money was going to come from."

Bill slipped back into the conversation, "Then, last March,
when just 1 of the 2 solid fuel rockets ignited at launch and
Atlantis, with its crew of 5, cart-wheeled off the launch pad
and was destroyed, the Shuttle Program and NASA's control of
the never-to-be-finished International Space Station Program
both came to an abrupt end. Once again, a Shuttle and a crew
were lost because NASA management would not listen to its
engineers and delay the launch, just as the Columbia Accident
Committee had feared would again happen. Instead of waiting until 2010 to retire the then 3 remaining Shuttles, as Bush
proposed in his January '04 speech, the 2 remaining Shuttles
were permanently grounded right then and there and the
never-to-be-finished Space Station was turned over to the
Russians, who, right then, had the only means of getting crews
and cargo to it. What a waste of more than 40 billion American
dollars and what a display of NASA's bungling."

George put the final touches on the conversation, "And that brings us to yesterday's announcement. Unfortunately, Bush ignored the cries of the space community and the American public to replace NASA with a purely commercially based, civilian space program, but he did respond to Congress' criticism that his Lunar/Mars Initiative was too expensive and decided to give NASA one more chance. As we all heard yesterday, he cut down his earlier proposal and told NASA just to build a lunar base. However, nobody I know outside NASA thinks NASA has a snowball's chance in hell of doing the job."

When George finished, both Sam and Joyce were at a loss for words and looked a little dazed. Noticing that, Nancy came to their rescue, "Well, enough of our complaining about NASA. There are other things in the world besides the space program to talk about."

Joyce wisely took the opportunity to escape and said, "Right, but it's late and we have to get to work early tomorrow, so I think we'll fight our way back home through the mosquitoes. We had a great time, thanks for the invitation."

George also took the hint and said his goodbyes.

After they left, Bill turned to Nancy, gave her a big hug, and said, "Well, I wonder what will become of Bush's lunar base. Will NASA succeed or will this be the end of NASA?"

Part One
PLANNING
THE FRA MAURO
LUNAR BASE

Chapter 1-1
The Call

July 22, 2005, 8:45 AM CDT

The next morning, shortly after Bill arrived at his engineering consulting company in Clear Lake, the telephone rang. Bill answered and heard the voice of his old friend Harry Caldwell. After exchanging greetings and a couple of banal comments about the July weather, Harry said, "The NASA Administrator asked me to call you, figuring you would not hang up on me without hearing me out."

Bill groaned, "Oh no, now what?"

"Here's the story, Bill. When Bush approached Congress a few weeks before his new Lunar Base speech, Congress agreed, but with several conditions. First, NASA has to keep within the Base's budget that Congress has set at no more than 20 billion. Second, the Base has to be operational by the 45th anniversary of the Apollo 11 Moon landing — in no more than 9 years. Third, unlike the International Space Station fiasco, the Lunar Base Initiative has to be solely an American effort. Fourth, again, unlike the Space Station, NASA has to define a simple plan and carry it out, without its usual modifications, additions, and growth. If NASA fails to meet these requirements, both the Lunar Base Initiative and NASA will be closed down," then Harry paused to wait for Bill's reaction.

Bill responded to the pregnant pause. "So far so good — what's the catch?"

Harry responded slowly. "You're the catch. Congress said NASA has to get you back to lead the effort."

Bill was struck dumb for a few moments and when he recovered, he asked, "Is Congress crazy? NASA hates my guts. They'll never accept my running the program."

"NASA has to — and already has. They have no choice. Congress and the President have no confidence in NASA, not after Challenger, Columbia, and Atlantis. They want a top notch engineer from outside NASA, who is critical of NASA and who will keep NASA's feet to the fire, or it's no deal."

"What if I say no?"

"There's a short list of acceptable engineers who the President and Congress will accept, but they made it clear, they want you to run the show."

Bill thought a few moments and asked slowly, "If I accept, will I have total authority to run the program and to choose my upper-level engineers and managers?"

Harry answered very carefully. "Hypothetically, yes. But you know NASA will fight to keep as much control as possible. I know you understand the politics. There are many Democrats who want to see Bush's initiative fail and will back NASA against you if you push too hard. So you'll have to compromise, how much, I don't know. That will depend on how many allies you can find in Congress and in NASA itself. Bill, this will be no cakewalk, but people in high places think you can do the job, and for what it's worth, so do I. You know this is important."

Bill let out an audible sigh. "I want to talk this over with Nancy and my boys. How soon do you need an answer?"

"A couple of days — a little longer if necessary, but don't take more than a week."

"Ok."

Harry added, "One more thing, and I think you'll like this. If you can hack it old man, Congress and the President want you to be on the first crew to go to the Base to check it out and get it operational. How's that for a kicker?"

Delighted, Bill answered, "That sounds great to me. I just hope Nancy doesn't have a conniption fit when I tell her that part."

"Me too. Well, give me a call ASAP. Bye."

Bill put the phone down absentmindedly, got up from his desk, left his office, told his coworkers he was going to be gone for the day, and drove the few kilometers to his home.

Chapter 1-2
Getting Started

August 1, 2005, 8:35 AM CDT

Ten days later, Bill walked into his new office in JSC's Building 1, after having spent a day going through all the rigmarole necessary to rejoin NASA, and told his new secretary on the way in, "June, I want a meeting with all the senior staff members who have been assigned to me at 1:00 sharp. Tell them I want to layout my tentative work plan and then I want a private interview with each of them, starting right after the meeting. Could you give me a list of them and set up a schedule for the interviews, a half-an-hour for each should do, ok?"

June answered, "I'll get right on it."

August 1, 2005, 1:00 PM CDT

Bill walked into the meeting room at exactly 1:00 and found nearly a dozen-and-a-half-men and women, only a few of whom he knew, seated and waiting for him. Bill was pleased that everyone was on time, but their body language and expressions clearly showed the majority of them resented his being forced on them by Congress.

Since the best way to defuse such a situation is to immediately take charge, Bill opened the meeting with, "There are two principles I work on, 'KISS — Keep It Simple Stupid' — and, 'If I wanted it tomorrow, I'd ask for it tomorrow.' Keep those two things in mind and we'll get along fine. The clock is ticking and we have no time or room for error.

"Numerous lunar base plans were developed during the SEI days. Go dig them out. We're going to choose the simplest one and I'm going to present it to Headquarters in a week to 10 days. If it's accepted, we're going to get to work on it. We have 12 months to modify it, but only where absolutely necessary to account for changes in technology and hardware that have occurred since the plan was drafted, and to develop an accurate budget and an accurate schedule.

At the end of those 12 months, we are going to have a polished and verified lunar base program we can accomplish within the time and budget constraints set by the President and Congress."

While Bill was talking, three in his audience were whispering among themselves and chuckling. When he finished, Bill looked directly at them and asked, "I assume you three already know how to do this, right?"

Without even the slightest trace of embarrassment, the ringleader said, condescendingly, "Yeah, Bill, we can do this without any outside help."

Bill replied, "Well, I'm glad you three are so competent you don't need my help. But unfortunately, I am running this program and since you don't need my help, you can find another program to work on where your considerable talents will be of more use than they would be to me."

Stunned, all three sat there for a second and then one of the other two said, "Hey, we didn't mea—— "

Bill cut him off, "You're done here. I don't need you on this program."

The ringleader got up and said haughtily, "Fine with me," but his two cohorts looked dejected as they left the room.

Bill said, "Anyone else want to leave?" and one more person got up and left with a look of disgust on his face.

Bill continued, "Ok, do any of the rest of you have any questions? — No. Good. If one of you still here is Marshall, you're the first on my list, please come to my office. I'll see the rest of you at your appointed times. June will notify you of the — ah — revised schedule of interviews."

Over the next few days, Bill interviewed the remaining staffers, told four more to find other assignments, and interviewed a number of others to fill out his staff.

During that time, his growing staff reviewed the numerous SEI lunar base scenarios and picked three to present to Bill for his final selection. After two days of reviews and discussions, Bill settled on the one he felt would get the job done, presented it to JSC's Director, and, with the Director's blessing, flew to Washington to present the preliminary plan to NASA Headquarters.

August 9, 2005, 9:00 PM EDT

Bill's reception at Headquarters was proper, but distinctly cool. After presenting the Base's preliminary architecture to the Administrator and his top aides, Bill said, "In addition, there are some important unknowns about the Moon and its resources we need to investigate before we can commit to the Base's final design and to determine where to locate it. For example, we need to know if the hydrogen deposits at the poles Lunar Prospector mapped are water ice or just enhanced deposits of solar wind hydrogen. And, I'm told we need to get more seismic data to understand the seismic risk factor. So, I — "

The Administrator interrupted, "I'm sorry to interrupt Bill, but due to the stringent financial and time restrictions, we have decided to forego any new unmanned exploration missions. Besides, our science advisory committee assures me we have enough information from Apollo, Clementine, and Lunar Prospector to plan and locate the Base. I'm sure the scientists who are telling you they need more data are just using the program as an excuse to get more missions for pure science. We want that, too, but only after the Base is finished and operational. After that, there will be plenty of time and money for science."

Since NASA's survival depended on the Base being done on time and on budget, there was little Bill could say against the Administrator's arguments. Nevertheless, Bill's expression revealed how uneasy he felt about the cavalier dismissal of the need for more data. But a good manager knows he has to carefully pick which battles to fight and which to forego, and Bill was a good manager, so he reluctantly let that one go.

Bill switched topics, "We have just begun to lay out the construction schedule and it looks like we can build the Base with 2 crews of 4 men over a period of — "

The NASA Administrator interrupted again, "Uh, Bill — I had assumed somebody at JSC told you we are going to build the Base tele-robotically. That will save time and money and we won't risk human lives during the construction phase."

Bill was dumbfounded and speechless for a few moments. "Pardon me, but that's just crazy. You can't build something as complicated as a lunar base tele-robotically. You have to have humans there to see that it's done properly."

"That's not correct and you know it. Humans didn't build the Space Station — each new section was sent up and docked with the existing structure. We can do the same thing on the Moon."

Bill, perplexed at the naiveté of the Administrator, who was neither an engineer nor a scientist, rather a career government bureaucrat whose upper level managers were feeding him BS, retorted, "The Space Station was a free-flying structure in zero-g, where aligning and securing the modules was relatively easy. The Base will be built in a trench on the lunar surface at ⅙-g. Aligning and sealing the junctions will be difficult. Also the Base will be buried under several meters of regolith, ah — lunar soil, for radiation protection when it's finished. That means we can't get to any of the junctures and seals to fix any leaks once the Base had been buried. No, building the Base tele-robotically is just asking for trouble and maybe a disaster."

Reddening, the Administrator said sharply, "NASA has spent considerable time and money developing tele-robotic capabilities. We are not going to waste that effort when we can utilize it to our advantage and prove to Congress that the money was well spent."

Clearly angered, Bill opened his mouth to reply, but the Administrator beat him to it, "Everybody out — I want to talk to Mr. Huff alone."

Without a word, but with the scraping sound of hurriedly moving chairs, the upper level lackeys speedily left the room.

As soon as the door closed, the Administrator said in a cold, threatening tone, "I know you think because the President and Congress forced me to bring you back to run the program, you can do what you want and get away with it. But as far as I am concerned, you're a turncoat who has been stabbing NASA in the back for years. I'll tolerate you as long as I have to, but if you don't get in line with agency policies, I'll go to the President and Congress, backed up by all my staff, and prove you're a detriment to the program and get you thrown out. There are many good NASA engineers who can do this job and who believe in NASA. So you can and will be replaced, if you don't cooperate. Do I make myself very clear?"

After a few moments of silence, Bill answered in a measured tone, "Yes, I fully understand the situation and I will do what is necessary to get the job done right."

The double entendre was not lost on the Administrator, who retorted, "I truly hope you do, but, just in case you don't, don't go running to some of the NASA bashing members of Congress to complain. You are well aware if any member of NASA lobbies Congress outside the approved channels — well, you know what happens."

Then, switching tactics, the Administrator said, in a very friendly and fatherly tone, "Bill, I know you are a fine engineer and you want to do the best job possible. But remember, NASA is filled with dedicated and exceptional people. Learn to use them as a resource and listen to them. If you do, we will get this job done together and everyone will benefit. Have a nice flight back to Houston."

The line had been drawn in the sand and Bill had two choices; tell the Administrator to go straight to hell right then and there or pretend to play ball. If he did the former, NASA would get some NASA weenie to run the show and, with all probability, end up with a useless and dangerous mess like the Shuttle and the Space Station. If Bill did the latter, and managed to keep his feet just at — but not over — the line, he might just get a Base built that would not be an accident waiting to happen.

Chapter 1-3
The Fra Mauro Moon Base Architecture

August 27, 2006, 8:45 AM EDT

Armed with a typical NASA PowerPoint presentation, Bill headed into the committee room to present the proposed Lunar Base Architecture to a joint meeting of the House and Senate Space Science Committees.

At 9:00 AM sharp, the Chairman of the meeting started his introduction and ended with, "Mr. Huff, we would like to hear the results of your hard work."

Bill stood up and said, "Mr. Chairman, distinguished members of the Committee, I thank you for the opportunity to present our recommendations for the Lunar Base Program the President and Congress requested 13 months ago. There are 4 parts to the architecture," and Bill made the appropriate keystrokes on the PC sitting on the table in front of him.

Bill waited for the first graphic to appear on the projection screen and the committee members began shuffling through the hard copies of his presentation they had received the day before. The graphic appeared and Bill said, "The first part of the architecture is concerned with the transportation of crew and cargo between the Earth's surface and Low Earth Orbit, or LEO.

"Regarding crews, we propose using the small, reusable Space Plane, which will be launched on a conventional, expendable Delta 4 rocket, to transfer crews back and forth between Earth and LEO. Regarding cargo, we propose using the Shuttle Derived Heavy Lift Vehicle, or HLV. As you know, the HLV will use reusable, Shuttle engine modules, the Shuttle's large external tank, and the Shuttle's 2 reusable, solid fuel booster rockets to lift heavy payloads to LEO.

"Since the Space Plane is in its final stages of development as the replacement for the Shuttle and the HLV is being developed for other NASA programs, they will be ready in time to support the Lunar Base Program and the Program does not have the large financial burdens associated with their development. However, they are not free. The Program will have to purchase its own fleet of Space Planes and HLVs. Are there any questions or comments before I go to the second part of the architecture?"

Senator Black, a harsh critic of NASA, said, "I am impressed you are using hardware from other programs to keep the cost down and to keep on schedule. That is a change from NASA's usual approach of starting from scratch on every new program." While Bill was visibly pleased, the NASA Administrator, seated to his right, reddened.

Bill said, "Thank you Senator Black, I hope you will like the rest of the plan as well," and a lighthearted chuckle ran through the room.

Pleased, Bill brought up the second graphic and said, "The second part of the architecture is concerned with the transportation of crew and cargo between LEO and Low Lunar Orbit, or LLO. The transportation of crews will be accomplished using, as the critical component of the system, the aerobraking shield NASA began developing in the early 90's, but never finished."

That statement of fact brought a scowl to the Administrator's face, an expression that suggested he would like to wring Bill's neck for bashing NASA in front of the Committee, but could do nothing since the Committee was eating it up.

Unaware of the Administrator's disapproving look, Bill never missed a beat. "Vehicles coming back from LLO, or from high Earth orbit, will use aerobreaking shields, rather than large amounts of fuel, to shed their high velocities. They will aerobrake in the Earth's upper atmosphere and do small circularization burns into LEO.

"The crew transfer system between LEO and LLO will consist of completely reusable, two stage, Orbit-to-Orbit Transfer Vehicles, or OTVs, with each stage using Shuttle derived LOX and LH — that is, liquid oxygen and liquid hydrogen burning engines and an aerobraking shield. The 1st stage will boost the OTV out of LEO into a highly elliptical

Earth orbit, giving the 2nd stage 97% of the velocity needed to reach the Moon. At 1st stage burnout, the 2nd stage, carrying the crew module, will do a very small burn — the last 3% — to put itself and the crew module on a minimum energy, trans-lunar trajectory and will reach LLO in $4\frac{1}{2}$ days.

"While the upper stage is on it way to the Moon, the 1st stage will swing back to Earth 4 days after launch, do an aerobraking maneuver in the Earth's atmosphere, and do a small circularization burn back into LEO. There it will be refueled and readied for its next launch, when the 2nd stage, with the crew module, returns from the Moon."

Bill paused, waiting for possible questions or comments. Since there were neither, Bill said, "The next graphic shows what will happen with the 2nd stage and the crew module," and he waited a few seconds for the graphic to appear.

"When the OTV's 2nd stage reaches the Moon, it will use its LOX/LH engine to burn into LLO, where it will rendezvous with a Lunar Lander in orbit there, leave off its crew, pick up the returning crew, and then burn out of LLO into a $4\frac{1}{2}$-day, trans-earth trajectory. When it reaches Earth, it will do an aerobraking maneuver, circularize its orbit, and rendezvous and dock with the waiting 1st stage and Space Plane. The stages would be re-stacked, the 2nd stage would be refueled, and the full OTV would be ready for its next trip from LEO to LLO and back again."

Much to the chagrin of the Administrator, Congresswoman Waterman interrupted, "Mr. Huff, what exactly is the current status of the aerobraking shield program we funded well over 10 years ago?"

"The test aerobraking shield was built, but never flown. The test hardware is in storage at JSC and can be brought out, refurbished, and flown in a short time."

The Congresswoman said sarcastically, "Well, I'm glad the money we spent will not be wasted after all. Also, is the OTV you talk about partially developed? I don't remember funding an OTV program."

"No, the OTV is not developed and no, there never was a funded OTV program. However, the basic engineering concept of the OTV was understood back in the SEI days, so we know how to build them. But the development of the OTV will be a major part of the cost of the Lunar Base Program."

Congresswoman Waterman said, "Thank you Mr. Huff."

Bill continued his presentation with the next graphic. "In contrast to crews, cargo will take an efficient 'slow boat to China' to the Moon. As you know, NASA began the development of a reusable Nuclear-Electric Tug, or just plain Tug, in 2002. The Tug uses low thrust, but very fuel-efficient, ion engines, powered by electricity produced by a nuclear reactor. Though the Tug will take a few months to slowly spiral out from LEO to LLO and a few weeks to get back to LEO, its efficiency will dramatically reduce the cost of the Lunar Base Program. Since the Tug's development is nearly complete, it will not cause any financial or scheduling problems for the Project."

Bill again waited for further comments, but it was clear the committee understood how he was making efficient use of existing hardware and hardware development programs to benefit the Lunar Base Program and had no comments.

"The third part of the architecture is concerned with the transportation of crew and cargo between LLO and the Moon's surface. Though NASA has conceptual plans for a LOX/LH fuelled Lander, which can carry either a cargo pallet or a crew module to and from the surface and LLO, the development of the Lander and the crew module will be a major part of the developmental phase of the Lunar Base Program."

Bill paused, but he had the committee's attention and was selling them his plan.

Bill called up the next graphic and said, "The fourth and final part of the architecture is the Lunar Base itself. Much of the equipment needed for the Base can be developed using and/or modifying existing equipment. The 4.26-meter diameter, 8.56-meter long modules developed by Boeing for the International Space Station, can to be increased in length to 12.80 meters and used for the habitation and lab modules of the Base. Similarly, the life support system developed for the International Space Station will be used for the Base. The type of nuclear reactor developed for the Tug will to be used to provide the Base with power, later to be supplemented by solar cells manufactured *in situ* from lunar resources. Tele-operated construction equipment will be built by various manufactures, based on plans NASA has already developed. Boeing has been asked to get out its 35 year-old design for the 2-man Rover used on Apollo 15, 16, and 17 and update it to provide the Base crew with local transportation with a range of 100 kilometers. Boeing was also asked to be ready to start the development of a pressurized exploration rover, or Traverse Vehicle, which can support a crew of 4 for 2 weeks and have a range of 1000 kilometers."

Before Bill could call up the last graphic for that part of his presentation, the Committee Chairman asked in an inno-cent tone, "You mentioned tele-operated construction equip-ment, correct?" Bill nodded affirmatively as the Chairman continued, "Rumor has it, you are opposed to having the Base built tele-robotically. Would you like to comment on that?"

Since discretion is the better part of valor, Bill looked at the Administrator, who wisely and literally rose to the occa-sion. Standing up, he said, "Mr. Chairman, I would like to address that issue, if I may," and the Chairman nodded. "With all due respect to the engineering and managerial capabilities Mr. Huff has so aptly demonstrated during the past year and here today, NASA has a very capable engineering staff in the area of tele-robotics. They have convinced not only me, but also all the rest of NASA's upper management, including Mr. Huff, that the most economical way to build the Base is to use tele-operated equipment. This also has the great benefit of reducing the risk to humans during the construction phase to zero. I believe everyone here can appreciate this fact. Clearly, I expect Mr. Huff will retain a healthy concern about all aspects of crew safety and about the ultimate integrity of the Base. But I can assure you, Mr. Huff fully understands the util-ity of using tele-operated equipment during the construction phase of the Base. Thank you."

Though the Chairman and most of the Committee Members knew of Bill's serious concerns, there was little use in pressing the issue. That would just put Bill, whom they trusted and who had no hard data to back up his objections, between a rock and a hard place for no clear reason. The Chairman simply said, "Thank you. Mr. Huff, would you like to continue?"

Bill nodded, called up the next graphic, and said, "We are planning to build an 8-module Base to support a crew of 16. The Program will buy 3 reusable Space Planes and 4 semi-reusable HLVs. The LEO to LLO transportation infrastructure will consist of 2 Tugs for cargo and 2 OTVs for crew transportation. The LLO to lunar surface infrastructure will consist of 4 Landers with 2 interchangeable crew modules. The total cost of the Lunar Base Program, through the first 6 months of its operations, will be 19.8 billion dollars — just under target of 20 billion. The Base will be operational by the 45th anniversary of Apollo 11. The details of the budget and the schedule are given in the handouts you received yesterday."

With a smile of satisfaction, Senator Black said, "Bill, that all sounds very good. But where are you going to build the Base, at one of the poles, where the water ice is?"

With a twinkle in his eye, Bill said, "I thought you would never ask," and everyone in the room broke out in laughter.

As Bill called up the first of the new set of graphics, he said, "We have several requirements for the Base Site. First, and foremost, we insist the Base be located where, in an emergency, the crew can leave the Base and get to an orbiting OTV within a few hours. This requirement means the Base has to be either at, or very near the equator or at, or very near one of the poles. In the former case, the 200-kilometer altitude, rendezvous orbit would be an equatorial orbit and in the latter case, it would be a 200-kilometer altitude, polar orbit. In both cases, the OTV will pass over the Base once every 127.5 minutes."

Almost every one of the Committee members nodded in agreement with that sensible safety requirement.

"Second, we insist the Base always have line-of-sight communications with Earth. This requirement eliminates the entire farside of the Moon. Though possible for a polar Base, line-of-sight communications would be difficult because of the 7° librations of the Moon."

Puzzled, Congressmen Peterson asked, "What are librations?"

"As seen from the Earth, the Moon seems to rock back and forth by about 7° in latitude and longitude as it orbits the Earth. This apparent movement in latitude is caused because of the Moon's orbital inclination of 5° and its polar inclination of 1½°, while the apparent movement in longitude is due to the fact that the Moon's orbit is slightly elliptical."

The Congressman's expression indicated he did not have a clue as to what that meant, but said, "Ah, thank you Mr. Huff," and smiled uncomfortably, which caused an amused smile to creep across Bill's face. Bill took a quick look at the Administrator, whose blank look put him in the same intellectual class as the Congressman, which only added to Bill's amusement.

Bill continued, "There were three different science areas to be considered in the selection of the site — lunar science, astronomy, and all the other sciences together. Lunar scientists want the Base in a region that will allow access to a variety of different petrological units and topographic features within the 500-kilometer radius of exploration of the Traverse Vehicle. There are 9 candidate sites along the nearside equator and one at each pole. They are given in the handout[1]."

Some of the Committee members began searching for the correct pages, but before they could get lost in the scientific details of each site, Bill quickly continued. "In contrast to lunar scientists, we found that astronomers have lost interest in using the Moon for astronomy, except for farside radio astronomy, which is excluded by the requirement the Base have line-of-sight communications with Earth.

"That surprised us. During the Apollo era and throughout the rest of the seventies and eighties, astronomers were excited about the possibility of having telescopes on the Moon. However, as a result of the great advances in active optics, optical interferometry, and detectors in the visible and infrared parts of the spectrum, Earth based telescopes have achieved their full resolution and work efficiently over wide

Note: [1]Appendix 2

parts of the spectrum at a fraction of the cost of space based telescopes like the Hubble Telescope. So astronomers see no reason to have a very expensive and modest sized telescope on the Moon, when the same amount of money would allow them to build many, very large telescopes on Earth and even additional space based telescopes. Telescopes that would produce better results than a lunar based telescope — at least, until there is a sufficiently robust lunar industrial capability to allow very large and very inexpensive lunar telescopes to be built *in situ*. In short, the astronomers have no interest in the Lunar Base at the present time."

Very surprised at those statements, the Chairman said, "Very interesting. But if I read that correctly, astronomers are not opposed to the Base, as long as it leads to bigger, cheaper, moon-built telescopes in the future, correct?"

Bill answered, "I believe that is a fair statement," and pressed onward. "In contrast, the other sciences, like cosmic ray physics and low gravity biology and medicine, do not place any constraints on the site — the needs of those sciences will be met no matter where the Base is.

"And that brings us to the final set of site selection criteria — the availability of lunar resources for the *in situ* manufacturing of construction materials, life support products, and rocket propellants. Dr. Binder argued at the Base Site Selection Committee meetings that the availability of lunar resources needed for the development of the Base into a lunar industrial facility and colony should dictate the selection of the site. I believe Dr. Binder's argument is correct. I am convinced the Base must be built in the most optimum location for its future development into an industrial complex, so we will have a return on investment. Thus, I would like to present all his arguments in some detail, if the Committee agrees that I do so."

The Chairman quickly polled the committee members and said jokingly, "We are on pins and needles."

Bill put up a graphic with a lot of numbers on it, "Based on the Apollo sample analysis program, we know lunar materials are made up almost completely of just 7 elements — oxygen, silicon, iron, magnesium, titanium, aluminum, and calcium[1]. As you easily recognize, most of these 7 are main-stays in our Earth's global economy and will be the mainstays in a future Moon/Earth economy. They are the building mate-rials of our cities and industries. Since all 7 can be found in economically important amounts anywhere on the Moon, the Lunar Base site should be selected on the availability of eco-nomically important minor or trace elements."

Bill paused to let that sink in. Seeing that the dull data on the abundances of the major elements on the Moon had perked up the Committee, Bill struck the second blow. "Again, based on the Apollo results, 7 of the 12 minor ele-ments, elements whose abundances are generally between 0.1 and 1% in lunar materials — as you can see from the graphic, the 12 minor elements are sodium, potassium, phos-phorous, sulfur, manganese, chromium, nickel, vanadium, zirconium, yttrium, barium, and strontium[2]. I think you all know how important most of these 12 are in the Earth's economy — anyway, as I started to say, 7 of these elements are concentrated in a material lunar scientists call KREEP and 4 are concentrated in mare volcanic rocks or the mare basalts, as they are called, while nickel is concentrated in the oldest lunar regoliths, such as in the Fra Mauro Formation — one of the most interesting sites to lunar scientists along the equator.

"The global maps produced by Lunar Prospector show one of the highest concentrations of KREEP is found in the Fra Mauro, the place the Apollo 14 Astronauts landed and col-lected samples. Thus we have detailed knowledge of the minor element resources there. Also, the Fra Mauro Formation is surrounded by mare basalts, which contain the other 4 minor elements. Dr. Binder concluded, and I quote, 'The Fra Mauro is not only one of the best lunar science sites, it is the very best site from the standpoint of the availability of all major and minor element lunar resources — except for hydrogen, which is present in significant quantities only in the Polar Regions. The Base should be built in the Fra Mauro,' and I agree."

Notes: [1,2]Appendix 3

Senator Black said, "Bill, that's all very interesting, but I don't understand why you don't want the Base where the water ice is. As I recall, everyone said when Dr. Binder's Lunar Prospector found the ice, it opened the door to the Moon, because you can make rocket fuel out of it and use it for life support."

Bill answered, "That's quite true, regardless of whether the polar hydrogen deposits are water ice or just enhanced deposits of solar wind hydrogen. Assuming they are water ice, the total amount is only a few billion tons, just enough to fill a small lake, and that small amount is spread over hundreds of thousands of square kilometers. Also, using the water to make rocket fuel has one big drawback — it would be lost from the Moon. Dr. Binder argued that the water or hydrogen should only be used for life support, so it can be conserved by recycling and be available for future use in an expanding lunar civilization, and I agree."

Senator Black retorted, "Maybe, but I hope you both are right."

"I am confident we are and so, we recommend the Base be built at the Fra Mauro Site. It meets all the logistic, communications, scientific, and resource criteria used in the site selection. After a detailed study of the Fra Mauro region, the exact site of the Base itself is at $0.2°$ south latitude and $16.3°$ west longitude, near the northern edge of the Fra Mauro Formation. The landing pads for the Landers are 5 and 6 kilometers to the north and straddle the equator. The Base will be 25-kilometers south-west-west of the 25-kilometer diameter crater Gambert and 117 kilometers north-north-east of the Apollo 14 landing site," and Bill brought up the last graphic, a beautiful picture of the Fra Mauro.

Satisfied, Bill said, "Mr. Chairman, Committee Members, I thank you for your attention and insightful questions. I am looking forward to Congress' decision."

September 10, 2006

Bill got a call from Senator Black two weeks later, "Congratulations Bill, we've got more than enough votes to approve your Lunar Base Plan. The vote is set for later this

FRA MAURO LUNAR BASE SITE

The Fra Mauro Base Site is located at X in this picture and the Apollo 14 landing site is located at A. The Base Site is 117 kilometers NNE of the Apollo 14 landing site and 25 kilometers SWW of the 25-kilometer diameter crater Gambert. North is up.

afternoon. I trust you will be watching. You did a great job. Goodbye for now."

Later that day, all of NASA knew it was on its way back to the Moon and NASA, with a fervor that was reminiscent of the Apollo days 40 years earlier, got very busy building the hardware for its Fra Mauro Lunar Base and its salvation.

Chapter 1-4
From Blueprints to Hardware

January 2007 through June 2007

By early 2007, NASA had a good start on what it touted would be its return to glory and Bill was working hard to keep everything going according to plan.

However, as 2007 marched on, the rejuvenated NASA and its major aerospace contractors were finding it hard to shake off their decades-long, bad habits. One day in June, George came to the JSC cafeteria to meet Bill for lunch. After getting through the lunch line, they took a window table in the corner and George said, "Well, let's get started — you bitch and I'll eat."

Bill bitched, "It's just like it always was, George. My authority is undercut every time I turn around. Everything still has to be done by committee — that way nobody is actually responsible for anything and nobody can be blamed when things go wrong."

George interrupted between bites, "Except you, of course. I know the routine — important decisions are delayed by indecision and the big aerospace contractors are happily going about their business as usual, with their fat, lucrative, cost plus fixed fee contracts. Am I right, or did this old fool quit NASA for nothing?"

Bill answered, "You know you're right. The thing that worries me most is the schedule is already beginning to slip and the costs are already beginning to rise — and we're not even a year into the program."

August 27, 2007

A couple of months later, the program had its first success. Though the refurbishment and preparations for its test flight took 2 months longer than the 8 months Bill had planned, the aerobraking shield was successfully launched on the maiden flight of the HLV, and essentially all the test objectives were met. The discrepancies between predicted and actual performances were well within the range that could be understood and corrected via computer modeling. NASA had gotten over a big hurdle in the development of the OTVs and Lockheed Martin, the OTV's prime contractor, was able to proceed with their design and construction. Bill was relieved.

January 2008 through March 2011

Despite Bill's best efforts, neither NASA nor its big aerospace contractors were capable of sticking to simple hardware designs, schedules, and budgets. So the development and construction of flight and Base hardware continued to slip and the cost overruns increased dramatically during 2008. Bill said to Nancy one evening after a particularly frustrating day, "What did I get myself into? Congress was crazy to think one man could make a difference in the way NASA works."

Nancy hugged Bill and whispered in his ear, "You'll make it work somehow, you always do," and she kissed him tenderly.

The real blow to the Program came on the first Tuesday of November 2008, when the Democratic candidate for President, Charles Jackson, soundly beat outgoing President Bush's handpicked Republican candidate and the Democrats took back the Senate, though the Republicans still held the House. Though the change in leadership did not immediately spell trouble for Bush's Lunar Base Initiative, the handwriting was on the wall, even if it was in invisible ink.

Given the insurmountable rift between the Democrats and Republicans after the scandal-plagued years of the Clinton Administration and Clinton's impeachment, followed by the Gore/Bush election fiasco, and Bush's ongoing war on terrorism in Afghanistan and Iraq, the newly elected President and his fellow Democrats were not going to give their full support to the Lunar Base Initiative started by the hated Bush.

President Jackson had said to one of his closest aides right after the election, "We're not going to kill the Lunar Base, or admit we're against it, but we're going to keep NASA on a very tight leash. Then we're going to figure out a way to turn the Base to our advantage and make Bush and his father look like the fools they are."

After President Jackson was sworn in and after his new administration got settled, NASA had to fight for every penny it needed to keep the Lunar Base Initiative going, a battle that was made even more difficult because NASA had not really changed.

As the scheduled flight test phase of the OTVs and the Landers approached in early 2010, NASA was in typical schedule and cost crises. There was no way around it, if NASA was to have the Base finished by July 20, 2014, and be within budget, NASA would have to scale down the Base and its transportation system.

In response to a stern request for a review, a tired Bill Huff again appeared at a joint meeting of the House and Senate Space Science Committees.

After reviewing the progress and problems, without overtly saying the new NASA was just the old NASA in sheep's clothing, Bill concluded with, "We can achieve our goal of having the Base operational by July 20, 2014 at a cost of 19.8 billion by reducing the scope of the initial facilities. Instead of a 16-man Base consisting of 8 modules, the Base would be an 8-man Base with just 4 modules. Instead of having 3 Space Planes dedicated to the program, there would be just 2. Initially, there would be just 1 Tug and 1 OTV for crew transportation between LEO and LLO — the 2nd Tug and the 2nd OTV would be added to the fleet as soon as possible after the Base becomes operational. Similarly, the lunar surface/LLO fleet would initially consist of just 2 Landers and 1 crew module, with the 3rd and 4th Landers and the 2nd crew module being added to the fleet after the Base becomes operational."

After a series of questions about the positive and negative impacts of scaling down the Base Program, Senator Black asked pointedly, "Are you not taking a very great risk, in terms of crew safety, by having just 1 OTV, 2 Landers, and 1 Lander crew module during the first several months of Base operations?"

Caught between a rock and a hard place, Bill admitted, "I cannot deny it would be safer to have the full complement of vehicles from the beginning of the operations of the Base. However, all manned space accidents — ours, the Russians, and the Chinese — have occurred during the most dangerous phases — launch or landing — of the missions, except Apollo 13, which was on its way to the Moon when it got into trouble. Even more so than Mir and the Space Station, the Lunar Base will be a stable safe haven with life support capabilities that will last many months. If a crew runs into trouble on the way to or from the Moon, there is little to do except try to save them the way NASA did with Apollo 13, whether or not the second OTV is available. If something goes wrong with a Lander or the Lander crew module, the crew can wait it out at the Base until the problem is fixed."

Finally, President Jackson and the Democrats had the stick they wanted to beat Bush and the Republicans with. After the hearing, the Democratic leader of the Senate said, "If NASA fails to get the Base done on time and at cost, we'll say, 'Bush and the Republicans started the nation down another blind alley — like Nixon's Shuttle Program and Reagan's Space Station — rather than canning NASA after the Atlantis disaster and restructuring the nation's space program.' If NASA succeeds in getting the scaled down Base built on time and within the 20 billion cap, we'll say, 'We took over a doomed program, scaled it back, and made it work,' and take credit for the success of the Lunar Base." Thus, NASA's continued incompetence had presented the Democrats with a win-win situation, much to the Republicans' consternation, and the President and Congress happily approved the scaled-down Lunar Base Program.

April 2011 through Early February 2012

With that crisis mastered, but with the clock ticking ever faster and the costs continuing to increase, Bill and NASA began to worry about the OTV and the Lander test program schedule. Originally, Bill had laid out a step-by-step test program for the flight hardware.

The 1st stage of the OTV would be assembled in LEO, checked out, and sent on a 4-day mission that would end with an aerobraking maneuver to get it back to LEO — exactly mimicking its normal mode of operation, except it would not carry the 2nd stage with the crew module.

Once that test was successfully completed, the 2nd stage and the unmanned crew module would be assembled in LEO, stacked on the 1st stage, and the entire OTV would perform a complete TLI[1] burn, the 2nd stage and crew module would insert itself into the 200-kilometer altitude LLO, stay there for 3 orbits, do the TEI[2] burn, and return to LEO using its aerobraking capability.

Nearly parallel with the two phase OTV testing, the Lander would be assembled in LEO and put through a series of burns that would simulate its activities while landing on the Moon. Then the OTV would take the Lander to LLO and it would execute an unmanned landing on the Moon and return to LLO.

When those unmanned test flights were successfully conducted, Bill intended to send a 2-man crew to the Moon — the first in forty years — to land at the Base site as the final, full-up test of the transport system. When that was accomplished, the tele-operated construction of the Base would begin.

However, there was no longer time nor money to conduct that carefully planned, step-by-step test program, so Bill went to Headquarters and told the Administrator, "I want permission to skip the flight test of the 1st stage of the OTV and go directly to the full-up-test of the entire OTV with its unmanned crew module and just do the LEO test of the Lander. NASA did something very similar back in December of '68, when it skipped a series of test flights and successfully used the first manned test of the Saturn 5 to launch Apollo 8 on the first manned orbital mission to the Moon."

Uninterested in Bill's arguments, but pressed by the need to get the Base done, the Administrator said, "Do what you need to do to get the Base up there on time and on budget."

After being assembled and fuelled in LEO, the unmanned OTV burned out of LEO on its way to the Moon on August 4, 2011. The 1st stage performed flawlessly and did its aerobraking maneuver 4 days later without error. The 2nd stage fin-

---

Notes: [1]Trans-Lunar Injection; [2]Trans-Earth Injection. Also see the **Glossary,** Appendix 5, for these and all other acronyms.

ished the TLI burn, coasted for 106 hours to the Moon, and inserted itself into the 200-kilometer altitude LLO, where it stayed for 3 orbits or 6 hours and 21 minutes. It then did its TEI burn, coasted for 106 hours back to Earth, performed a flawless aerobraking maneuver, and rendezvoused with the waiting 1st stage. NASA was exuberant — it had the old Apollo touch after all — and Bill was relieved.

NASA then assembled and fuelled the 1st Lander in LEO and it was successfully put through its unmanned LEO test on October 9, 2011. NASA had hit two homeruns and was back on schedule, actually a little ahead of schedule, and again within budget.

With the much abbreviated test phase of the transportation hardware finished, Bill flew to Boeing in California for a program review — and an inspection — of the Base hardware that would soon be on its way to the Moon. The second afternoon of a boring, but successful review, Bill was taken to a very large hangar that housed the completely assembled Base. As Bill walked into the hangar, an exuberant look spread across his face. Before him were the 4 modules, the 2 access tunnels, and the 4 airlocks, fully assembled and sitting in their alignment cradles, just as they would appear on the Moon in less than 2 years. As he admired the gleaming, aluminum hardware, he said, "It's beautiful — I never dreamed it would be so beautiful. It's too bad it will all be buried under a layer of regolith and never seen again."

His Boeing guide replied, "Yeah, that was one nice thing about the Space Station before it was decommissioned, every time a crew went up or came down, you got all those beautiful shots of it floating above the Earth. Even the Base's first crew won't get to see it like this. But at least we'll have the videos from the tele-operated construction equipment, before it's buried."

Bill sighed and said, "True, but I'd still like to see it sitting on the Moon, gleaming in the Sun."

After they walked around the Base and Bill inspected every nook and cranny of its exterior, they entered the Base through its NE airlock for an inspection of the interior, and it almost took Bill's breath away.

Very late that evening, Bill arrived home. He gave Nancy a big hug and kiss and said, "Well, somehow we did it. That part of my job is finished and I can relax a little. Tomorrow I hand the management over to Tom Taylor, who will run the tele-operation construction activities, and Wayne Sharp, who will run the Earth/Moon transportation part of the program. And in two weeks, I'll start the medical and psychological testing to see if I can be on the first crew to the Base. But I'm so beat, I doubt I'll even be able to pass the stand-up-for-five-minutes test."

Nancy replied, "Cheer up, I've got our vacation in Hawaii all set up — see, here are our airplane tickets. After two weeks on those beaches and in the sun, you'll be your old self again and you'll kickass during those tests."

Part Two
FRA MAURO'S FIRST OPERATIONAL CREW

Chapter 2-1
The Press Conference

March 3, 2013

NASA was about halfway through the tele-operated construction of the Base and Bill had to admit to the Administrator, "Though the operations are going slower than we had hoped, there have been relatively few problems."

Despite the success of the tele-operated construction activities, Bill was still quite concerned about the integrity of the Base. But that was no longer his responsibility; he had spent the previous year becoming an astronaut. And so it was that, shortly before 9:00 AM CST, Bill entered the Auditorium in JSC's Building 2 with 7 other individuals, who took their seats at a long table on the stage, to take part in a press conference.

The press conference was as well attended as the press conference 44 years earlier, when the Apollo 11 crew was introduced to the world. Judging by the large attendance, the world was much more interested in the Lunar Base Program than it had been in any of NASA's programs during all the intervening years.

At 9:00 AM sharp, a middle aged, very neatly dressed man stepped to the microphone and said, "Ladies and gentlemen, welcome to the First Fra Mauro Lunar Base Operational Crew Announcement Press Conference. My name is Peter Weller and I am Chief of the Johnson Space Center Public Relations Department. Today I have the great pleasure of introducing the 8 astronauts who have been selected as the First Operational Crew of the Fra Mauro Lunar Base. After the tele-operated construction work is completed in March of next year, this crew will go to the Base and start the Base's Operational Phase. The crew will spend 6 months at the Base and then be replaced by the second crew.

"The form of the press conference is as follows — I will introduce each of the crewmembers, starting with the command and engineering personnel, then the medical and health personnel, and last, but not least, the scientific personnel, and give you a brief summary of each person's background. After each introduction, that astronaut will say a few words concerning what he or she hopes to accomplish during the 6-month tour-of-duty at the Base. When I have finished the introductions, you will be invited to ask questions. Finally, you will find additional biographical information on each crewmember in the press kits you have received[1].

"I am confident you will find that NASA has selected 8 exceptional individuals to start Base operations. However, the makeup of this crew is quite different from the crews we have previously sent into space. During the earlier programs, starting with the Mercury Program and going through the Shuttle and International Space Station Programs, the emphasis was on learning how to get to — and from — space safely and learning how to live and work there. As a result of the experience NASA gained during those 50 years, we have reached a level of maturity that allows us to concentrate on applications at the Lunar Base. Thus, the need for traditional, flight-experienced astronauts has lessened. That is the reason, with the exception of the Base Commander, the crewmembers are all highly skilled professionals in various fields, without previous flight experience.

"Now, without further ado, I am extremely pleased to present to you the First Base Commander, Pilot Astronaut Colonel John Harrison Roberts. Colonel Roberts is 48 years old and a Texan — he was born and grew up in Kerrville, Texas, just northwest of San Antonio. As Commander of the Base, Colonel Roberts will be responsible for the safety of the crew and the success of all the planned activities that will be carried out during his crew's 6-month mission. John retired from the Air Force 12 years ago and immediately joined NASA. He is one of NASA's most experienced and most capable astronauts. He has flown three times. First, as a member of the 14th crew of the International Space Station, second, as the Command Pilot of the 2nd orbital test flight of the Space

---

Note: [1]Appendix 4

Plane, and third, as the Commander of the 23rd crew of the International Space Station. Colonel Roberts is married and has two daughters of college age, all of whom live here in the greater Houston area. John, would you like to say a few words?"

John stood up and took the microphone. In keeping with NASA's unwritten policy of selecting attractive astronauts for their high profile missions, John was strikingly handsome; 5' 9"; had wavy blond hair; piercing blue eyes; an athletic, medium build; and was impeccably dressed.

Grasping the microphone with obvious confidence, John said, "Thank you, Pete. I would like to thank NASA for trusting me with the Command of the First Operational Crew of the Fra Mauro Lunar Base. I am greatly honored that NASA saw fit to choose me for the task, knowing that many of my colleagues are as qualified as I am to do the job. I am also pleased with my crew, all of whom you will meet in the next half-an-hour. They are all highly qualified for their positions and I am looking forward to getting to know them very well during our training over the next year and to the 6 months we will be living and working together at the Base. Back to you Peter."

"Thank you, Commander Roberts. Next I would like to introduce the Deputy Commander and Base Engineer, Engineer Astronaut Mr. William Peter Huff. As you all know, when President Bush announced the Lunar Base Initiative, NASA just knew it had to get Bill out of retirement to manage the Definition and Development Phases of the Program. We also hoped Bill would be on the first crew, to get the Base up and running properly. When we called, Bill immediately stepped up to the huge challenge and now here he is, ready to go to the Base, which he is largely responsible for."

Bill was scowling at the load of BS he was hearing, but just then, Peter's revisionistic introduction was interrupted by a scattering of applause, which rapidly turned into a standing ovation, which embarrassed Bill — he turned red as a beet. When the applause finally stopped, Peter turned to Bill and said, "Well deserved Bill, well deserved," and turned back to the audience to continue.

"Bill is 50 years old and was born and raised in Shelbyville, Indiana. He got his Bachelors and Masters Degrees in Mechanical Engineering at Purdue University, the latter in 1984. After graduating, he joined us here at JSC and distinguished himself on many programs before retiring from NASA in 1994. He rejoined NASA in 2005 to manage the Lunar Base Program and became an Engineer Astronaut a year ago. Bill, along with John, will be responsible for getting the Base operational after arriving there and will be responsible for the maintenance of the Base. He will also be the primary driver of the Traverse Vehicle when the science team goes on the 2-week exploration excursions as far as 500 kilometers from the Base. Bill and his wife live here in Nassau Bay, across from JSC, and their three sons are away at various universities getting undergraduate and graduate degrees. Bill, would you like to say a few words?"

Bill was pleasant looking; 5' 7"; had dark brown, short, straight hair; blue-green eyes; a medium build; and was dressed casually. However, Bill's stature as an engineer and manager, as well as his air of self-confidence and competence, commanded everyone's respect, as exhibited by the standing ovation.

"Thank you, Peter. Like Commander Roberts, I am honored to be a member of the First Operational Crew of the Fra Mauro Lunar Base. I am looking forward to our stay at the Base and the exploration of its surroundings. Thank you."

Peter, caught off guard by Bill's curt statement, looked up from his notes with a surprised expression, "Ah — well, just like an engineer, short and sweet. Thanks, Bill."

"Now I would like to introduce the third member of the command and engineering staff, Engineer Astronaut Tom Wong. Tom is 30 years old and was born and raised in San Francisco. He got his Bachelors Degree in Computer and Electrical Engineering at Stanford University in 2003, after which he joined NASA at the Ames Research Center in the Bay Area. Tom became an Engineer Astronaut two years ago and has been working on the computer and communications systems of the Base. Logically, he will be responsible for the maintenance of the computer and communications hardware and software and is the Base Communications Officer. In addition to English, Tom speaks Chinese. Tom and his wife and young daughter live in Friendswood. Tom, would you like to say a few words?"

Tom, who was short — 5' 3" — had strong, pleasant, oriental features; black hair; black eyes; a slight build; and was very quiet and reserved, simply said, "Thank you, Mr. Weller. Like Commander Roberts and William Huff, I am honored to be a member of the First Operational Crew of the Fra Mauro Lunar Base."

After Bill's short statement and knowing Tom was quiet, Peter was prepared for Tom's very short statement and said, "Well folks, as you can see, our Communications Officer is a man of few words. I hope he will be more talkative when he is at the Base.

"Next are 2 of the 3 women astronauts in the crew and these ladies make up the crew's medical and health team. First, I introduce to you Scientist Astronaut Dr. Isabel Luisa Rodriguez, MD. Dr. Rodriguez is 42 years old and was born and raised in Buenos Aires, Argentina, where she got her pre-med education at the Medical Institute of the National University of Argentina. Then she came to Houston to complete her medical education at the Baylor College of Medicine, where she got her MD at the head of her class in 1998. After finishing her MD, Dr. Rodriguez practiced medicine at Baylor for four years and then joined the medical staff here at JSC. She became a Scientist Astronaut one year ago. Her responsibilities at the Base will be caring for the mental and physical health of the crew and she will also do physiological studies of human adaptation to living on the Moon. She speaks Spanish, English, and French. Dr. Rodriguez is married and has a son and a daughter in high school. They all live in Houston proper. Dr. Rodriguez, would you like to say a few words?"

Isabel was tall, 5' 8"; slender and perfectly proportioned; with handsome, classic Spanish features; brown eyes; black, straight, and shoulder length hair, but drawn back in a Spanish chignon; and she was fashionably, but professionally dressed.

"Thank you, Peter. Ever since I was a little girl in Buenos Aires, I was interested in medicine and space exploration, so it was natural for me to combine those interests into the study of human adaptation in space. While humans have spent up to a year in weightlessness in Earth orbit, the Apollo Astronauts spent no more that 3 days on the Moon. Our crew will be the first humans to spend an extended period of time in the ⅙-g lunar environment. Thus, I am pleased to have the privilege of being able to study how well we adapt physiologically to lunar gravity and the 0.3 bar, atmospheric mixture of 50% oxygen and 50% nitrogen, as well as how we adapt psychologically to the closed environment of the Base. In addition to my scientific duties, I will also look after the health of the crew and I will have a well-equipped little hospital, but I doubt I will have much occasion to practice healing medicine at the Base. Finally, I would like to thank NASA for giving me the chance to fulfill my most precious dream. Thank you."

Peter, visibly relieved that someone had finally said something of substance, said, "And I thank you Dr. Rodriguez for giving our audience such a complete synopsis of your hopes and expectations for your stay at the Fra Mauro Lunar Base.

"The second member of our medical and health team is Scientist Astronaut Pamela Ann Gray. Pam is 35 years old and comes from Cedar Rapids, Iowa. She got her BS in nutritional science and fitness training at Iowa State University. A few years later, she joined our staff at JSC and was part of our team that looked after the nutritional needs and exercise requirements of the astronauts, both during training and in space. Pam became a Scientist Astronaut one year ago. Her responsibilities at the Base will be to monitor the nutritional needs of the crew and their exercise programs. She will also assist Dr. Rodriguez in the Base hospital whenever necessary. Pam is married and has three sons and a daughter. They all live in League City. Pam, would you like to tell the audience something about your work at the Base?"

Pam was 5' 4" and cute; had a medium, solid build; dark blond, shoulder length, wavy hair; blue-green eyes; and she was rather plainly dressed.

Bubbling with her characteristic enthusiasm, she began, "Thank you, Pete. Well, my real duties are those of the cook, the maid, and the aerobics instructor. Though I love to cook,

I'm afraid most of the food we will be eating consists of pre-packaged food like you find in the freezers at Safeway, so my 'cooking' will generally be limited to heating up the food in the microwave or oven. I will also make sure everyone is eating a well balanced diet — I will be logging everything each person eats. Also, part of my job is to see that the Base stays neat and clean, but I'm really not the maid — at least I hope I'm not — since everyone is supposed to clean up after him- or herself. So I'm more of a hall monitor than a maid. The really fun part will be making sure the crew keeps up their daily physical fitness training, so I'm also the gym teacher. Thanks, Pete."

"Well Pam, it sounds like you're going to be very busy at the Base and, knowing you, I'm sure you will keep things very lively up there.

"Last, but not least, I have the pleasure of introducing the three members of the crew who are going to study the Moon itself and, since ladies are always first, I am pleased to introduce Scientist Astronaut Dr. Maria Selena Gutierrez. I should point out that Maria's middle name, Selena, is very appropriate for someone who is going to the Moon — or Selene in Greek. She has a PhD from the University of Arizona in Selenology — the study of the Moon — and Selenopetrology — the study of Moon rocks. Dr. Gutierrez was born, raised, and spent all her educational years in Tucson. Maria is the youngest of the crewmembers, she is 28 years old. Maria was accepted as a Scientist Astronaut almost immediately after getting her PhD a year ago. While at the Base she will study the structure, morphology, and stratigraphy of lunar craters, tectonic features, and volcanoes — that sounds like a lot of exciting work. Maria speaks English and Spanish and a little German. Dr. Gutierrez is single, but is engaged to another member of the crew, whom I will introduce shortly. Maria lives in Clear Lake. Dr. Gutierrez, would you like to say a few words?"

Maria rose demurely; she was 5' 3" tall; had a slight, but nicely proportioned build; soft, beautiful Hispanic features; dark brown, very long, straight hair; and dark brown eyes; her dress was feminine, but professional.

"Thank you, Mr. Weller. Growing up in Tucson, which has one of the highest concentrations of observatories, astronomers, and planetary scientists in the world — at the University of Arizona, Kitt Peak National Observatory, the Planetary Science Institute, the Lunar Research Institute, and Lunar Exploration Inc. — it was only natural I would become interested in exploring the Moon. As a high school student, I was fortunate to get a job as a junior assistant at the Lunar Research Institute, where I was also an undergraduate assistant while I attended the University of Arizona. I also worked at LRI as a graduate research assistant while I was getting my PhD at the Lunar and Planetary Lab at the U of A. Like all my colleagues, I wanted to go to the Moon, not just study it using unmanned spacecraft data and the Apollo samples. When it became possible to apply for a position as a Scientist Astronaut, I did. So here I am, getting trained to fulfill my dream of going to the Moon to study it first hand. I am especially looking forward to the 2-week Traverse Vehicle excursions we have planned, as well as exploring the Fra Mauro. Thank you."

"Now I would like to introduce the lucky man who is going to explore the Moon with his fiancée, Scientist Astronaut Dr. Karl Frederick Meyer. Dr. Meyer has a PhD from the Technical University of Munich in Selenophysics — the study of the Moon's interior — and, like Maria, in Selenopetrology. Dr. Meyer was born and raised in Herrieden in northern Bavaria, Germany. Karl is 29 years old and became a Scientist Astronaut a year ago. While at the Base he will set up the first of several Selenophysical Stations to study moonquakes and the properties of the lunar interior and he will study the volcanic rocks of the lunar maria and lunar volcanoes. Karl speaks German and English, as well as some Spanish. As you already know, Dr. Meyer is engaged to Dr. Gutierrez and they plan to marry after their return from the Moon. Karl lives in Clear Lake. Dr. Meyer would you like to say a few words?"

Karl got up somewhat awkwardly. He was 5' 7"; nice looking, but not handsome; had short, straight blond hair; blue eyes; and a muscular, medium build. When Maria and Karl had gotten up and dressed for the press conference, Maria had laid out a blue shirt and a pair of black slacks, both freshly pressed, and his one suit jacket. But, no matter how hard she tried to keep Karl looking neat or how often she tried to brush his blond hair out of his blue eyes, Karl always managed to look disheveled within minutes of getting dressed, and so he appeared as he stood up.

"Yes I would, Peter. First I would like to thank NASA for selecting both Maria and me to be on the First Operational Crew of the Fra Mauro Lunar Base. We are both very excited about the scientific opportunities that lay ahead.

"I am particularly happy about being able to set up the first few Selenophysical Stations of what will become a global network of such stations. While the 4 Apollo stations gave us a first look at the internal structure of the Moon, its heat-flow, and the magnetic and electrical properties of its interior, those 4 stations were too few in number, far too limited in their distribution over the Moon, and functioned for far too short a time for us to have more than a first order knowledge of the physical and compositional properties of the Moon's interior and, from the standpoint of safety, the lunar seismic risk factor. It is unfortunate that nearly 40 years have passed since the Apollo seismometers were shut off without having a global array of Selenophysical Stations set up to replace it. Had we had such a global array, as proposed by Dr. Binder in the late seventies[1], we would have 30 years of seismic data and hence a very good idea of the seismic risk factor, as well as the internal structure of the Moon. So, I am particularly interested in starting to set up the Selenophysical Stations and I am looking forward to the future when Stations will be placed in all areas of the Moon, not just within 500 kilometers of the Base. Thank you."

Peter, forewarned that Karl might bring up the touchy point of the unknown seismic risk factor, turned to Karl and said, "Thank you, Karl. I know you are very excited about starting to set up the seismic network." Turning back to the audience, Peter continued, "But I should add that our team of top NASA science advisors has assured us that large moon-

---

Note: [1]Selene, ein Mondlandungsprogramm mit unbemannten Sonden [Selene, a Moon landing program with unmanned probes], Project Leader, Alan Binder, Universität Kiel, Kiel, Germany, 1977

quakes are of no concern in terms of the safety of the Base, because they occur only once every 100,000 years, even by Dr. Binder's and Dr. Meyer's calculations — if ever. So, the Base will be safe for a long time."

Karl opened his mouth to respond, but apparently realized it would be better to wait for reporter's questions than to challenge the standard NASA BS directly, so he just sat back and kept quiet.

Peter continued, "Now I would like to introduce Scientist Astronaut James Eugene Williams. Mr. Williams has a MS from Cal Tech in Industrial Engineering. Mr. Williams was born and raised in Edmonton, Alberta, Canada. He is 46 years old and was accepted as a Scientist Astronaut two years ago. While at the Base, Jim will begin developing what will eventually become a lunar resource processing facility and start using lunar materials to improve and expand the Base. Jim is married and has a son and a daughter, who are away at college. Jim and his wife live in Dickinson. Jim, would you like to say a few words?"

At 5' 10", Jim was the tallest of the crew; he was well built; nice looking; had light brown, medium length, wavy hair; brown eyes; and was very neatly dressed.

"Yes, thank you, Peter. To date, everything needed on the Moon during the Apollo era and the current construction phase of the Base had to come from Earth at great expense. If we are to live and work on the Moon, we have to use lunar resources to cut the expense of expanding the Base and keeping it supplied.

"The first step in this process will soon be undertaken, when the tele-operation crews bury the completed Base under 5 meters of unsorted regolith that was dug up to make the large trench the facilities will set in. This is being done to protect us from the deadly effects of galactic- and solar flare-cosmic rays, as well as micrometeorite hits, and to eliminate the effects of the 300° C swing in the lunar surface temperature during the 4-week lunar day-night cycle.

"The next step we, the first crew, will undertake, is sieving the regolith, first to eliminate rocks larger than 10 centimeters and then to sort out the cobble, which we will use to line the craters that serve as the North and South Landing Pads. You may remember the tele-operator construction crews began the development of those craters as landing pads. But the craters have to be lined with cobble that is too heavy to be blasted out of the craters by the high velocity exhaust of a Lander as it lands or takes off, otherwise smaller debris would be blasted out at high velocity — like bullets — and it could damage Base equipment.

"Next we will sieve out the gravel sized rocks and use them as road bedding to protect the surface vehicles from the abrasive lunar dust.

"We will then use the coarser fraction of the remaining fine material to start testing the equipment designed to make cast basalt construction materials and the finest fraction will be used by follow-on crews to produce oxygen and metals, which will be used for life support, rocket fuel, and construction materials for Base expansion.

"Needless to say, I am looking forward to using lunar materials to improve the Base, even at the primitive stage of development that I will begin with. However, the real benefit of our work will come when the Base has expanded to the point where we have a functioning industrial complex and are making products from lunar resources that can be used to further develop the Base into a colony, directly benefit humanity on Earth, and help us expand into the rest of the solar system and beyond. Thank you."

Peter had looked impatiently at his watch several times as Jim went on with his rather lengthy and detailed explanation of his Base activities. When Jim finally finished, Peter quickly said, "Thank you. Now I would like to open the press conference to questions. Please state your name and affiliation before you ask your question and please, only one question at a time. Yes, the gentleman in the first row."

"Buddy Nelson, *KCBS Radio*, San Francisco. While I welcome the crewmembers from Canada, Argentina, and Germany, I seem to remember the Lunar Base Program was going to be solely an American venture — or am I wrong?"

Peter immediately said, "I'll answer that. You are correct, the Lunar Base Program is administratively, budget-wise, and management-wise solely an American program. But, as has been NASA's practice since the beginning of the Shuttle Program, foreign nationals can apply to become astronauts, though both Dr. Rodriguez and Mr. Williams became naturalized US citizens long before they became astronauts. So Dr. Meyer is our only foreign national. Next please — the lady in the fourth row."

"Betty Cramer, *Time Magazine*. My question is for Drs. Gutierrez and Meyer. How did you meet and did you both want to go to the Moon before you met?"

Karl turned to Maria and asked quietly, "Schatz[1], do you want to answer that?"

Maria answered quietly, "Sí[2]," and then in a louder voice, "As I explained earlier, I was an assistant at the Lunar Research Institute in Tucson from my high school days through my graduate student days. The last year of my PhD program, Dr. Binder was giving a series of seminars at various German Universities and met Karl, who had just gotten his PhD. As fate would have it, Karl's family farm is just outside of Herrieden and the farm of one of Dr. Binder's cousins is in the village of Höfstetten, a few kilometers away. Because of their family ties in northern Bavaria and because Karl's interests in selenophysics and mare basalt petrology are the same as Dr. Binder's, he offered Karl a post-doc position at the Lunar Research Institute. When Karl arrived at the Institute, we met and — well, I guess the rest is obvious. The answer to your second question is yes, we both wanted to go to the Moon long before we met."

Before Peter could call on another reporter, Ms. Cramer shouted, "If you two are already engaged, wouldn't it be appropriate for you to get married before you go to the Moon and spend your honeymoon there? That would surely be a first for NASA."

Everyone laughed at the good-natured question and Karl, who had a typical German's lack of a sense of humor, answered in all seriousness, "Well, I would like to get married first, but Maria believes, since there are considerable risks in

---

Notes: [1]Sweetheart; [2]Yes

what we are doing, we should wait until we are safely back on Earth before we get married."

Peter, whose pained look clearly indicated he was not pleased with Karl's direct answer, the serious tone in which he delivered it, and the negative impact his statement might have on any safety concerns the press might have about the Base, quickly said, "Maria's concerns are only natural for anyone who is about to embark on a space venture. After all, we are dealing with a very hostile environment, but NASA has done everything possible to make the Base completely safe. Nevertheless, as we all know from the accidents that have occurred in the Russian, Chinese, and NASA Manned Space Programs, the exploration of space and the expansion of humankind into space do occasionally exact a price in human life. The gentleman on the right in the last row."

Despite Peter's attempt to control the situation, Karl's statements opened up a can of worms and the reporter said, "John Waverly, *New York Times*. This is a follow-up for Dr. Meyer. If you are so worried about moonquakes, why are you going to spend 6 months at the Base along with your bride-to-be and your other crewmates?"

Though Karl was always on thin ice with NASA, but being fearless by nature, he answered in his usual direct manner. "You misunderstand my comments. I am not worried about our safety and have no concerns whatsoever about going to the Base for 6 months with Maria and the other crewmembers. While I believe we wasted 30 years by not setting up a global network of Selenophysical Stations in the early eighties, that would have provided only part of the answer to the scientific question about the seismic risk factor proposed by Drs. Nakamura and Binder.

"Remember, even in the most seismically active areas of the Earth, like California, magnitude 8 and larger earthquakes only occur once per century. Even if we had a seismic network on the Moon since the eighties, we would not know exactly how big moonquakes can get, how often they occur, and where they generally occur. But we would at least have some idea if there is a problem, though the Apollo seismic data and the photoselenological observation of young thrust fault scarps all point in that direction. If there is a problem, the engineers could have taken that into account in designing the Base, just as they earthquake-proof buildings in California and Japan. So no, I am not worried, but as a selenophysicist, I want to know the answer to this important question — as well as many others. Finally, though I speak for myself, I know I speak for Maria and I believe I speak for the others — even if it were far more dangerous to go to the Base than we know it is, we would still all go because the rewards of doing so are so great and the failure to do so is unimaginable."

Peter got a smile of relief on his face as Karl's answer nicely defused the issue and put an end to that line of questioning and said, "Thank you Karl, for that excellent clarification. Now, the gentleman in the far left of the middle."

"James Mason, *Houston Chronicle*. My question is for Dr. Rodriguez. You said something about a 0.3 bar, atmospheric mixture of 50% oxygen, 50% nitrogen. What does it mean in layman's terms and why doesn't the Base have a normal atmosphere."

Isabel smiled and said, "That is a very good question and the answer is — the standard pressure in the Base will be 0.3-bars or about 30% of that at sea level here on Earth. With a gas mixture of 50% oxygen and 50% nitrogen, we will be breathing the same amount of oxygen per breath as people do who live in the towns and cities in the high Rocky Mountains, like Vail and Leadville, Colorado.

"There are three reasons for having the pressure lower than normal down here at sea level. First, the low pressure reduces the stress on the modules and access tunnels of the Base, second, it eliminates the danger of crewmembers getting the bends when they go outside the Base in their spacesuits, since the spacesuits use 0.2 bars of pure oxygen, and third, the 50/50% mixture of oxygen and nitrogen, along with the low pressure, reduces the chance of fire — like the Apollo 1 fire in 1967 that killed astronauts, Grissom, White, and Chaffee, who were inside the capsule in a 100% pure oxygen atmosphere at 1 atmosphere pressure."

Mr. Mason said, "Thank you, that was such a good explanation even I could understand it."

What followed was a series of questions about lunar science, lunar resources, and the medical studies for Maria, Karl, Jim, Isabel, and Pam, but none about the Base or its commander. Though Tom and Bill seemed to be pleased they did not have to answer any questions, John, who had always been the center of attention at previous press conferences, appeared to be annoyed that he was being ignored.

Finally, about an hour after the press conference started, Peter said, "Ladies and gentlemen, the formal press conference is over, but you are welcome to stay and talk with the crewmembers on a one-on-one basis for half-an-hour or so, then they have to get back to their training." With that, the reporters, photographers, and TV cameramen stormed the stage, formed little groups around each astronaut, and engaged in animated conversations for as long as they dared without missing their deadlines.

NASA had every reason to congratulate itself on the success of the press conference. In fact, shortly after Peter returned to his office, the Administrator called and said, "Congratulations, that went very well. However, one of you JSC guys had better find a way to force Karl to keep his mouth shut and get off Binder's infernal NASA-bashing bandwagon. His girlfriend, ah — Maria, did fine. Apparently she's too smart to have become tainted by him, but Karl's attitude is far too in tune with Binder's for my liking. Maybe you can get Maria to change his attitude, if you know what I mean."

As Peter and the Administrator were conspiring, the 8 crewmembers were drifting away from the auditorium and Bill stopped Karl and Maria and said, "Karl, I'd like to talk to you about the moonquakes. How about the three of us having a long lunch down at Landry's in Kemah tomorrow."

Karl looked at Maria, who nodded, and answered, "Sure, we'd love to."

Chapter 2-2
The Seismic Risk Factor

March 4, 2013, 12:15 PM CST

After Maria, Karl, and Bill were shown to their table at Landry's, they spent a few minutes looking at the menu and ordered their drinks and lunches. When they were finished, Bill said, "I'm interested in the seismic risk you talk about. When the Lunar Base Initiative got started 8 years ago, I wanted to have the kind of commercial, unmanned missions flown that Dr. Binder has been advocating, in part to get the seismic data you guys want, but the Administrator axed the idea on budgetary grounds. So what's the story about the moonquakes?"

Karl asked, "What do you know about moonquakes? I don't want to waste your time by telling you things you already know."

"Well, before Apollo, astronomers thought the Moon was dead, with no volcanic or moonquake activity. But when Apollo came along, scientists wanted to have seismometers put on the Moon to study its interior. As I understand, they intended to use the seismic waves generated by meteoroid impacts to study the Moon. Correct?"

Karl answered, "Ja[1], but that effort started in the early sixties with the unmanned Ranger Program. The second block of Rangers was designed to hard-land simple seismometers on the Moon that would each function about 30 days. Unfortunately, all three Block 2 Rangers, which were all launched in 1962, failed."

Bill said, "I was just born then, but I do remember the Apollo 11 Moon landing on July 20, 1969. Didn't Buzz Aldrin set up the first lunar seismometer then?"

Maria said, "Yes, but unfortunately the seismometer obtained only 21 day's worth of data before someone sent up an erroneous command and turned it off."

Note: [1]Yes

Karl said, "Nevertheless, the seismometer recorded several signals, though there were far too few data to understand what they meant. But, unlike earthquakes, which have impulsive beginnings and generally last just several seconds, the lunar events had emergent beginnings — that is, the first vibrations to arrive were very small and gradually built up in amplitude, the vibrations took several minutes to build up to a maximum, and they took up to an hour to die out. But what that meant was a mystery."

Just then the waiter brought the drinks and said, "Your lunches will be out shortly."

After they had thanked the waiter, Karl continued, "Four months later, Alan Bean, one of the Apollo 12 Astronauts, set up another seismometer. The Apollo 12 seismometer was the first in a 4-seismometer network set up during the next 3 years in a triangle, 1100 kilometers on a side. The network functioned for several years, before NASA shut it down to save money. What a waste of a good and productive network."

Karl stopped talking to take a drink and then continued with zeal, "The most surprising thing happened after the Apollo 12 seismometer was set up. A few hours after the Apollo 12 Astronauts lifted off the Moon, the Lander was intentionally crashed 80 kilometers from the Apollo 12 landing site. About 25 seconds after the impact, the seismologists saw the arrival of an emergent signal that took 7 or 8 minutes to reach its maximum and took nearly an hour to die out. The newspapers headlines blared out 'Moon wave rings bell for scientists,' and the scientists said, 'We have never seen anything like it.'

"That seismogram showed that some, if not all, of the observed signals with emergent beginning and that lasted up to an hour, were meteoroid impacts, but nobody knew what the strange characteristics of the signals meant. But, within a couple of months, they figured out why the lunar seismic signals were so different from their terrestrial counterparts.

"First, the long duration of lunar seismic events is due to the fact that the Moon has neither air nor water. On Earth, the air and water in the rocks and soil very quickly damp out the vibrations. Since the Moon has no atmosphere or water, there is very little damping, so moonquakes last for an hour or more.

"Second, because the outer few kilometers of the Moon's crust are highly fractured, or brecciated — by the innumerable meteoroids that have impacted the Moon over the eons — seismic waves are strongly scattered when they pass through this breccia zone. Thus, the seismic waves diffuse through the breccia layer, so the first waves to reach the surface have a very low amplitudes and it takes several minutes for the main part of the seismic energy to diffuse to the surface — hence the emergent beginnings, the several minute rise-times to the maxima, and the long decay times of the lunar seismic signals. That was the first big step in understanding lunar seismology."

Just then the waiter brought their lunches and Karl said, "A good place for a break," and took a big bite out of his hamburger. But as soon as he had swallowed that bite, eaten a couple of French fries, and took a swig of Coke, he rattled on. "A short time later, the Apollo Team discovered the first true moonquakes. They noticed that several of the Apollo 12 seismograms were identical in appearance and the events occurred at exactly the same time during the monthly lunar tidal cycle. These periodic moonquakes are caused by the monthly variations in the tidal stresses in the Moon due to Earth's gravity and their focal points are very deep, 700 to 1100 kilometers deep, in the lunar mantle."

Bill asked, "Ah, lunar mantle?"

Karl said, "Give me that napkin — thanks. Ok, here's the Moon with a radius of 1738 kilometers," and drew a circle on the napkin. "At the center is a very small iron core with a radius of 300 to 400 kilometers — about this big. Above the core is the lunar mantle — similar to the Earth's mantle — composed of heavy olivine and pyroxene. The tidal moonquakes are found in this zone, somewhat above the core in the mantle — here," and Karl drew a bunch of crosses in his cartoon Moon.

After finishing that part of his napkin drawing, Karl continued, "The tidally induced moonquakes are very weak — they have maximum magnitudes of only 1.3 on the Richter

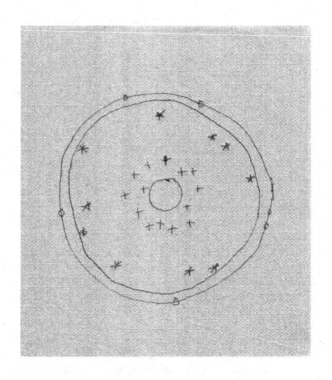

KARL'S NAPKIN DRAWING

The Moon's radius is 1738 kilometers (1080 miles) and that of its core is 300 to 400 kilometers (190 to 250 miles). Very weak moonquakes (crosses), caused by Earth induced tidal stresses, occur between depths of 700 and 1100 kilometers (430 and 680 miles). Weak tectonic moonquakes (stars), caused by tensional, thermoelastic stresses, occur in the upper mantle to depths of 200 kilometers (120 miles). Strong tectonic moonquakes (circles), caused by compressional, thermoelastic stresses, occur in the outer few kilometers of the 60 to 100 kilometers (40 to 60 miles) thick crust.

scale and the biggest release only about as much energy as a car hitting a brick wall going 170 km/hr. So the first moonquakes discovered pose no threat to the Base — they are too weak and too deep in the Moon. So, unfortunately, by the end of the Apollo Program in December of '72, the available seismic data, along with the 3.3 billion year age of the youngest volcanic rocks collected by the astronauts, seemed to confirm the old idea that the Moon was dead, since the only moonquakes found were due to the tidal forces exerted on the Moon by the Earth.

"Two years later, things got interesting. Dr. Nakamura found a new type of moonquake in the Apollo seismic records. There were just 28 of them spread over the 6 years of data. He found that they occurred in the upper most crust and upper 200 kilometers of the Moon's mantle, got as large as 5.8 on the Richter scale, and are true tectonic moonquakes."

Karl added the lunar crust to his drawing and said, "The crust is made of light plagioclase plus pyroxene and some olivine and is 60 to 100 kilometers thick." He added some circles at the top of the crust and some stars in the upper mantle and said, "See here and here are Nakamura's tectonic moonquakes."

Bill nodded in acknowledgment and Karl continued, "Nakamura pointed out the destructive power of such quakes and the need to define the lunar seismic risk factor. But NASA was not interested in the Moon then and virtually no one listened.

"That's where Dr. Binder came in. He spent 10 years, between 1973 and 1983, working and teaching at German universities. While there, he calculated the stresses caused in the Moon as it cooled from its initially totally molten state. He found there are two types of stresses.

"The first type consists of large compressional stresses in the outer few kilometers of the lunar crust, stresses that became strong enough to cause thrust fault moonquakes in the last 500 million to 1 billion years of lunar history. The second type consists of weak tensional stresses in the upper 200 kilometers of the mantle and causes weak normal fault moonquakes. So Dr. Binder's stress model nicely explains the origins of the tectonic moonquakes.

"He was especially interested in the first type, since, if his model were correct, the Moon's surface should have numerous, young thrust fault scarps that are up to 20 kilometers in length. So he studied the Apollo 1-meter resolution imagery and found over 70 thrust fault scarps in the 5% of the lunar highlands photographed during Apollo. His analysis showed the thrust fault scarps are all less than 700 million old — exactly as his model predicted.

"Dr. Binder concluded that all the available data — the seismic, photoselenological, and stress model data — showed convincingly that large, perhaps up to Richter magnitude 10, moonquakes occur in the upper few kilometers of the lunar crust, that the moonquakes last for hours, and that big ones occur once every 100,000 years or so. Based on that — as I mentioned during the press conference — he proposed Selene, a joint German/American program to set up a 16 station, global, Selenophysical Array using unmanned spacecraft, but NASA was not interested. So here we are, about to set up a Base and we don't have a clue as to what the seismic risk factor is."

Karl finally stopped talking and began eating. That gave Bill a chance to ask, "Ok, but you indicated at the press conference that we shouldn't worry, didn't you?"

Karl swallowed his half-chewed bite of hamburger and answered, "The Base would have to be very near the epicenter of a big quake to suffer any damage. Since the Moon's surface area is equal to that of North and South America combined, it is very unlikely that a magnitude 9 or 10 quake would occur anywhere near the Base. So, no — there is no need to be overly concerned, but as a scientist, I would like to know the answer to the seismic risk factor question and if it is high, then the engineers would have to build the Base to take a good shaking.

"Right now, NASA doesn't believe there is a moonquake problem at all. That's because NASA's hand-picked science advisory panel is telling Headquarters what it wants to hear and so NASA just ignores the possibility. Nevertheless, as I said at the press conference, I'm not worried — do the people in San Francisco worry about living right on the San Andreas fault, one of the most active in the world? No they don't. Look, if a big moonquake occurs once every 100,000 years somewhere in the 40 million square kilometers of the surface, the chances one would be close enough to the Base to cause damage, even during a 100 year period, is astronomically small."

Maria stopped eating and said, with a twinkle in her eye, "Gee, mi amado[1], isn't that what Professor Tyrannosaurus Rex said to Mr. Brontosaurus just before the asteroid hit, 'The chances of an asteroid hitting Earth and wiping out us dinosaurs is astronomically small?'"

Bill and Karl laughed and Karl retorted, in a vain attempt to make a joke, "Don't be silly Schatz, Brontosaurus died out well before the end of the Cretaceous, so a T-Rex could not have said that to one of them." His effort was rewarded with just polite smiles, so Karl went back to eating his half-finished hamburger and cold fries.

Since Karl was again eating, Maria had a chance to ask, "Bill, what do you know about the others in our crew?"

Bill answered, "Well, from what little I know, Pam is always cheerful and positive. She's the motherly type and will probably drive us nuts trying to keep us fit and eating healthy food."

Karl, with his mouth half-full of food, added, "Ja, she seems like a Mutter Henne — a mother hen to me."

Bill continued, "In contrast, Isabel is a cool professional. She knows her stuff and she won't take crap from anybody. I like and respect her a lot. I'd trust her to fix me up right, no matter how bad a shape I was in."

Maria said, "Sí, I like her, too. I love her Latin aristocratic air and her self-confidence. I'm sure we will become good friends. I'm really glad I'll have two nice women companions at the Base, so we can have some girl time together, when you men get on our nerves." Karl and Bill smiled at her last remark.

Note: [1]darling

After sipping some tepid iced tea, Bill said, "I don't know Jim at all and though I have been working with Tom on the Base computer- and com-systems for over a year, he is so quiet and reserved, I hardly know him, except, he really knows his stuff."

Maria prompted Bill. "That leaves John — you have known him for quite a while, haven't you?"

Bill answered slowly, "Yes I have — Peter wasn't kidding about John being one of the best astronauts in the corps. In reality, he's probably the very best. There's no one I would trust more to fly with. If we get in trouble, John has the guts, experience, and skill to get us home safely. You can bet your life on that, and you might have to."

Maria had a dubious expression on her face, "I don't doubt that, but the women in the corps, and at JSC in general, all tell me he's a real ladies man." Karl, who was remarkably puritanical for a European, stiffened at Maria's comment.

Bill said with great care, " Yeah, well — a lot of the ex-military astronauts, and some of the non-military ones, too, take full advantage of their hero status. It's one of the perks for some of them, and from what I know, John takes full advantage of that. However, there is little to worry about, most of those guys limit their extracurricular activities to the bimbos they find in the bars around the JSC and Houston area. The guys, and some of the gals, too, know all too well that the government takes sexual harassment charges between NASA personnel very, very seriously and, of course, NASA wants the public to think its astronauts are above reproach."

Clearly disgusted, Karl asked, "Why does his wife put up with that? If I were her, I'd kick him out in the street," and Maria nodded in agreement.

"Well, as far as I can tell, John and Betty get along just fine. Maybe they have an open marriage, though Betty doesn't seem to be the type. Maybe she enjoys being the wife of a national hero and accepts his cheating as something she has to put up with to get all the other perks. Whatever, she always seems proud of John and pleased to be with him at the various JSC and Headquarter functions. I just don't know.

"However, and I find this very funny, when his two girls were in high school, they were never — and I mean never — allowed to date. We thought he wanted them in a Nunnery. I suspect he's all too aware of the creeps out there just waiting to seduce his precious daughters. Even now, though they're away at college, John keeps close tabs on them and is a very doting father. Interesting enough, they seem to have the same affection toward him and Betty. Go figure."

Maria had a frown on her face and Karl looked unconvinced and said, "I hope you're right about him behaving himself during training and when we are at the Base. There has always been something I didn't like about him, and that must be it."

Bill said, "Maybe, and maybe not. Maybe you're detecting some of John's prejudices against us nonmilitary astronauts and against Germans."

Karl asked incredulously, "What are you talking about?"

Maria seconded that. "Yes, what do you mean?"

Bill answered, "First and foremost, like many of the military jet jockey astronauts from the Mercury, Gemini, Apollo, and even the early Shuttle days, John detests nonmilitary astronauts. Like Deke Slaton and Alan Shepard, who together ran the Astronaut Program in the early days of NASA, John firmly believes only military pilots should be allowed in the few seats available for space missions. The fact that Jack Schmitt — a geologist — was assigned a seat on Apollo 17 happened only because the science community put so much pressure on NASA to have a geologist finally go to the Moon on the last Apollo Mission. NASA was forced to bump Joe Engle and put Jack in his place. Except for Jack, all the Apollo Astronauts were or had been military pilots and many of the Shuttle and Space Station Astronauts were also ex-military pilots. So here he is, the Commander of the First Operation Crew at Fra Mauro, the only 'real' astronaut in the crew, and the only one of his crew who, in his mind, should be at the Base, especially you women."

Maria said, "That's revolting and sexist."

Karl asked, "Ok, why does he hate Germans — and now that you mention it, I believe you're right, he doesn't like me."

"Ok, but don't forget, you asked for it. Though World War II is 70 years and 3 generations behind us, John still considers all male Germans 'Nazi Krauts,' or so he has been reported to say. Look at you, you're blond and blue eyed, nice looking, and solidly built. You're the classic movie caricature of an SS man in jackboots, though you are a little short for that role — and you've got the most beautiful girl in the movie."

Maria looked sick and Karl looked like he was about to explode. Maria was the first to respond, "If that's true, why did NASA choose him as Commander?"

"Because he is an exceptional astronaut, he keeps his views just below NASA's radar, and, just like his sexual escapades, as long as things like that don't get too public, NASA just ignores them. Besides, John is too much of a professional to let his feelings get in the way of a mission. If NASA tells him his crew is a bunch of weenie astronauts, he'll make sure he gets the best out of the weenies."

Chapter 2-3
From the Earth to the Moon

April 5, 2014, through April 14, 2014

With a year of intensive training behind them, the crew flew to Cape Canaveral on the first leg of their trip to the Fra Mauro Lunar Base.

A week later, the pilot and his passengers, John, Tom, Isabel, and Pam, climbed aboard a Space Plane and a few hours later, as the remaining 4 Base crewmembers watched, a Delta 4 launched the Space Plane into LEO. Rendezvous and docking with the fully fuelled OTV was smoothly accomplished in 3 orbits, or some 5 hours later, and John and his 3 crewmates transferred to the OTV. The Space Plane returned to the Cape, while John started the careful checkout of the OTV, backed up by Houston.

The next day, Maria, Karl, Bill, and Jim were lying on their acceleration couches in the Program's second Space Plane, waiting for their first space venture to begin. Karl, who had tossed his cookies every time he had been in NASA's zero-g training airplane, or the Vomit Comet as it is lovingly called by all at NASA, held his breath as the Delta 4's main- and venire-engines and its strap-on solid motors ignited, violently shaking the vehicle and producing a very loud rumbling noise. Despite that, despite the violent shaking as the vehicle passed through the sound barrier 60 seconds after liftoff, despite the maximum acceleration of 3.4-g just before 1st stage burn out, and despite the protracted zero-g after the Space Plane was inserted into orbit, Karl miraculously did not get sick.

Five hours later, Karl was still not sick, as he, Maria, Bill, and Jim transferred from the Space Plane to the OTV. Maria went in first and was greeted by John, who said, "Welcome to the Lunar Base OTV. I hope you had a pleasant flight from the Cape." Then John welcomed each of the others as they came onboard.

Early Morning, April 15, 2014

One day later, the OTV blasted out of LEO. Unlike the Delta's rough, noisy ride, the OTV-ride was very gentle. There was no noise when the OTV's 1st stage engines ignited, just a very slight vibration and the slight return of weight as the OTV started to accelerate at a mild 0.3-g and the g-load never exceeded 0.8-g. Even the separation of the stages after 1st stage burnout almost 11 minutes later was hardly noticeable, there was just a mild jolt as the explosive bolts fired and the very slight return of weight as the 2nd stage engine kicked in at a low acceleration of 0.3-g. Just over 30 seconds later, the 2nd stage finished its burn and the crew was once again weightless.

Shortly after 2nd stage burnout and after everyone, except John, had unbuckled themselves from their acceleration couches and started floating around the cabin, Karl said miserably, "Isabel, I'm not feeling well, can you give me some Dramamine — quickly?" but it was already too late and Karl desperately grabbed a vomit bag and began to retch.

Both Isabel and Maria came to Karl's aid, while the others kept to themselves, since the smell of vomit permeating the cabin could well set them off vomiting, too.

Isabel prepared a dose of Dramamine she would give Karl as soon as he could hold the medicine down, while Maria held Karl to keep him from floating around and kept saying, "It's ok, cariño[1]. Just keep still and keep your eyes closed and you will feel better in a little while."

As Isabel came with the Dramamine, she said, "Get him back to his couch and buckle him in. If he's not floating around, he might get over being sick sooner."

Though John had maintained a professional attitude towards his crewmates throughout the training, even when Karl, Tom, Pam, and Bill had gotten sick in the Vomit Comet, he could no longer hold back his resentment of Karl. In complete contempt and disgust John said, "Christ, if you damned Krauts can't take space flight without puking all over the place and stinking up the entire cabin, you should stay in

---

Note: [1]darling

Kraut-land where you belong and leave flying in space to real astronauts."

Maria bristled, but before she could say anything, Isabel said sharply, "Shut up John. You know very well space sickness can hit anyone and you had better watch your personal slurs. Don't forget, I will be writing up your psychological report and I won't let you get away with that kind of verbal abuse. This is no way to start our mission."

As the crew's MD and psychologist, Isabel's sharp reprimand had enough teeth in it to shut John up, so Maria kept quiet and Karl was too miserable to give a damn what John said. Since Isabel had backed John into a corner, all he could say was, "Yeah, yeah, just see to it he doesn't make a mess in the cabin," and that ended that.

A little over an hour later, after Karl stopped vomiting and kept the Dramamine down, he was beginning to look better. John announced cheerfully, "The OTV and our trajectory are in excellent shape." He unbuckled himself from his couch and drifted over to where Maria and Isabel were still fussing around Karl.

As John arrived at Karl's couch, he suddenly got a peculiar look on his face. Not saying a word, John steadied himself in an apparent attempt to will an unpleasant sensation away. No fool, Isabel asked, "John, are you getting sick, too? If you are, get back to your couch and get stabilized. Maybe it will pass. I'll get some Dramamine."

Looking quite peaked and nodding weakly, John headed back to his couch. As soon as he got buckled in, he looked a little better — but then, as he vainly tried to grab for a sickness bag, and for the first time in his entire, long and distinguished career — John vomited.

Isabel, the most immune to such messes, immediately grabbed some paper towels and sprang to John's aid, followed by Maria, Bill, and Jim, who held their breaths to avoid getting sick themselves, while Pam and Tom, who had more frequently battled sickness in the Vomit Comet, and poor Karl, cowered as far from the action as possible.

As John continued to retch, but by then into a vomit bag provided by Maria, the helpers were making good progress cleaning his vomit off the surfaces where it had collected and capturing the spherical gobs of it that were floating around the cabin.

The latter phenomena shook Pam and Tom out of their lethargy and they sprang into action, helping to corral the disgusting, floating gobs, while Karl just tried to keep himself from vomiting all over again.

As the cleanup activities were in full swing and the cabin's air system was just making headway cleaning the air of the offensive odor, John suddenly groaned in misery, "God no. Get out of my way. I've got to go, and bad."

John unbuckled himself and literally hurled himself towards the zero-g toilet and locked himself in the little compartment. Like Frank Borman — Commander of the Apollo 8 Mission, the first manned mission to orbit the Moon in December of 1968 — John was hit by all the symptoms of space sickness — headache, vomiting, and diarrhea — a few hours after TLI.

It was a couple of hours before a naked — John had taken all his soiled clothes off while in the toilet — and humbled Commander emerged from the toilet to finish cleaning himself up and to put on some fresh clothes.

Still wobbly, John made his way to Karl and said loud enough so especially Isabel and Maria could hear, "Karl, I'm sorry about my remarks when you got sick. I guess I got what I had coming. Next time — and I hope there never will be a next time for either of us — I'll keep my mouth shut."

Karl, somewhat taken back by the first friendly thing John said to him in a long time, but one to let bygones be bygones, replied, "That's ok John. No hard feelings. And I agree, I never want anyone to get space sick again."

April 16, 2014

After that rough beginning, the boredom of space flight quickly set in and, as the Earth got smaller and the Moon got bigger, the crewmembers wiled away their time as best they could. The highlight of each day came when each crewmember got to talk with his or her family. Tom, Karl, and Maria had an advantage in that, because of the lack of privacy in the confined space of the OTV crew module, they spoke in Chinese, German, and Spanish, respectively, to their families. Unfortunately, Isabel's husband and children did not speak Spanish, so she, like Jim and Bill, kept her conversations from becoming too personal.

In contrast, Pam let her emotions run free in conversations that almost always took the same course — with minor variations — such as the first one the second day out, "I miss you so much sweetheart. Is everything ok at home? Are the children behaving and eating properly, or are you taking them to Pizza Hut or McDonald's every day?"

Her husband answered, "I miss you, too. The house is fine and so are the kids," but avoided the question about Pizza Hut and McDonald's.

Not noticing that lapse, Pam said, "Let me talk to the children." She then proceeded to say, more or less, the same thing to each child. "Mommy misses you so much. Lots of hugs and kisses," followed by several loud kissing sounds and then, "You behave, mind your daddy, and clean up your room like you promised me you would while mommy is on the Moon. Don't forget to look up at the Moon tonight and wave to mommy. Bye, bye, sweetheart, I love you." When she was finished, there were tears in her eyes and she retired to her couch to compose herself.

When John talked with his wife, he told her, "The mission is going very smoothly, though some of my crew got space sick after injection. But everyone is doing just fine now and, though this phase is a bit boring, everybody is excited about getting to the Moon and getting the Base up and running. I love you babe and I'm looking forward to being home with you again, but that will just have to wait another 6 months.

"How are the girls doing? Is Margaret still going with that oversexed jerk?" When his wife answered in the affirmative, John said, "Damn it, next time we talk, get her patched in so I can tell her to dump that bozo and you make her listen to me, understand. What is Beth up to, the same thing?" and so on.

Given what Bill had told Maria and Karl at Landry's a year earlier, both of them found John's conversation confusing and amusing.

April 17, 2014

About halfway through their 107-hour transit time, John said, "Boy, I agree with the Apollo Astronauts, the trip to the Moon is boring as hell, and their travel time was just 62 hours," and everyone agreed.

April 18, 2014

The boredom led the crew to become engaged in an animated discussion about NASA, the space program, and the origins of the Lunar Base Initiative.

Bill had started the conversation with many of the arguments, about how bad NASA is and how it had wasted all its money and time since Apollo, that he, Nancy, and George had bombarded the Whites with that July evening 9 years earlier.

When he took a breath, John jumped in, "I couldn't agree with you more. NASA sucks and I can tell you, most of my kind of astronauts think the same thing."

Pam said, "I can't believe you two. Here we are, on our way to the Moon because of NASA and all you can do is criticize it. You're biting the hand that feeds you. Shame on you. NASA has done great things for the nation and space exploration — look at the Mars exploration program and the Hubble and the other space telescopes. You should appreciate all that and accept that not everything goes well all the time."

John retorted, "Pam, take your head out of your butt. NASA management killed 3 Shuttle crews through some of the worst, self-serving, management decisions imaginable and wasted 40 years of time and technology before getting the 8 of us back on the way to the Moon — and the Lunar Base Initiative was not even NASA's idea, it was forced on NASA by Bush and Congress after the Columbia and Atlantis disasters. No, if NASA had its way, we would not be on the way to the Moon — we would still be screwing around with that deathtrap Shuttle and the useless Space Station."

Bill added, "Yeah, even when Bush senior suggested the Space Exploration Initiative back in '89, NASA screwed it up by planning a 500 billion-dollar program. Though Bush was just as much to blame for the failure of his SEI as NASA was."

Isabel asked, "What do you mean?"

Bill answered, "Look, Bush senior was a do-nothing President. When he announced the SEI, he did absolutely nothing to sell it to the public or to Congress. He just sat back, expecting it would somehow happen just because he suggested it. It was just like the Berlin Wall, when the East Block Nations began to break away from the Soviet Union. Bush did nothing to encourage the tearing down of the Wall, even though West Germany and the rest of the free world were putting as much pressure on the Commies to free East Germany as possible. Bush just sat back, afraid to hurt the Commies feelings, but when the Wall fell, he suddenly stood up and took credit for it.

"Basically I'm a Republican, but that pissed me off and I was really fed up with his half measures, like when he stopped the Gulf War after 100 hours and left Saddam Hassein sitting in Baghdad, so he could torture and kill his own people and cause unrest in the region for the next decade. I was so disgusted with him I even voted for Clinton in the next election. What a mistake that was, though I have to admit, had I known how depraved, corrupt, and immoral Clinton is, I still would not have voted for Bush. I probably would not have voted at all."

John said, "I agree about Bush," and added emphatically, "but it's absolutely nobody's business what Clinton did with women or what anybody else does with them either."

Isabel jumped in, "That's nonsense, John. He was the President — he should have set a high moral standard for the country and he had his trysts in the White House. That is our House, not his. If any executive of any company, big or small, did what he did, he would have been ousted immediately. As far as I am concerned, I'm glad he was impeached, but I am very disappointed he was not convicted by the Senate and removed from office."

Pam was indignant, "While I agree that President Clinton should not have done what he did with poor Monica, I think he was a fine President and deserved the second chance he got from the nation and from Hillary."

Bill rolled his eyes in disbelief at Pam's comment and said, "Pam, Pam, what can I say to that? The only good thing about Clinton is that Bush junior's desire for revenge for his father's defeat at the hands of Clinton prompted him to run in 2000. Though I was all for it, I believe Bush junior went to war with Saddam to make up for his father's failure to end the Gulf War with total victory.

"Likewise, I'm sure one of the motives behind Bush junior's Lunar/Mars Initiative of '04 was to make up for his father's failure to get his SEI pushed through. Regardless, I'm happy we're here, on our way to the Moon and to the Lunar Base, even if it's 30 years late and NASA is falling apart."

Uncharacteristically, Tom said, "I am sorry, Bill, but I do not share your feelings about NASA. I tend to agree with Pam. NASA cannot do more than Congress wants and NASA has accomplished much during its history. I believe the Lunar Base will prove NASA is an important and viable part of our national space program and it will continue to lead the program for decades to come." Then, having said his piece, Tom quietly withdrew from the conversation.

Finally Jim said something, "As a born Canadian, I don't care about American politics or the fate of NASA. All I care is I'm on my way to the Moon and I can finally start using its resources to build something. Long after NASA is gone and forgotten and America is just another dirt poor country on Earth, the Moon and it resources are going to be important for the Earth and for our expansion into the solar system."

Though the conversation continued a while longer, drifting between politics, NASA, and the Lunar Base, it had lost momentum and finally died a natural death.

Late Afternoon, April 19, 2014

Finally, the OTV arrived at the Moon, did its LLO insertion burn and 2 orbits later, rendezvoused and docked with the orbiting Tug and Landers that were already docked with the Tug via remote control from Houston. The Tug had arrived in LLO, after its slow trip from LEO, just 4 days earlier, and was loaded with supplies for the Base — life support LOX, liquid nitrogen, water, and food; fuel for the construction crane, bulldozer, and Traverse Vehicle; LOX and LH propellants for the Landers and the fuel cells of the Rovers and

Traverse Vehicle; the Traverse Vehicle itself; and miscellaneous equipment.

John had taken control of the rendezvous and docking of the OTV to the waiting Lander/Tug complex. Then he began the extensive checkout of the OTV, both Landers, and the Tug, with Houston verifying all his activities.

When he was finished, John remotely undocked the Lander with the crew module from its Tug berth, maneuvered the Lander so its upper access hatch was directly above the upper access hatch of the OTV's crew module, and docked the two.

Finally, everything was ready for the crew's landing on the Moon, scheduled for the next morning, after the crew had a good night's sleep.

Early Morning, April 20, 2014

John was the first to awaken and said in a loud and jovial voice, "All hands on deck. The Lander leaves in 3 hours. Anybody who's not onboard, will be left in orbit for the duration."

John's threat notwithstanding, the crew quickly got up, dressed, ate a light breakfast, and began to carefully checkout and put on their hard spacesuits.

After John had made sure everyone was properly suited, he carefully opened the hatches between the OTV crew module and the crew module on the Lander and entered the Lander's crew module. When he was satisfied everything was in order in the crew module, he said, "Ok everybody, come on in and get ready to land on the Moon."

Once everyone was ready, John undocked the Lander and set it drifting away from the Tug/OTV/2nd Lander complex at 1 m/sec. Some 20 minutes later, he started the de-orbit burn sequence and turned control of the Lander back to the computer, as the Lander, and its excited crew, dropped towards its landing at Fra Mauro's South Landing Pad, which was still halfway around the Moon and some 70 minutes away.

As they were dropping towards the Moon, the crew was quiet, except for John, who was exchanging trajectory, altitude, and velocity information with Houston. Some 10 minutes before the projected landing, the Lander's main engine kicked in and began to slow the Lander for its touchdown. When the Lander was about 110 kilometers from the South Landing Pad, it picked up the signal from the Pad's beacon and began automatically steering itself directly down the prescribed path.

At 10:43:22.7 GMT[1] on April 20, 2014, the contact probe touched the lunar surface in the partially modified, 30-meter diameter, 3-meter deep crater that served as the South Landing Pad and the engine immediately shut off. The First Operational Crew of the Fra Mauro Base had landed exactly 3 months ahead of the President and Congress' deadline.

Note: [1]Greenwich Mean Time

Chapter 2-4
Getting the Fra Mauro
Moon Base Operational

The Rest of April 20, 2014

"Welcome to the Moon, everybody. Let's get cracking and get this Base operational." Despite John's cheerful greeting, they could not "get cracking" until John had finished the post-landing checkout of the Lander, which took 30 minutes. Then John pumped the air out of the crew module, opened the front access door, and went down the ladder to become the 13th human to step on the Moon, just 3 months shy of 45 years after Neil Armstrong became the 1st human being to step on the Moon on July 20, 1969.

Trying to emulate Neil's first words, John said, as he stepped off the Lander, "That was a small step for a man, but it was the first step in the colonization of the Moon and beyond," and added somewhat caustically, "Too bad it took us nearly 45 years to take that next step."

John enjoyed the moment for a few more seconds and then began walking around the Lander to give it a good visual inspection. After finding no visible damage, he went under the Lander, opened a box that was partially buried in the crater floor by the tele-operation crews and that contained an electrical connector and hoses to the LOX and LH cryogenic refrigerators located just outside the crater's rim. John attached the connector and the hoses to the appropriate ports on the Lander in order to provide it with power from the nuclear power generator located 4 kilometers to the SE and to reliquefy the LOX and LH boil-off from the fuel tanks and return the fluids to the tanks.

When John was finished preparing the Lander for its 6-month stay on the Moon, he radioed, "Bill, come on down — let's inspect and turn-on our home-away-from-home."

Bill and John walked through the man-made breach in the east wall of the landing pad crater to the area just outside

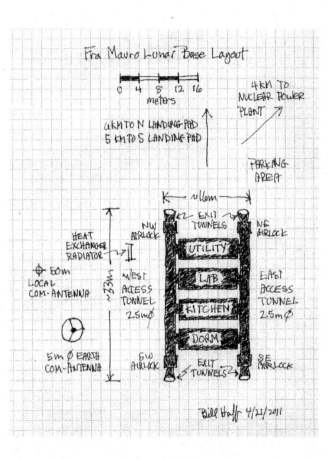

FRA MAURO LUNAR BASE LAYOUT

ROUGH SKETCH FROM BILL HUFF'S NOTEBOOK

the crater's rim where the 2 Rovers were parked. Bill disconnected the electrical cable from one of the Rovers and the power outlet box from the nuke, jumped in the driver's seat as John jumped in the passenger's seat, and started the 5-kilometer drive to the Base.

They had landed late in the lunar day, some 2 Earth days before local sunset. Because the Sun was about 30° above the western horizon, there was only the slightest hint of shadow visible on the steepest slopes in the small, young craters that littered the surface of the Fra Mauro. Both Bill and John were struck by the stark beauty of the rolling hills of the Fra Mauro, and like the Apollo 14 astronauts who preceded them over 43 years earlier, they exclaimed in childish delight, "Fantastic. Amazing. Breathtaking."

After a 25-minute ride, Bill pulled up to the parking place next to the NE entrance to the Base and said, "End of the line. Let's go, John."

As they quickly walked to the mouth of the entrance tunnel, John said, "As Base Designer and Base Engineer, you should have the honor to be the first to enter."

Bill said, "Why, thank you, John. I appreciate that."

With flashlight in hand, Bill went into the short tunnel that led to the NE airlock, which served as the main entrance to the Base, and manually opened its outer door. Following the bright light of his flashlight, he entered the dark and airless airlock. Then he manually opened and closed the outer and inner doors of the airlock several times, to insure they worked properly and inspected the interior of the lock.

Satisfied, he stepped into East Access Tunnel, which led to the east or front doors of the 4 modules and to the SE airlock at the south end of the tunnel, and said to John, "Ok, come on in."

Once inside, they proceeded down the dark, airless tunnel, with flashlights in hand, inspecting the junctions and their seals, the modules' vacuum doors, which they opened and closed several times, and then they inspected the SE airlock. They exited the SE airlock and re-entered the Base via the SW airlock, inspected it, and entered West Access Tunnel, or West Utility Tunnel, which carried all the utility cables,

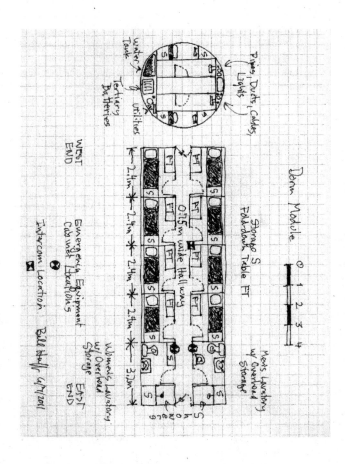

Dorm Module

Water Tank

Pipes, Ducts, Cables, Lights

Tertiary Batteries

Utilities

WEST END

2.4m 2.4m 2.4m 2.4m 2.4m 3.7m

0.75m wide Hallway

Storage S
Foldaback Table FT

Men's Lavatory w/ Overhead Storage

Emergency Equipment Cabinet Locations

Women's Lavatory w/ Overhead Storage

EAST END

Intercom Location. Bill Huff 4/7/2011

DORM MODULE DETAILS

ROUGH SKETCH FROM BILL HUFF'S NOTEBOOK

pipes, and airshafts to the modules and which was the back-up access tunnel to the modules.

After inspecting West Utility Tunnel, the west or back doors at the rears of the modules, and the NW airlock, Bill said, "Ok, I'm satisfied we have safe access to the entire Base."

The next step in the very meticulous checkout procedure was the checkout of the battery powered, tertiary emergency power system in each module, starting with the Dormitory Module — or Dorm for short, at the south end of the Base; followed by the next module, which housed the kitchen, hospital, and recreation/exercise area — called Kitchen; then by the Selenophysical/Selenological/Selenopetrological Laboratory Module — or just Lab; and ending with the Utility Module — or Utility, at the north end of the Base. Kneeling just inside the rear access door of each module, Bill had lifted the floor panel that covered the batteries, checked their voltages, and then switched on the tertiary emergency lighting for a few seconds. Once that step was done, and being in Utility, Bill checked the battery powered, secondary emergency power system, whose batteries were also housed below the floor of Utility. The secondary system ran not only the secondary emergency lighting in all the modules, access tunnels, and airlocks, but also the air control system, so Bill was extra thorough in his testing of that crucial system.

Then Bill checked out the primary power control unit in Utility and said, "John, we have to be absolutely certain that all the electrical systems in the entire Base are turned off before we switch the power on. You check Dorm and Kitchen and I'll check Utility and Lab and make sure each system on this list is off before you check it off, ok?"

When they were finished, Bill said, "John, go out the NE exit and plug the big power cable from the nuke into the external power receptacle of the Base."

By the time John came back into Utility, Bill was checking the voltages and other readings on the then functioning power control unit. Once satisfied that everything on the check-off list was correct, Bill turned on the power from the nuke to the primary power circuit. After he verified there was still no current flowing, that is — there were no electrical

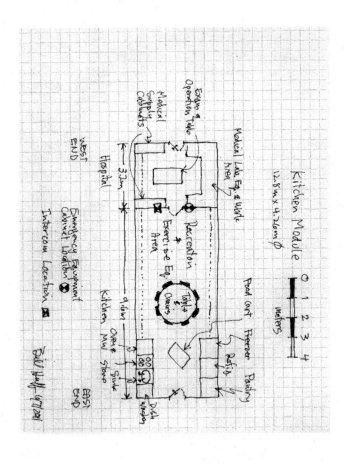

KITCHEN MODULE DETAILS

ROUGH SKETCH FROM BILL HUFF'S NOTEBOOK

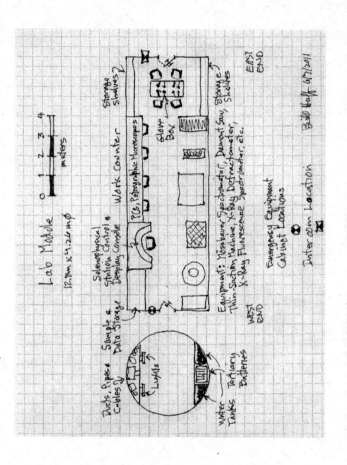

LAB MODULE DETAILS

ROUGH SKETCH FROM BILL HUFF'S NOTEBOOK

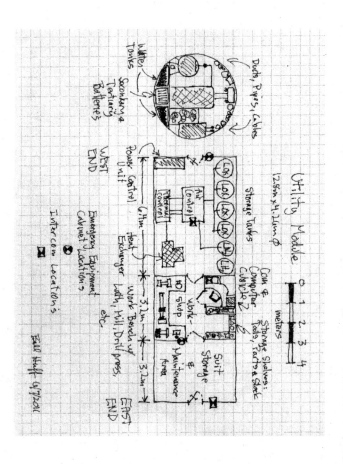

UTILITY MODULE DETAILS

ROUGH SKETCH FROM BILL HUFF'S NOTEBOOK

shorts in the primary power grid, he said, "John turn on the primary lights in here," and when he did, the lights in Utility came on perfectly. Bill then turned on and off each system — the air control system, the heat exchanger, etc. — in the module and repeated the procedure for the other 3 modules, the access tunnels, and the airlocks, leaving the lights on. When they were finished, the entire Base was under external power, with fully functioning secondary and tertiary emergency power systems.

Having spent nearly 7 hours in their spacesuits and being very tired and hungry, they left the Base and returned to the crew module on the Lander for food and a good night's sleep with the rest of the crew.

April 21, 2014

The next day, Karl and Jim, who had the necessary physics background to assist in the inspection and preparation of the Base for habitation, joined Bill and John. They first drove the bulldozer, which like the construction crane, could be tele-operated from Houston or driven on the Moon by humans, and its trailer to North Landing Pad 1 kilometer north of South Landing Pad. Like its southern counterpart, North Landing Pad was located in a 30-meter diameter crater and in it was the second Lander, which was loaded with supplies from the Tug and which had been landed via remote control by Houston the day before. Once the trailer was loaded with the transfer tanks of LOX, LH, liquid nitrogen, water, and the transfer pipes for those fluids, the 4 astronauts drove to the Base, with Bill manning the Bulldozer and Karl hitching a ride with him, followed by John and Jim in one of the Rovers.

As they drove to the Base, each of the crewmembers was absorbed in the desolate beauty of the lunar surface. Though the vista enthralled everyone, it sent Karl into raptures of delight. He babbled, to the delight and/or amusement of the others, "Mensch[1], look at that young crater, it can't be more than a few 100,000 years old, if that," and, "Look over there, that big boulder has a contact running right through it, just

---

Note: [1]Man

like Contact Rock the Apollo 14 Astronauts photographed," followed by, "Hey, see that bunch of breccias around that little cluster of secondary craters," and on, and on, as they drove though a selenologists paradise.

When they arrived at the Base, John and Jim attached the transfer pipes to the external couplings leading inside Utility to the storage tanks for the LOX, LH, and liquid nitrogen and to the water storage tanks below the floors of 3 of the modules.

While they were busy with the pipes, Bill and Karl went inside the still airless, but no longer dark Base and into Utility to make a final inspection of the pipes and storage tanks and to turn on the air control unit.

As he turned the unit on, Bill said, "As the LOX and liquid nitrogen flow into these warm storage tanks, oxygen and nitrogen will rapidly boil off until the tanks chill down to their boiling points and the flow of those gases into the Base has to be regulated, or all hell could break loose," and he checked all the gauges to see if the unit was running properly.

"Next we close all the air conduits to the access tunnels and to Dorm, Kitchen, and Lab, and bring the atmospheric pressure here in Utility up to the standard 0.3 bars. Then we check for leaks of any kind and check the pressure readings on the gauges mounted inside the module at the access doors to East Access Tunnel and West Utility Tunnel during the next hour. I hate to say it, but I'm still worried about the integrity of the Base. I just don't trust anything put together tele-robotically."

By that time, John and Jim had rejoined Bill and Karl and they all went to close off the rest of the Base from Utility and Bill proceeded with its pressure test. An hour later, after Bill was satisfied Utility was airtight, he pumped the air out of Utility. Then they repeated the pressurization and checkout procedure for each of the other 3 modules, the access tunnels, and the airlocks.

Finding that the entire Base was airtight, Bill said, "Well, maybe I was wrong. Maybe a base can be built with tele-operated equipment and it won't fall apart the first time a door slams. Let's get all the conduits and vents open and get air in this Base."

That long, careful checkout procedure lasted 12 hours and when they were done, the crew returned to their home in the crew module for food and rest — and the Base had a breathable atmosphere.

April 22, 2014

With a breathable atmosphere in the Base and with the air management system working, much to the relief of Maria, Isabel, Pam, and Tom, who were beginning to get cabin fever, the entire crew would be able to go into the Base, take off their spacesuits, and work efficiently.

After the crew had gotten suited up and passed their suit checks, John started the pump to evacuate the crew module so they could egress. As the air was being pumped out, John said over his suit radio, "Today is a historic day. Isabel, Maria, and Pam — you will be the first women to step on the Moon's surface, so you 3 go out first and say something appropriate for the TV. I'll leave it up to you who goes first."

Having completely forgotten the facts that only men — and only 16 men at that — had ever walked on the Moon and that they had been the first 3 women to land on the Moon, Isabel, Maria, and Pam were taken by surprise at John's comment. Isabel was the first to recover and replied, "How thoughtful, but now you put us on the spot."

Maria immediately said, "Isabel, you're the oldest and most experienced, you go first."

Pam added emphatically, "Yes, you should go first."

Isabel hesitated, smiled broadly, and finally said, "Ok, let's go?" as John opened the front access door.

Isabel, followed by Maria and then Pam, started down the ladder to the surface. When she reached the surface, she stepped off the ladder and waited for Maria and Pam. After they were all on the surface, Isabel said, "Those might have been small steps for Neil and John, but they were giant leaps for women."

The historical act finished, the men came out and down the ladder and the crew drove to the Base on the rovers.

The first task at hand at the Base was to get the water system checked out and running. By early afternoon, hot and cold water for drinking, food preparation, showers, and the toilets were available throughout the Base and all those systems were checked out and functioning properly.

In the few remaining hours left in their workday, the crew began the final checkout of all the subsystems in the Base, e.g., the oven, microwave, refrigerator, and freezer in Kitchen and the power tools and life support equipment in Utility. When they were finished, they left the Base to go back to their living quarters in the crew module to get supper and rest.

April 23, 2014

Early the next morning — one day after lunar sunset — they loaded their duffel bags on the Bulldozer's trailer, which they had already loaded with food and other supplies from the cargo Lander on North Landing Pad. When they were finished, John said, "Come on, let's get to our new home," and the caravan of the Bulldozer and trailer, followed by 2 Rovers, set out on its 12 km/hr trek to the Base.

Upon arriving at the parking site, as the crew gathered their duffel bags and assembled at the mouth of the NE entrance, John again graciously said to Bill, "As Base Engineer, you should be the first to enter."

Bill laughed and replied, "Thanks," and proceeded to the airlock door. Seeing the expected red status light on, indicating that the airlock was evacuated, he pressed the open button, and the door effortlessly opened. He and John stepped inside, closed the door, and started the airlock cycle. The remaining crewmembers saw the status lights change from red to green, as air was let into the lock and turn back to red after John and Bill had stepped into East Tunnel, had closed the door, and had started the pump to evacuate the airlock again.

Over their suit radios, they heard John say, "The next two can come in."

In pairs, the remaining 6 crewmembers entered the Base. Maria and Karl were the last — they wanted to look at the selenology in the bright, blue earthlight as long as possible.

After everyone was inside, they entered Utility in pairs — there was too little room in Utility's suit area for more that 2 people to take off their suits at one time.

After Tom, John, and Bill had de-suited and while the others were still at that task, the three went to Tom's com-cubicle and radioed Houston. Once Tom had established contact, John reported, again mimicking Neil Armstrong, "Houston, Fra Mauro Base here, the operational crew has arrived," and then he and Bill gave Houston a short status report and Tom signed off.

When everyone had de-suited, John said, "Let's go to Kitchen for a celebration."

Though it was strictly against NASA's rules, John had smuggled 2 bottles of wine to the Base in his personal belongings.

When they assembled in Kitchen, John brought out his contraband, to everyone's surprise and delight, and said, "Pam, get 8 glasses, so we can properly toast the official opening of the Base."

Pam responded, "Gladly John. What a nice surprise."

As Pam went for the glasses, John opened the wine, saying, "I thought about bringing champagne, but I was a little worried about the bottles exploding because of the launch or landing vibrations and what would happen when I uncorked the bottles at $\frac{1}{3}$ of an atmosphere of pressure. Also, I figured Isabel would get on my case if I brought something stronger than wine, so wine will have to do."

Isabel laughed and shook her head.

Pam said, "Wine is fine by me," and the others agreed wholeheartedly, as John began to pour the amber liquid into the glasses. Under lunar gravity, the wine took a perceptible 0.5 sec to go from the bottle to the glasses, where on Earth the trip would have lasted just a barely detectable 0.2 sec.

As they all slowly raised their glasses in a toast, being careful not to let the wine slosh out of the glasses by any abrupt movements, John said, "Here's to the brand-new Fra Mauro Base and her First Operational Crew. Cheers," which was followed by a chorus of, "Cheers," and everyone took a sip or a slug of their wine.

After some lighthearted conversation, the little party began to breakup as the crewmembers took their duffel bags and drifted to Dorm to start getting their personal belongings stashed away in their private quarters and to make their beds. Tasks that were difficult, since the rooms — on either side of a 0.75-meter wide, 12.8-meter long, central hallway — were only 2.4 meters long, 1.7 meters wide at their widest, and 3 meters tall.

Each room had just enough space for a narrow bed that served as a sofa during the day, a fold down table, and storage spaces below, above, and at the end of the bed.

Similarly, the small lavatories at the east end of Dorm had just enough room for a shower, sink, toilet, and storage cabinets.

The modules gave one the feeling of being in World War II submarines, a feeling that was enhanced because each of the vacuum doors at the ends of the modules had a small, round escape door, or submarine hatch, in its middle.

John said, "Since the women's and men's lavatories are on the left and right sides of the hall, I suggest the rooms on the left side should be mainly for the women and those on the right side should be for the men, with the odd man on the women's side of Dorm, ok?" and no one disagreed.

"As Commander, I want the first room right next to the men's lavatory and the front door, so I can get to the other modules fast, if I have to. And since you're the Base MD, Isabel, you need to be near the front door so you can get to Hospital fast, if you're needed there."

Isabel replied somewhat suspiciously, "I don't agree. As Base Engineer and Second in Command, Bill's room needs to be right across from yours, so you both can get out fast in case of an emergency."

Maria and Pam backed Isabel up, while the rest of the men remained neutral. Thus, Isabel won and Bill took the room next to the women's lavatory, directly across from John's room.

Pam said, "I'll take the room behind Bill's."

And Isabel said, "I will take the next one, if that ok with you Maria?" and it was.

As soon as Maria had agreed, Karl said, with a smile, "I'll take the room across from Maria's," and Maria blushed more than a little.

Tom took the room next to John's, and Jim ended up with the one between Tom and Karl.

Then, each crewmember went to his or her room and got busy trying to make their mini-domains as homey as possible.

When they were finished, Maria, Karl, and Jim went to Lab to start getting it ready for work; Isabel went to her hospital in Kitchen; Pam went to kitchen proper; Tom went to his small com-cubicle in Utility; and Bill went to Utility to fuss with the life support equipment and to checkout his mini-workshop tools. That left John, who did not know exactly what to do with himself, except to patrol around the modules to see if everyone was finding everything in order and to flirt a little with Isabel, who had been trying to avoid him.

April 24, 2014, through April 28, 2014

During the next few days, all the rest of the cargo, including the Traverse Vehicle, was brought down from the Tug via remote control from Houston. The Tug then started its slow journey back to LEO. Simultaneously, the OTV started its 4½-day trip back to LEO and the crew finished getting the facilities and all the equipment checked out and ready for full operations.

Bill and Jim finished filling the tanks in Utility with life support LOX and liquid nitrogen and the LOX and LH needed for the fuel cells and the water tanks under the floors of Utility, Dorm, and Kitchen. Then they loaded the external fuel tanks with diesel fuel and hydrogen peroxide for the construction crane, bulldozer, and Traverse Vehicle. Finally they began setting up the regolith sorting machinery, so they could start the work of lining the landing pad craters with cobble and covering the roads with gravel — tasks that would keep Jim, and whoever would help him, busy for half of the crew's 6-month stay on the Moon.

Tom, characteristically, kept to himself, tending to the Base's computer net and faithfully maintaining communications with the crewmembers when they were working outside the Base and with Houston.

Isabel began her medical studies of the crew's adaptation to the Base environment by starting her weekly physical and

psychological examinations of each crewmember and collecting their urine, feces, blood, and tissue samples.

During John's first exam, Isabel, having noticed that John
seemed a little lost, asked, "John, now that we've been on the
Moon nearly a week and settled in the Base for a few days,
what are your thoughts, good and bad?"

John thought a minute and answered cautiously, "Well,
I'm used to a little more action. As I had expected, the trip
here was boring. But I thought things would liven up when
we got here at the Base. Of course they did the first couple of
days. But once you guys got busy with your research, there
has not been a hell of a lot for me to do."

Isabel asked, "Didn't you sense that would be the case
during our training, when we were in the Base mockup for a
month?"

"Not really, I mean, yeah, I was bored, but I figured that
was just because we were on Earth in a mockup. Training is
never as interesting as the real thing. So I figured once we
were here, things would be exciting — like it was for the
Apollo Astronauts."

"But John, they spent no more than 3 days on the Moon
and were outside the LM, exploring the surface for up to 8
hours a day. You, Pam, Tom, and I will hardly ever be outside
and even our intrepid pair of selenologists will spend only a
few weeks outside. Most of their work will be in their Lab.
Though Jim and Bill will apparently spend more time outside
doing resource utilization work. You are supposed to help
Jim and you could volunteer to do more outside work with
him."

"Sounds boring to me. I want some real action. I would
enjoy going on the Traverse Vehicle trips, but they're all
booked with the science geeks and Bill. There's no room for
the Commander. What a load of crap."

Isabel asked, "Well, how did you handle this when you
were back on Earth? You were not flying jets and spacecraft
all the time."

John looked as if an opportunity had just presented
itself, "Do you want me to be bluntly honest?"

"Yes."

"Well, I chased around. There's nothing like beautiful women to put a little spice in your life during dull times. In fact, you're a beautiful and desirable woman and I'm a handsome and desirable man. So why don't we take advantage of our isolation from Earth. There's no reason for us to be lonely up here and — "

Isabel bristled and interrupted sharply, "John, I am not interested in having any kind of relationship with you, except that which is required by my duties as the Base Doctor. Is that clear?"

Since John's direct approach had almost always worked on the bar bimbos, he appeared quite surprised that Isabel had rebuffed him. But, unabashed, John replied, "Don't give me that. A beautiful, sexy woman like you needs a real man around to keep her satisfied and I'm just the one to satisfy you. And don't give me that married woman routine. Your husband is half-a-million kilometers and 6 long months away. Do you think he's waiting around for you to return — not if he is a real man with — "

Isabel cut John off again, "You know nothing of my husband and don't be so arrogant to think that all men — all real men, as you like to say — have to chase every skirt that walks by to prove how macho they are. Real men do not have to prove it. It's self-evident by the way they conduct themselves."

John responded, "Think what you like. Your husband is on Earth, while you're here and I'm here. Given the circumstances, I'm sure you'll come around to my way of thinking — anyway, I can wait."

Having nearly reached her Latin boiling point, Isabel visibly struggled to keep her Castilian upbringing from being overwhelmed by her anger and finally said, calmly, but contemptuously, "You will have to wait until hell freezes over. Now take off your shirt, so I can start your physical," which she conducted without attempting to be gentle while taking John's blood and tissue samples.

While Isabel was starting her medical studies, Pam was busy recording what everyone was eating and making out menus to make sure everyone was eating well-balanced meals. Though those activities bothered no one, Pam's rigorous attention to making sure everyone kept up with the required 2 hours of physical fitness training everyday was a pain in everyone's behind, except John's. John actually liked to work out and used the time to flirt with Pam. But after Isabel's rebuff, John's flirting changed from innocent fun, to something more serious. During one workout, John said, "Gee Pam, why don't we go off somewhere and get sweaty together, instead of wasting all this energy on the treadmill?"

Pam just laughed and answered in a motherly tone, as if she was talking to one of her children "Johnny, Johnny, don't be a naughty boy, or I'll have to send you to bed without supper?" which quickly cooled John's desire and added to his humiliation.

Without a word, John left Kitchen and went to his room in Dorm.

Maria and Karl spent most of their time in Lab, getting all the scientific equipment calibrated and ready to use, as well as planning their first Rover excursion to collect Fra Mauro samples and to set up a Selenophysical Station, the first in the new network and the first in 45 years, 19 kilometers south of the Base. They were planning to do their Rover fieldtrip 3 days after local sunrise, on May 9.

The First Rover Fieldtrip

April 29, 2014, through May 8, 2014

As the first several days passed, each crewmember had fallen into his or her daily routine and John became both more withdrawn and more belligerent, especially towards Karl, and more sexually aggressive towards the women — a state of affairs that annoyed everyone. And Isabel became more and more concerned about John's mental state.

Though it was still deep lunar night outside the Base and the surface temperature was $-165°$ C, Karl and Maria went out twice to collect rock, soil, and 2-meter core samples within a few 100 meters of the Base and spent many happy hours in Lab cataloging and doing preliminary analyses on the samples, in preparation for their eventually being sent to Earth. Those activities gave Maria and Karl practice doing fieldwork on the Moon, instead of in the deserts and volcanic areas of Earth, and got them used to using Lab's equipment on real samples. But they were really looking forward to their first Rover fieldtrip and even more to the Copernicus Traverse.

May 9, 2014

Maria and Karl had gotten up early the morning of their first real lunar fieldtrip. After showering and dressing, they went to Kitchen, well before Pam, and heated up a substantial breakfast of pancakes with honey and sausage, coffee for Maria, and carbonated grape juice for Karl, who hated coffee.

As they were eating, Pam came in and, finding they had beaten her to her domain, said cheerfully, "Well, you two lovebirds are up early. All excited about your fieldtrip, huh?"

Between mouthfuls, Karl said, "We want to be ready to go as soon as Tom is in the com-center. I hope he's up and ready to go on time."

Pam said, "Yes he is. He was going into the men's lavatory just as I was going into the women's. But since you have to wait for John, too, don't get your hopes up that you'll get off on time."

Just then, to their surprise, both Tom and John came into Kitchen.

Uncharacteristically, John had gotten up early and when he entered Kitchen, he said, "I have to make sure you two don't screw up and get killed out there. Nobody under my command is going to do that. As soon as you are done with breakfast, I want to go over the safety checklist again, before I give you my final permission to leave on your little field-trip."

Karl bristled and said sarcastically, "Both Maria and I really appreciate your concern about our safety and the success of our little fieldtrip, danke schöne[1]."

John retorted maliciously, "I don't care about you, buddy, just Maria."

Seeing that the insult to Karl and the sexual innuendo to Maria made Karl mad as hell, Pam stepped in before the confrontation escalated any further and said, "Boys, boys, enough of your friendly banter. Maria and Karl — finish your breakfasts and get suited up. John, I'll fix you and Tom something special, while they're getting ready."

Karl and Maria left their unfinished breakfasts — an act they later regretted, since, except for the juice and water they could sip from their suit's liquid reservoirs, they would not eat for another 12 hours — and left Kitchen for the suit area in Utility.

Once inside Utility, Karl exploded, "That filthy Schwein[2]. If he so much as looks at you again, I'll break his filthy neck."

Maria responded quickly, "I know Karl. But don't let him get to you. He does that just to make you angry."

"I know, but I also know he's after you just as much as he's after Isabel and if I weren't with you all the time, he'd bother you as much as he does her. What in hell is the matter with NASA for having such an Arschlock[3] in the Astronaut Corps, let alone having him be the Commander of the Base with 3 woman for him to hound?"

Notes: [1] many thanks; [2] pig; [3] asshole

"Karl, you know NASA and its good-old-boy mentality. There's nothing you can do about it, so let's just do our jobs and forget him. Ok?"

"Ok, but there are limits to what I'll put up with for the sake of science. Let's get into our suits."

Wisely, Pam told Bill, who came to Kitchen after Karl and Maria had left, "Bill, why don't you go to Utility to help Karl and Maria with their final suit checks and to see them off. The rest of us will stay here."

Bill, noting that something was amiss and since it did not take a genius to guess what, replied, "Sure, I'll check them out and see them off," and left for Utility, as a furious John brooded over his breakfast.

Later, when she was alone with Isabel, Pam told her about John's behavior and Isabel said, "John is really beginning to worry me. He is getting more and more confrontational with everyone and more aggressive with his sexual advances towards me — and I assume towards you and Maria, too. He has become all too aware he has little to do here. NASA's having put a Pilot Astronaut in command of 7 highly skilled, professional people, who have useful research to do, has put John is a position of authority with no real authority — we do not need him to tell us what to do. He's used to being the center of attention and his macho ego can't take the fact that he's useless here. I'm afraid we have a real problem building up, especially since he can't get any of us in bed, which seems to be the only way left for him to prove he is a man. He is getting frightening. If he gets worse, I'll have to inform NASA. Help me keep an eye on him, ok? "

Pam nodded and answered, "Yes, of course I will."

By the time Isabel and Pam had that private conversation, it was nearly 8:00 GMT and Maria and Karl had arrived at their first sample collection stop, the south rim of a 2-kilometer diameter, very young crater, 6 kilometers SSW of the Base.

By then, Karl and Maria had forgotten about John, in fact, it had taken Karl only until they were exiting the NE exit tunnel to cool down. There was nothing like being on the lunar surface, surrounded by the beautiful, low rolling hills of the Fra Mauro, with its plethora of craters — from the tiniest pits to those several meters across and that range in morphology from bowl shaped young craters to highly degraded, shallow old crater — as well as numerous rocks of all sizes and shapes to calm both Maria and Karl down. They were in their dream world, about to embark on their first lunar fieldtrip and nothing, not even John, could spoil that for them.

Karl started the narration to go along with the TV pictures being periodically sent to Earth for public viewing, "The 2-kilometer diameter crater we have driven to has excavated rocks from as deep as 280 meters below the surface and deposited the deepest rocks at the rim and those from near the surface, farthest from the rim. Since the crater is so deep, it probably brought up samples from the pre-existing surface on which the Fra Mauro Formation was deposited when a giant impact formed the 1000-kilometer diameter Imbrium Basin 3.8 billion years ago. By collecting ejecta samples along a radial traverse from the crater rim, we will have a continuous set of samples from the ancient, Pre-Imbrium rock unit just below the Fra Mauro Formation, to the very top of the Fra Mauro."

Karl stopped the Rover, just short of the crater rim, among boulders ranging from a meter in dimensions to those that were bigger than a large house. He said, "We've stopped on the rim to collect our first samples. We're going to collect a standard set here — a double core soil sample, a set of 1 to 3 centimeter diameter rake samples — so named because they are collected with a rake, a few 10 to 20 centimeter, hand-sized rocks, and we are going to chip off some samples from the big boulders."

Then he asked Maria, "Schatz, since these are all highland samples, do you want to collect them and have me do the documentary photos, or the other way around?"

Maria answered, "I'll collect and you photograph," and she got off the Rover, went to its cargo bed, and collected the sampling tools and the rock box in which the samples would be put and sealed, while Karl grabbed the camera.

Loaded with their equipment, they walked some 30 meters up the slope to the very rim of the crater. When they arrived, they were stunned by the beautiful panorama before them. Having stood many times on the rim of the 1-kilometer diameter Meteor Crater in northern Arizona and on the rims of the 1-kilometer diameter volcanic craters in the Pinacate Volcanic Field in northern Sonora, Mexico, as well as having seen the pictures taken from the rim of North Ray Crater by Apollo 16 Astronauts, John Young and Charlie Duke, Maria and Karl thought they knew what to expect — but they didn't.

The view into the 330-meter deep crater, with its opposite rim 2 kilometers to the north, was spectacular. With absolute crystal clarity, they saw the exposed rock beds in the inner wall, just below the crater's rim — outcrops they could follow around most of the crater's circumference and down to the point where streaks of dark and light talus and fallback had buried the original surface of the bowl shaped crater.

Looking at the bottom of the crater, they saw a 300-meter diameter pool of very dark, solidified impact melt and Maria said, "Boy, I wish we could get down there to sample that impact melt rock to get a good age on this crater. But since we can't, let's look for impact melt pools round the rim area and some glassy samples of impact melt in the ejecta."

After absorbing the beauty of the crater for a minute, Karl began taking a series of photos, from which they could make a 180° panoramic mosaic back at the Base. As he did, Maria noted, "Cariño, you know we are looking into the biggest crater anyone has seen from the Moon's surface. The biggest seen during Apollo was North Ray at the Apollo 16 site and that was only a kilometer in diameter."

Karl answered, "Ja Liebling[1], but just wait until we do the Copernicus Traverse and look down into Copernicus — this view will pale in comparison."

Maria replied, "Sí, I can hardly wait."

Then they got busy collecting and documenting the various samples they wanted from the rim area, tasks that took about forty minutes. Taking one last look into the breathtaking crater, they turned to walk back to the Rover and put their equipment and the rock box back on the cargo bed.

Note: [1]darling

Karl then used a portable gravimeter and a portable magnetometer to measure the local value of gravity and the local magnetic field.

Finally finished at that site, Karl climbed aboard the Rover and they drove off through the boulders, almost due south, following a prominent eject ridge that turned into a ray, a kilometer to the south, with many secondary craters and plenty of the eject blocks and rocks they sought.

As they drove southwards to their second collection area, ½ kilometer from the rim, they chatted about the stark, beautiful landscape they were driving through, a landscape that reminded them of the beautiful, barren deserts and lava fields of Arizona, New Mexico, and Mexico. Both of them were in heaven — they were together, sharing an adventure that was beyond description, absolutely on their own, alone and away from the Base and the annoyances caused by John's increasingly erratic behavior.

They reached their second stop, where they collected more rock, rake, and soil samples from the crater's ejecta and Karl made a second set of gravity and magnetic measurements.

They stopped again 1 kilometer from the rim and then every 2 kilometers along the ray, collecting and documenting the soil, rake, and rock samples they needed to study the stratigraphy of the Fra Mauro Formation and the pre-Imbrian surface and for Karl to make his selenophysical measurement. As they did, they kept up a running dialog with Tom, Bill, and Jim, the latter two having gone to Tom's com-cubicle to follow Maria and Karl's progress, and for the benefit of the listening public.

As expected, by the time they reached their seventh stop, which was 15 kilometers south of the Base, they began to notice the communication link was breaking up — they were passing over the horizon as seen from the 50-meter tall antenna used for local communications between the Base and crews working on the surface. Tom said, "Karl, you had better switch over to the Earth-link. I have already told Houston you would be doing that at the seventh stop."

Karl replied, "Ok, I'm doing it now — do you have us on the Earth-link?" He waited — instead of the radio signals going just 15 kilometers between the Rover and the 50-meter antenna and taking an inconsequential 0.1 milliseconds for the round trip, the signals had to go 384,000 kilometers to the Earth and back again, for a round trip time of 2.5 seconds.

About 3 seconds after asking the question, Karl and Maria heard Tom's voice loud and clear as he answered, "Yes, I have you on the Earth-link."

Maria and Karl continued their work at that stop and proceeded to make 2 more stops, the last one being 19 kilometers from the Base, the farthest point they would go on that fieldtrip. There they would set up the first Selenophysical Station of the new network and the first one to gather data since the Apollo Stations were shut down nearly 40 years earlier.

Karl stopped the Rover in a broad, flat, inter-crater area and he said, "This is an ideal place for the station. Let's set it up first and then do the sampling over by that small secondary crater over there," pointing a little to the west.

Maria answered, "Fine, you get the station and I'll get the camera. Let's go," and they happily jumped from the Rover and went to the cargo bed. Karl unlatched the bulky Selenophysical Station and picked it up as Maria got the camera.

Just before they started to leave the Rover, Bill radioed, "Ok you guys, you have been on your PLSSs[1] for over 7 hours and you have less than an hour of life support left in them. You need to put the spare PLSSs on now — before you do anything else."

Maria responded, "Copy that. We'll change PLSSs right now."

When they were finished, they started walking 15 meters from the Rover to where Karl wanted to set up the station. He was having trouble carrying the bulky station and said, "This thing might not be heavy in ⅙-g, but it's hard to carry in this spacesuit."

Like the Apollo Astronauts, Maria and Karl tended to babble euphorically at times and that was one of them. Maria laughed and teased, "Oh, come on, be my macho man. Quit complaining about that little load. Or do you want me to carry it?"

Note: [1]Portable Life Support System

Karl just laughed and said, "No, mi señorita pequeña[1], I'll manage just fine."

By then they reached the site where Karl wanted to set up the station. He sat the station down, oriented it properly, and adjusted its antenna so it was pointing towards Earth, as Maria photographed what he was doing.

Karl said, "I'll dig the hole for the seismometer and then I'll drill the holes for the heat-flow probes, if you'll set up the RTG[2], the magnetometer, and the tidal gravimeter."

Maria replied, "Ok, that shouldn't take me very long. When I'm finished, I'll get the seismometer and the probes ready to put in the ground."

Maria took each piece of equipment off the Central Station, carried it the 10 meters its cables would allow, sat it on the surface, properly oriented it, and photographed it. When she was done, the RTG, the magnetometer, and the tidal gravimeter were 10 meters north, west, and south of the Central Station, respectively. Satisfied, she returned to the station, unlatched the seismometer and the 2 heat-flow probes, and carried the former 10 meters to the SE of the Central Station to the ½-meter deep hole Karl had laboriously dug. Since Karl was still busy drilling the second of 2 holes for the heat-flow probes, Maria asked, "Shall I go ahead and bury the seismometer?"

Karl, huffing and puffing from the strain of drilling the holes, answered, "Ja, go ahead. I'll be done soon. Mensch, this is as hard as the Apollo Astronauts said it was. I would have thought that the engineers would have improved the drill."

Maria carefully put the seismometer package, which contained a standard 3-axis, broadband seismometer with a short period vertical seismometer, as well as an ultra-long period, vertical seismometer, in the hole Karl had laboriously dug. She carefully aligned the package, photographed it, and began to shovel the loose regolith over the seismometer package, to protect it from the 300° C swing in temperature between lunar noon and lunar night.

Notes: [1]my little miss; [2]Radioactive Thermal Generator

Knowing full well it is very hard to dig up the regolith, since it is tightly compacted by the innumerable impacts that pounded it over the eons, but once loosened, it is very easy to shovel, Maria teased, "Gee, cariño, I don't see why you are so tired, shoveling this little bit of regolith is very easy."

Karl stopped the drill and replied, "If you don't stop making fun of me, I'll make you walk back to the Base," and they both laughed giddily.

After Maria buried the seismometers, she took the 2 heat-flow probes to Karl, who carefully inserted them into the 1.5-meter deep holes he had finished drilling. Karl said, "There, we're done with the station. Let's get the samples. I'll make the gravity and magnetic measurements and then we can head home. I'm starving."

It was 15:00 GMT and they still had 2 hours of sample collection and driving to do. Except for water and juice, they had eaten nothing since their abbreviated breakfast and they were regretting they had let John spoil their breakfast.

Finally, at a little after 17:00 GMT, they arrived at the Base. They were greeted by everyone but John, as they came in the NE airlock carrying their precious rock boxes, which they let Bill and Jim take to Lab as they de-suited.

They went to Kitchen, where Pam had warmed prepared dinners of roast beef, mashed potatoes with gravy, green beans, rolls, juice, tea or coffee, and dessert of apple pie with ice cream. As everyone assembled for the celebration meal, John walked in and sat down to eat, without joining in any of the conversation.

After dinner, Maria and Karl showered and got ready to go to bed early. Besides being very tired from being in space-suits all day, they wanted to get an early start on the sample work and Karl wanted to checkout the new Selenophysical Station as early as possible. They embraced and kissed and Karl said, "Tomorrow, we'll be alone in Lab, so we can properly celebrate our first fieldtrip. Sí, mi señorita hermosa[1]?"

Maria blushed a little and whispered, "Sí, mi amor[2]."

Notes: [1]my beautiful miss; [2]my love

Chapter 2-6
The Copernicus Traverse

Thursday, July 4, 2014

The 4th of July, Independence Day for the US, was celebrated at the Fra Mauro Lunar Base by a very early breakfast and an early start of the long anticipated Copernicus Traverse — the first use of the Traverse Vehicle.

Lunar sunrise had occurred 2 days earlier and the crew had readied the Traverse Vehicle for its maiden voyage across the frozen lunar seas. It was fully fuelled and carried life support and fuel cell power for 3 weeks. Though mission rules limited the traverse to 2 weeks, the Traverse Vehicle always carried a 50% life support and power contingency and the planned Copernicus Traverse was to last only 12 days — 13 at most, so there was plenty of food, oxygen, water, and power to spare. Also, the southern rim of Copernicus, the goal of the traverse, was only about 250 kilometers to the NNW of the Base, and so the round trip was only going to use half of the 1000-kilometer range of the vehicle. Thus, the maiden voyage would not stretch the capabilities of the Traverse Vehicle, but would give it a good shakedown.

Shortly before 7:00 GMT, the crew went out the NE airlock and walked around the Traverse Vehicle for a last visual inspection. To reduce costs, Boeing had built the Traverse Vehicle using the same basic, 4.26-meter diameter, 12.8-meter long module used for Dorm, Kitchen, Lab, and Utility for its body. In fact, the Traverse Vehicle was just a mobile minibase with all the functions found in the Base's 4 modules crammed into just 1 module. It had four, 2.5-meter diameter, springy, metallic wheels, a large front window, and 2 smaller side windows just aft of the front of the vehicle.

At 7:32 GMT, Bill, sitting in the driver's seat, with Jim next to him in the passenger seat and with Maria and Karl standing immediately behind them, called Tom on the radio, "Ok, we're ready to go. Is everything ready on your end?"

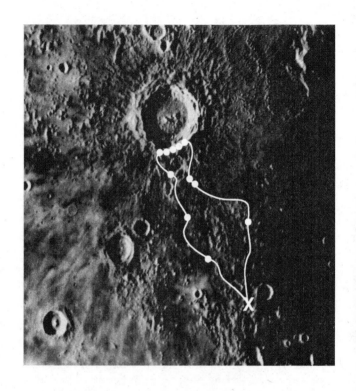

COPERNICUS TRAVERSE

The Copernicus Traverse started at the Base (X) and proceeded NNW to the southern rim of the 92-kilometer (57-mile) diameter crater, Copernicus, which is 250 kilometers (155 miles) from the Base. The return leg of the traverse was to the east of the leg to Copernicus. The dots along the traverse path mark the sites where the vehicle was parked while the crew slept. North is up.

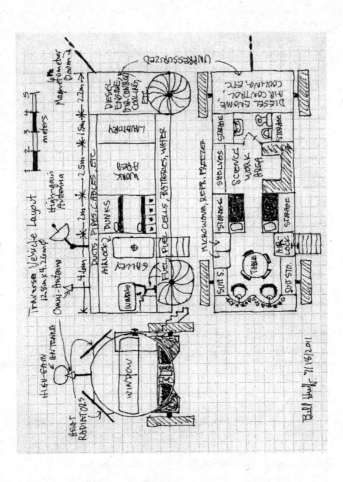

TRAVERSE VEHICLE DETAILS

A ROUGH SKETCH FROM BILL HUFF'S NOTEBOOK

Tom answered, "Yes, we are getting excellent engineering telemetry and we have clear voice communications. You can get started. Have a nice trip."

With the final ok, Bill started the diesel and hydrogen peroxide motor and began driving north along the graveled road to the landing pads at a brisk 15 km/hr.

Twenty minutes later, they passed South Landing Pad and just before 8:00 GMT, they passed North Landing Pad and the end of the graveled roadway. Thus their speed dropped to 12 km/hr as Bill drove through the bumpy, cratered moonscape. About 45 minutes later and 15 kilometers from the Base, Tom called and said, "You're signal is beginning to break up. Please switch to the Earth-link."

Some 2½ hours later, at a distance of 45 kilometers from the Base, Bill drove the Traverse Vehicle off the light colored Fra Mauro onto the dark mare basalt units that stretched 150 kilometers to Copernicus' continuous ejecta blanket. Once Bill had driven a couple of kilometers onto the mare surface, that was peppered with innumerable, large and small secondary craters from Copernicus, he stopped at Karl's first mare basalt sample collection site. Since they were stopped and since it was nearly 11:30, Bill said, "Let's have lunch, then you three can go hunt rocks."

Since Bill liked to "cook," he went about heating the TV dinner-type lunches in the microwave in the little galley behind the right front seat. As Bill tended to the food, Jim, Karl, and Maria inspected their suits and PLSSs in the adjacent suit-area, in preparation for their leaving the vehicle.

As the quiet and brief lunch ended, Karl said, "Schatz, do you want to be the first to go, before we suit-up?"

Laughing a little, Maria answered, "That's very gallant of you, cariño," and she walked from the galley, though the narrow passageway between the two sets of bunk beds and through the small work area to the little lavatory at the far end of the Traverse Vehicle. She was soon finished and was ready to start suiting up.

As Karl started towards the lavatory, Bill said in a light-hearted tone, "Make sure your aim is good in there. I don't want to have to cleanup after you and Jim," and Karl and Jim chuckled, knowing full well that, even after living at ⅙-g for 2½ months, the males of the crew still did not always correctly compensate for the differences in gravity while unconsciously calculating the trajectories of their urine streams. Though the three males laughed at what they considered to be great humor, Maria said, in mock disgust, "Can't you men ever stop behaving like Neanderthals?" which made Karl, Jim, and Bill laugh even louder and longer.

Soon, Maria, Karl, and Jim each cycled through the airlock and began their standard sample collection activities, work that lasted about an hour. Using the same strategy as on their Rover fieldtrip, in addition to collecting mare basalt samples, they would also collect samples of Copernicus ejecta that came from deeper and deeper depths in the pre-impact crust, as they got closer to Copernicus. Since Copernicus is 92 kilometers in diameter, they expected to find rocks from depths as great as 13 kilometers below the original crust — an important and exciting possibility.

Karl also made some gravity measurements, which could only be made when the vehicle was stopped and when he was on the surface with the gravimeter. But Karl did not have to use the portable magnetometer, except when he wanted to measure the magnetic fields in an area within walking distance of the Traverse Vehicle. The Traverse Vehicle had a magnetometer mast sticking out the back, which carried an inboard magnetometer to monitor the magnetic fields generated by the vehicle and an outboard magnetometer that, when its data were corrected for the effects of the vehicle's magnetic fields, made continuous magnetic field measurements as they drove the vehicle.

When their hour's work was over, they stashed the rock box and equipment in the external bays of the vehicle and cycled back in through the little airlock and de-suited. When they were done, Bill began to drive in the direction of Copernicus at the fast clip of 8 to 12 km/hr, depending on the roughness of the moonscape.

Towards 19:00 GMT, and some 90 kilometers from the Base, they reached the second sample collection site and the "night's camp site." While it was possible to lie in the bunks when the Traverse Vehicle was moving, it was not possible to sleep as the vehicle bounced along the rough lunar surface. Protocol demanded they stop for the "night" and do the sample collecting the next "morning."

After Bill microwaved a simple supper, each crewmember took a turn in the lavatory to cleanup before bed. As always, Maria was given the honors first. Unfortunately, because of the limited supply of water and space, there was no shower. So all one could do was to take a sparse sponge-bath, which removed only a limited amount of the sweat and soil accumulated after a day of riding in the bouncing vehicle and after spending a few hours in a spacesuit.

Maria emerged from the lavatory 25 minutes later, dressed in modest pajamas and a robe, looking somewhat refreshed and smelling of her White Diamonds perfume. She hugged Karl, gave him a quick kiss, and got into the lower bunk on the right side of the passageway, as Jim and Bill discreetly kept busy at the front of the cabin.

Friday, July 5, 2014

After breakfast the next morning, it was Bill's turn to assist Karl and Maria in their fieldwork and then they drove off towards their next stop. By evening, they were close to the southern edge of Copernicus' continuous ejecta blanket and they made more frequent stops to collect samples and make measurements.

Saturday, July 6, 2014

The day began with a call from Houston. After the usual technical communications, Houston said, "Bill, we have someone here who wants to talk to Jim."

Having heard that, Jim took the mike and said, "Jim here, go ahead."

A female voice came through the ether, "Jim, honey, you're not going to believe this, but I'm pregnant — it must have happened the last night you were here. At first, I didn't think anything about it — you know how irregular I am. But after the second month, I went to the doctor to see if something was wrong. He did some tests and said I was pregnant.

I didn't want to tell you until he did additional tests to see if the baby is all right — given my age. But the baby is fine and so I came to JSC to tell you, we're going to have the third baby we always wanted."

Jim was ecstatic; in his excitement, he jumped up, forgetting about the low lunar gravity, and banged his head against the top of the cabin. Ignoring the growing bump on his head, he said, "Honey, that's great — that's wonderful. Hey, I'll be back home before he's born. Have you told Ben and Jan? What did they say?"

Patty answered, "No I haven't, I wanted to tell you first. Oh, I'm getting the sign to wrap up now. I love you. Bye"

After the light-time delay, Jim said, "I love you, too, darling, bye."

Jim turned to Bill, Maria, and Karl and said, with tears in his eyes, "I'm going to be a dad again, and I'm on the Moon. Could life get any better?"

Maria said, as she hugged him, "Congratulations Jim, I'm so happy for you."

Bill slapped Jim on the back and shook his hand, "Way to go old man."

Karl shook Jim's hand and said with Germanic seriousness, "Congratulations."

By the end of that happy day, they were on the ejecta blanket and less than 30 kilometers from Copernicus' rim. The next day, Karl and Maria, with Bill's help, planned to set up the 2nd Selenophysical Station, about 15 kilometers south of the rim, and then they would camp that night on the rim and spend the next 4 days exploring the rim area.

Sunday, July 7, 2014

As Karl, Maria, and Bill were setting up the Copernicus Selenophysical Station on the 4th day, things came to a head between John and Isabel back at the Base.

Having determined that Pam was with Tom in the com-cubicle and that Isabel was alone in Hospital, John barged into Hospital without knocking. As Isabel looked up from her work with a mixture of surprise, anger, and a little fear on her face, John said, forcefully, "Well beautiful, it looks like we're finally alone and can get down to business." Before Isabel could say a word, John continued, holding up his right hand to ward off any response, "I know, I know, you're married, etc., etc., but I'm tired of your little game of hard to get, which I don't believe for a minute. The traverse crew is hundreds of kilometers away and Pam and Tom are glued to Tom's radio, so there's no one to bother us and no one will know. Do you want it here or shall we go to Dorm?"

Isabel was boiling. She had had enough and was getting more than a little frightened at John's persistent passes and increasingly erratic behavior. She "screwed her courage to the sticking place" and said sternly, "John, I am sick and tired of your persistent sexual advances. If you do not stop bothering Maria, Pam, and me right now, I will have Pam put something in your food that will stop you from having an erection for the next year and I will inform Houston officially that you are no longer fit to command the Base or be in the Astronaut Corps. Do I make myself absolutely clear?"

John turned red with anger and humiliation and, taken back by her serious threat, he could say nothing — he just glared at Isabel.

Seeing that she had him where she wanted him, she added the very unprofessional comment, "However, I recognize you have a very high sex drive. So as your physician, I recommend that, in the privacy of your bedroom, you masturbate at least twice a day. That will relieve your sexual tension and you will, at last, have a willing partner here at the Base."

The insult enraged John even more, as well as added to his humiliation. The twisted expression of hate on his face suggested he wanted to smash her in the face, throw her on the floor, rip her clothes off, and rape her on the spot. But, despite John's exploitation of women, he was neither a rapist nor had he ever physically hurt a woman. All he could do was to shout at her, "Go to hell, you conceited bitch. We'll see who gets who thrown out of the Corps," even though he knew full well he could do nothing to harm a flight MD, and he left Hospital in a total rage.

Though she had put up a brave front against a physically larger and stronger adversary, Isabel began shaking uncontrollably as John rushed out of Hospital and slammed the door as hard as he could. Though she had won without John getting physically violent, he was clearly capable of violence. To calm herself, she took out a bottle of medicinal whisky — a bottle known only to her — and took a big swig right from the bottle. As the whisky took effect, she called Tom's cubicle over the Base Intercom and said urgently, "Pam, come to Hospital, immediately!"

When Pam arrived, Isabel told her about her encounter with John, gave her some tranquilizers to put in John's food, and said, "Pam, be very careful of John. Let me know if he does anything strange or threatens you in any way, ok?"

Pam answered uncharacteristically, "I sure as hell will. I'm as sick of him as you are and I'm glad you put him down. But we do need to be careful of him. I assume you'll warn Maria as soon as she gets back. And you better say something to Karl, too. John hates Karl with a passion, especially because of Maria — if you know what I mean."

Isabel answered, "Yes I do, and yes I will."

Isabel paused and added, "If we can't keep him in check with tranquilizers, I'll have to report this to NASA. I hate to do it unless it's absolutely necessary. If I do, they will relieve him of his Command and that might make him become psychotic — and we do not have the means to deal with a potentially violent madman here for 3 months. Also, it would mean the end of his career, and I would hate to destroy his career over something we might be able to handle with tranquilizers and that might pass when we get back home."

Worried, Pam responded, "I hope you're right. Just to be sure, shouldn't I put a double dose in his food at lunch today? It's a good thing he never fixes his own food, or we might not be able to keep him loaded with pills. Just give me the amounts you want and I'll see to it he gets them."

Isabel nodded and gave Pam the extra pills for the double dose she had suggested.

To Isabel and Pam's surprise, John appeared at dinner in an apparently good mood. He was friendly and, for the first time, almost polite and that frightened Pam and Isabel even more. As Isabel said later to Pam, "I don't think the change in

LUNAR ORBITER II PHOTO OF COPERNICUS

John's mood is just because of the tranquilizers, I think John has gone over the edge and is a danger to all of us, including himself. We have to be very careful."

By the time supper was over at the Base and at Copernicus, and against all mission rules that at least 1 crewmember had to be in the Traverse Vehicle at all times, Maria, Karl, Bill, and Jim were all standing on the rim of the gaping hole — 92 kilometers from rim to rim and over 3 kilometers deep — called Copernicus. The panorama before them was breathtaking. Though Maria had the famous Lunar Orbiter II, oblique angle photograph of Copernicus on her office wall back in Houston, a picture whose beauty had stunned the non-scientific world back in 1966, seeing the beautiful expanse before them was beyond description.

Bill was the first to speak and was thrilled by the magnificent view, "Man, what a view. This makes the Grand Canyon look like a brook. No wonder you guys like studying the Moon — it's just beautiful. But what exactly are we seeing?"

Karl, keeping the good-natured banter alive that always exists when scientists and engineers work together, replied teasingly, "Gee, I didn't know an engineer could find anything beautiful, except some kind of machine. Aber ja[1], the Moon is extremely beautiful, though most uninformed people think it's just a dead lump of rock. Now you see how wrong they are."

Then Karl said, wanting his Maria to show off her stuff and because he was also in a giddy mood brought on by the enthralling sight before him, "As to what you are seeing, you had better ask the beautiful and talented selenologist to my right."

Taking Karl's cue, an equally excited Maria explained, "All along the inner wall, you see multiple, irregular terraces caused when huge sections of the initial, unstable crater wall slumped down, as the transient crater collapsed immediately after the impact. The individual terraces are up to 4 kilometers wide and there are 4 to 6 of them before the floor is reached, some 3 kilometers below the rim and the drops

---

Note: [1]Sure

along the scarps between the terraces are up to a kilometer. As you can see, the depressions in the terraces' surfaces were immediately filled with impact melt that rained down with the fallback — to form kilometer-scale lakes of impact melt. See how some of the impact melt overflowed the terraces and cascaded down to the next ones and over and over again, until it reached the growing lake of impact melt that was filling the floor of the crater?"

What Maria described and what the mesmerized crew saw, were solidified lakes — and contorted, solidified cascades — of impact melt, all of which dramatically depicted the incredible events and processes that had formed the magnificent crater. If selenologists were correct, the crater had formed a billion year earlier, a deduction that would be tested when the samples from similar solidified lakes of impact melt, that Maria and Karl would collect along the rim, were age-dated back on Earth.

The floor itself displayed a fantastic amount of detail, which Maria began to describe. "Now to the floor. As you can see, except for the young impact craters that pepper it, its northwest quadrant has a relatively smooth surface of solidified impact melt. In contrast, the northeast quadrant is covered by innumerable hummocks that are hundreds of meters in dimensions and that formed when large chunks of fallback ejecta fell into the growing impact melt lake at the bottom of the crater. You can also see the entire southern half of the floor is covered with similar hummocks, but their dimensions are up to the kilometer-scale. Also, the floor has numerous secondary vents and associated flows, where molten impact melt from below the solidifying crust erupted and spread short distances across the floor."

Maria stopped a minute to again take in the beauty of the scene before her and then continued, "Finally, there, in the middle of the floor, is its magnificent central peak complex — a complex of about a dozen mountains, the tallest of which reaches a kilometer above the crater floor."

There was just too much detail for the crew to grasp; only the pictures that Karl and Maria started taking would capture all the features they were looking at. Below them was a selenologist's paradise and Maria said, "I'd give anything to go down there." But that was far too dangerous with the equipment they had; such magnificent fieldtrips would have to wait until there was a Lunar Lander-like ballistic research vehicle available to "fly" into craters like Copernicus. Though, if NASA would allow it, the existing Lunar Landers would do the job nicely, but. . . .

After spending a couple of hours at the rim, absorbing the majestic scene and photographing it, they went back to the Traverse Vehicle for a night's rest.

Monday, July 8, 2014, through Thursday, July 11, 2014

They spent the next 4 days exploring the outer slopes along some 20 kilometers of the rim, gathering numerous samples of ejecta and impact melt rock from the solidified pools and lakes that had formed on the outer slopes.

Friday, July 12, 2104, through Sunday, July 14, 2014

Finally, on the 9th day of the traverse, they began driving to a 5-kilometer diameter, dark halo crater blasted into Copernicus' continuous eject blanket, some 40 kilometers from the rim. Selenologists believed that the impact had punched through Copernicus' light colored ejecta and excavated dark mare basalts from the pre-Copernicus mare surface — thus causing the dark halo. The crew spent the next day at the dark halo crater, collecting samples at various distances from its rim — to get samples from different depths in the Copernicus ejecta blanket and from the pre-existing mare basalt units below the ejecta.

The next day, they drove further to the SE and off Copernicus' eject blanket to get more mare basalt samples from another mare volcanic unit and then they turned towards the Base, which was more than a hard days drive — and more than 150 kilometers — away.

Monday, July 15, 2104, to Tuesday, July 16, 2014

At 20:40 GMT, at the end of the 12th day of the traverse, the vehicle came within the 15-kilometer range of the 50-meter antenna and Bill switched transmitters. A little over an hour later, Bill parked the Traverse Vehicle near the NE Access Tunnel and the tired, dirty, and smelly crew began cycling out the Traverse Vehicle's airlock.

As Bill began hooking up the power cable from the nuke to the Traverse Vehicle, Maria, Karl, and Jim retrieved the precious rock boxes from the bays in the sides of the vehicle and carried them into the NE airlock. When all the rock boxes were inside, Karl and Maria entered, pushed the cycle button, and were soon standing in East Access Tunnel, where Isabel, Pam, Tom, and a well-behaved John were waiting to greet them.

Maria and Karl took off their suit helmets and almost everyone shouted, "Welcome back. We're glad the trip went so well."

Too tired and dirty — Karl had a two day stubble and like Karl's formerly nice, blond hair, Maria's previously beautiful, shiny, dark brown hair was greasy and stringy and their faces were smudged — to really care about their crewmates' heart-felt greetings, they smiled and said exhausted, "We're glad to be back and to be able to shower."

To which John said, "Whew, we can smell that."

Karl asked, "Would somebody take the rock boxes into Lab, so Jim and Bill can get in through the airlock and so Maria and I can start getting out of these smelly suits."

John, in a surprisingly helpful mood, which Karl and Maria were too tired to notice, answered, "Sure. Tom, will you help me with the boxes?"

An hour later, shortly after 23:00 GMT and after quick showers, the tired and hungry traverse crew sat down at the table in Kitchen as Pam said, with pride, "I've made a special celebration dinner for everyone — not prepared meals, but real steak, grilled to perfection, with baked potatoes and corn on the cob, both dripping with butter, and a freshly baked blackberry pie, not from scratch of course, rather a Mrs. Smith frozen pie I just baked."

Isabel said in surprise, "I though it smelled exceptionally good in here," and the traverse crewmembers were too weary to say much more than, "Thanks, let's eat," which they did with relish, after 12 days of TV dinners and canned meals.

After supper, Maria and Karl went to Lab to check on the sample boxes and for Karl to take a quick look at the data coming in from the Copernicus Selenophysical Station.

While they were in Lab, Bill went to Utility for a quick check on the status of the Base and then, at a little before midnight, everyone went to his or her room in Dorm.

As Karl gave Maria a quick kiss and hug in front of their opposing doors, he asked, "Schatz, if I wake up early, do you want me to wake you up so we can get an early start on the samples?"

Maria, who usually slept later than Karl, who almost always woke up with the chickens, answered, "Sí cariño, wake me up when you are ready to shower. Te quiero muchísimo, mi amado[1]."

And Karl responded lovingly, "Ich liebe Dich auch, so sehr, mein Liebling[2]," and gave his sweetheart another good-night kiss and hug.

Then they went inside their small rooms, flopped into their beds, and almost immediately fell fast asleep.

A few minutes later, the Base's master clock ticked to 00:00:01 GMT, Tuesday, July 16 — the new day had started.

Notes: [1]I love you very much, my love; [2]I love you, too, very much, my darling

Part Three
THE DAY OF DESTRUCTION

Chapter 3-1
An Hour-and-a-Half in Hell

Tuesday, July 16, 2014, 05:45 GMT

Despite having gone to bed just before midnight, Karl woke up refreshed and ready to go to Lab to start looking at the plethora of samples he and Maria had collected during the Copernicus Traverse. He quietly left his room, being careful not to awaken the rest of the crew, and stepped across the narrow hall to Maria's door. He knocked softly and whispered, "Liebling, are you awake?"

Hearing no answer, he knocked a second time, a little louder, and whispered even louder, "Are you up?"

Then came the faint rustle of a blanket and sheet being moved back, followed by the sound of light, bare feet on the plastic floor and Maria's sleepy voice. "Sí, I'm up. Go take your shower and make some breakfast. I'll meet you in Kitchen in 20 minutes — 25 tops."

Shaking his head in skepticism at hearing "25 tops," Karl went to the men's lavatory and started his morning toiletries. After having spent nearly 2 weeks in the Traverse Vehicle and up to 8 hours per day in a surface exploration suit, and despite having briefly showered shortly after their arrival at the Base the previous evening, his morning shower, if you can call the fine spray of hot water that lasted just a few minutes a shower, finally seemed to remove the cumulated effects of sweat and the mixture of human and mechanical odors of the enclosed environments of his suit and of the Traverse Vehicle.

Refreshed after his shower and blow-dry, Karl shaved his three-day stubble, halfheartedly brushed his wet hair, and slipped on a clean pair of white briefs, a blue short-sleeve shirt, a pair of Lederhosen, white socks, and white sneakers. He quietly left the men's lavatory, paused at the door of the woman's, and listened to see if Maria was really up and taking a shower. Upon hearing the soft sounds of the shower water playing on her beautiful body, a smile crept onto his lips. Sighing softly, Karl left Dorm, carefully closing and sealing the vacuum door behind him, and went to Kitchen.

Karl got Maria's instant coffee and a pre-prepared Spanish omelet ready to heat up. Then he poured himself some carbonated grape juice and thawed out his raspberry sweet roll. As he was busy doing that, Maria was breaking a water conservation rule by taking a 10-minute shower. As if to justify her doing so to some unseen Base monitor in Houston, she said defiantly, "I had to go without a shower for two weeks. The one I took last night was short and I need a nice long, hot shower to properly wash my hair."

After showering and blow-drying her body, it took her another 20 minutes to dry her long hair with a hand-held hair dryer, even in the low humidity and low pressure of the Base. She then fixed her hair by taking small bundles of it from the right and left front sides of her beautiful mane, bringing them to the lower back of her head, and uniting them with a little white bow, to form a mini-ponytail that ran down the middle of her long train of hair, just the way she liked it. She slipped on her favorite pair of white, silky, lace trimmed, bikini panties and matching bra, a beautiful, white, Mexican peasant blouse that had been embroidered by her mother with multi-colored flowers, a pair of white short-shorts, and white sneakers. Looking at herself in the mirror, she smiled and said, "Finally, I feel like a woman again." She added a little red lipstick, tawny eye makeup, and topped it all off with a wisp of White Diamonds perfume, her favorite.

Clearly feeling far prettier than she had in nearly 2 weeks, Maria left Dorm, closed the vacuum door as quietly as Karl had done well over 30 minutes earlier, and walked the 6 meters through East Access Tunnel to Kitchen — some 45 minutes after she had told Karl she would be there in 25 minutes, "tops."

Tuesday, July 16, 2014, 06:31 GMT

Karl was experienced enough not to say anything about her arrival time and was smart enough to have just heated her omelet and coffee, and to have just made her buttered toast.

But, he had been too hungry to wait for her so they could eat together. As Maria enter Kitchen, Karl said, "Sorry beautiful — I was hungry, but your breakfast is hot and waiting for you."

He hugged her very tightly and gave her a tender kiss, which she returned with more fire than he had expected and she said, "Guess what I've got on under my blouse and shorts," which caused Karl to kiss her again, with considerable passion.

Putting their desires on hold, Maria started eating her breakfast, while Karl drank a second grape juice to keep her company. They discussed the day's work ahead of them and Karl wrote a note to Pam, explaining that Maria and he had an early breakfast and wrote down what each had eaten, so Pam could fill out her nutritional logs.

While Maria and Karl were talking over Maria's breakfast, Pam, closely followed by Isabel and Jim, had awakened and begun their morning routines.

When Pam entered Kitchen, she found Maria and Karl clearing away their dishes and preparing to leave for Lab. After exchanging good morning pleasantries, Karl said, "Here's the list of what we ate."

Pam nodded approvingly as she read what Maria had eaten, but gave Karl a motherly look of disapproval and said, "You're eating far too much sugar. We're going to have to have a little talk about your diet."

Karl muttered, "Ja, ja Mütterchen[1]."

Then Maria and Karl left Kitchen, holding hands, and Pam smiled approvingly as she closed and sealed the vacuum door behind them.

Tuesday, July 16, 2014, 06:49 GMT

Several minutes later, while Pam was thawing and heating a pre-prepared, but substantial breakfast of pancakes, sausage, orange juice, and coffee for the remaining crew, Jim sleepily entered Kitchen in his robe — and no one could tell what else — followed a few minutes later by Isabel, neatly dressed in stylish tan slacks and a navy polo, with her black

---

Note: [1] Yeah, yeah, little mother

hair drawn back in her usual Spanish chignon. She was eager-
ly looking forward to starting her medical tests on the traverse crew later in the morning.

Because everyone had been up so late the previous
evening, John, Bill, and Tom were still sleeping in Dorm,
much to Pam's consternation, when she realized that half of
her culinary efforts would end up as reheated, reheats. But
never one to let a setback, little or big, spoil her nearly eternally cheerful mood, Pam, along with Isabel and Jim, lingered
over breakfast and even longer over a second cup of coffee.
Clearly, the day was going to get off to a slow start, except for
Maria and Karl, who were excitedly beginning their work on
the lunar samples.

After walking the 6 meters between Kitchen and Lab,
Maria and Karl entered their work place, closed and sealed
the vacuum door, and in the privacy of Lab, gave each other
several proper and lasting embraces and kisses, but decided
they should get to work and leave their more romantic activities for a little later in the day — after Isabel had given them
their post-traverse physical exams.

As Maria started checking the sealed rock boxes, Karl
took a look at the readouts from the new Copernicus
Selenophysical Station. A quick look at the seismometer data
showed the usual low-level seismic noise, caused mainly by
thermal effects, and, going back through the seismograms of
the last 24 hours, he saw what appeared to be a weak, deep-
seated, tidally induced moonquake.

Karl said, "I'd like to pull up the stored data to see what
the Copernicus seismometer detected since we set it up and
look at the Fra Mauro Station records from when we were
gone, or do you need me to help you right now?"

Maria answered, "I'm almost ready, but you can take a
quick look if you want to."

Karl quickly called up the seismometer readout for the
last 24 hours from the Fra Mauro Station and found, as
expected, the same low-level noise and the signals of the
probable deep-seated, tidally induced quake he had seen in
the data from the Copernican Station. He quickly looked at
the temperature data from the heat-flow probes at both sta-

tions, as well as the readings from the magnetometer and mass spectrometer at the Copernicus Station and the data from the long period seismometer, the magnetometer, and the tidal gravimeter at Fra Mauro, as well as the engineering data from both stations. Seeing that everything was normal, he returned his attention to Maria and the rock boxes.

While Karl was looking at his beloved selenophysical data, Maria had put the first of several rock boxes in the airlock of the glass walled, evacuated glove box, required to keep the oxygen and moisture in Lab's air from altering the pristine lunar samples, and had manipulated the rock box out of the airlock and into the glove box itself.

As soon as Karl stuck his hands and arms into the armlong, rubber, vacuum gloves that reached inside the glove box, he helped Maria open the rock box and watched as she carefully took out the first clear plastic sample bag that contained about 30 rake samples he had collected from the regolith of the Imbrium mare basalt units to the south of the outer edge of Copernicus' continuous ejecta blanket.

Maria typed the sample bag number into the computer log, as Karl photographed the still unopened bag with the digital camera that was in the glove box. Maria then carefully opened the bag and even more carefully dumped its precious contents of dark, charcoal colored, mare basalt fragments into a stainless steel tray in preparation for their being individually photographed, measured, weighted, cataloged, and examined.

As Maria and Karl were just starting to process the largest rake sample — a 3¼ centimeter diameter rock, Pam, Isabel, and Jim were just about to finish their second cups of coffee in Kitchen — John had awakened and was in the men's lavatory, and Bill and Tom were just stirring from their slumbers, since John had, characteristically, made no attempt to be quiet in Dorm. It was 07:23:39 GMT.

Tuesday, July 16, 2014, 07:23:39 GMT

At 07:23:39 GMT, 57.2 kilometers SW of the Fra Mauro Base and 4.3 kilometers below the surface of the Fra Mauro Formation, the compressional stresses that had been accumulating in the outer crust during the past 3.5 billion years — since the beginning of the period when the stresses caused by the cooling of the Moon's interior had become compressional — finally exceeded the 3.1 kilobar crushing strength of the local rock. Once the first tiny fracture occurred along a relatively weak interface between a plagioclase crystal and a pyroxene crystal, the fracture propagated upwards at a flat angle of 21° and fanned out towards the NE in a conical pattern at 2.8 km per/sec.

The resulting thrust fault fracture reached the surface in 4.3 seconds, forming an arcuate, thrust fault scarp, 17 kilometers long and 11 meters high. The fault scarp became the youngest of over 2000 such scarps that had formed during the past 700 million years, or since the epoch of lunar crustal thrust faulting began 150 million years before the explosion of multi-cellular life on Earth that marked the beginning of the Cambrian Period of Earth History. The scrap was also the first to have formed in 83,127 years or since early man roamed the Earth, 8 of whose great, great . . . great grand children, some thousands of generations later, were going about their business, 47 kilometers to the NE.

Though the fracturing of the rock and the thrust fault movement lasted only 4.3 seconds, the amount of seismic energy released, over 4×10^{27} ergs, caused a 9.1 magnitude moonquake on the Richter scale — over 1000 times stronger than the 7.8 magnitude earthquake that destroyed San Francisco in 1906. The seismic energy spread out from the focus throughout the Moon at P-wave and S-wave velocities as high as 7.8 and 4.5 km/sec, respectively, in the deep lunar mantle. But because the P-wave had traveled only through the crust, and hence at a much slower average P-wave velocity, to reach the Fra Mauro Base, it did so 16 seconds after the moonquake had occurred, or at 07:23:55 GMT. But, because of the emergent nature of moonquake signals, no one at the Fra Mauro Base noticed the arrival of the first, tiny seismic vibrations.

Tuesday, July 16, 2014, 07:24 GMT — Lab

Maria had just finished dusting off the rake sample she and Karl were processing and Karl was just getting ready to photograph it, when he noticed the first humanly detectable effects of the monstrous moonquake that had occurred just

21 seconds earlier. He hesitated a second and asked urgently, "Maria, do you feel that?"

Maria, who had been concentrating on getting the sample correctly positioned for the first of several documentary photographs, answered with a little laugh, "Feel what?"

"The shaking. It must be a moonquake — and a big one for us to feel it."

By then, the vibrations had become quite noticeable, so much so that light objects on the table and counters and the rake samples and dust in the tray in the glove box were dancing around. Maria said, somewhat alarmed at Karl's comment, "Sí, I sure feel it now. Do you think it could do any damage to the Base?"

"I don't know, but I'm going to alert the others. If it gets any worse, get under the counter. Stay there and I'll be with you is a second."

Not waiting for it to get any worse, Maria got into a cubbyhole under the nearest counter, as Karl walked, with some difficulty, to the Base intercom. He quickly switched it on and hurriedly shouted, "We're having a fairly big moonquake. Get under something sturdy and stay put until it's over — remember moonquakes last an hour or more."

Not waiting for a reply, Karl turned to go back to Maria. But by then, the shaking was bad enough it was very difficult for Karl to keep his balance and he had to hold on to shelves and the counter to make it to the cubbyhole, where Maria was waiting for him. And the loud noises caused by moving equipment and furniture were joined by the low, ominous rumble of the moonquake itself.

Karl reached the counter under which Maria was sitting, slid down next to her in the cubbyhole, and grabbed her very tightly. She returned the favor, not out of affection, but to protect both of them from banging around in their small, and hopefully, safe-haven. Maria immediately asked loudly above the ever-increasing noise, "Is it going to get much worse?"

"Ja, I think so. It takes several minutes to build up to the maximum and we've only felt it for a minute or so."

Just then, one of the PC's that was sitting on the counter above them, was thrown against the wall hard enough to shatter its screen and then it was thrown in the opposite direction and hence off of the counter. Despite the $\frac{1}{6}$ gravity, it crashed noisily to the floor, followed very shortly by other loose items, all over Lab.

By then, the ever increasing moonquake rumble and the noise of falling and breaking equipment was so loud Karl had to shout to be heard as he responded to the sound of shattering glass with, "Scheisse[1], if the glove box glass walls shatter, the air in Lab will be sucked out through the box's vacuum vent and we'll die of asphyxiation in a couple of minutes. I have to shut the vacuum vent — und schnell[2]."

Maria shouted, urgently, "We might need the oxygen masks, too. You close the vent and I'll get the masks."

Karl shouted, "Nein, Du bleibst hier — I mean, you stay here. There's no need for both of us to risk getting hurt."

Maria started to protest, but Karl cut her short, shouting above the increasing din, "Nein, kommt nicht in Frage[3]. You stay put — I'll be back in a minute."

Just then the lights flickered for a couple of seconds, threatened to go out, but then came back on as bright as ever. Given the distinct possibility that the power could go out before he could use the electric motor to close the vacuum vent of the glove box and thus have to try to close it with the manual crank in the dark, Karl hurried, as best he could, to get that critical job done as fast as possible.

As Karl let go of Maria to leave the cubbyhole, they were both being shaken so violently that the right side of Maria's head banged hard against the wall she was setting next to. She cried, "Ouch," but did not feel the blood that trickled down her temple and cheek.

Karl hesitated a second to see if Maria was all right and then, with even greater urgency, scrambled to the nearest chair he intended to use to steady himself, since walking without aid was, by then, out of the question.

Pushing the chair ahead of him, Karl successfully crossed the 3-meter obstacle course of fallen and broken equipment and reached the glove box vent open/close buttons, whose

---

Notes: [1]Crap; [2]and fast; [3]No, out of the question

red status light was glowing, indicating the box's vent was open to the vacuum of the Moon. Karl, steadying himself as best he could, reached up with one hand and hit the close button. Then, with great relief, he watched for a few seconds as the red status light went out and the green one came on. At least they were safe if the glove box glass shattered.

Tuesday, July 16, 2014, 07:24 GMT — Kitchen

Pam, Isabel, and Jim were sipping the last dregs of their second cups of coffee and chatting about their families. Jim waxed eloquent about his pending fatherhood, "I'm really excited about the new baby, but it's going to be strange having a little baby in the house when our other two kids are all grown up and away at college. It'll be like having a second family. Patty and I always wanted more children, but it just never happened. Ben and Jan are excited, too. Patty says you'd think each of them was having the kid instead of a little brother or sister."

In contrast, Pam was concerned about her family's health. "I'm sure Henry is taking good care of the children, but I always worry about their nutrition. Henry hates to cook and I just know he's taking them to restaurants and worse, to fast food places, no matter what he tells me during our com-sessions."

Isabel replied, "Oh, I wouldn't worry about it too much — hey, what's the shaking all about?"

Jim laughed and said, "I'll bet its one of Karl's dreaded moonquakes. He should be so lucky as to have one hit just after he set up his first couple of seismometers."

Isabel replied, "I don't think this is funny Jim. This might — "

Isabel was interrupted by Karl's voice on the Base intercom, "We're having a fairly big moonquake. Get under something sturdy and stay put until it's o——— ," and all that followed was static, increased shaking, the noise of falling objects, and the low, ominous rumble of the moonquake itself.

Pam looked panic stricken, Jim was still smiling and clearly still thought the moonquake was some kind of cosmic joke for Karl's benefit, so Isabel took charge, "I have no idea what this is all about, but remember what Karl said about moonquakes lasting a long, long time. We should get under the table as Karl says. I'm worried that, since the intercom went dead, some vital things might get damaged. Hey, we need to get the oxygen masks, just in case."

Jim, whose smile had completely disappeared and had been replaced by a look of deep concern, said, "Good idea, you stay here, I'll get the masks," and struggled to keep his balance as the violent motion of the module increased. He reached the emergency cabinet on the wall separating Kitchen and Hospital, grabbed 3 masks, and struggled — using chairs and exercising equipment in the recreation area to steady himself — back to the table, under which Isabel and a very frightened Pam sat, holding on for dear life.

As Jim joined them, he gave them their masks. Isabel immediately put hers on, as did Jim as soon as he had braced himself between the table legs. But as the shaking had became more violent, so had Pam's panic and she would not put her mask on.

Isabel shouted at her, "Pam, put the mask on, now — I mean it."

Pam screamed, "I can't, I just can't. I've got to get out of here," and she crawled out from under the table and through fallen and broken debris towards the area in Kitchen where the appliances were located.

Isabel shouted over the increasing racket, just as the lights flickered, "Jim, we have to get something to restrain her."

Jim shouted, "Stay here, I'll go find something," and started to crawl towards Hospital. As he was underway, the shaking and the noise of falling and shattering objects and of the moonquake were becoming almost unbearable. Suddenly, there was a very loud crash, followed immediately by a very loud, metallic screeching sound.

Tuesday, July 16, 2014, 07:24 GMT — Dorm

John had awakened a few minutes earlier, had made his noisy way to the lavatory, and had stepped into the shower, which he had going full blast and where he was making as much of a ruckus as possible. John's commotion awakened Bill and Tom, who stretched and yawned as they tried to shake off the last vestiges of their sleep. They were still half asleep, when the Base intercom burst into life and they heard Karl shouting, "We're having a fairly big moonquake. Get under something sturdy and stay put until it's o—— ."

Startled by Karl's warning, by the failure of the intercom, and by a low, ominous rumbling sound, Bill and Tom were suddenly fully awake and sprang out of their beds. Only then did they become fully aware that Dorm was shaking with increasing violence and that clothing and other personal items in their rooms were being thrown around.

John was singing loudly in the shower, unaware of what was happening, when he suddenly stopped and exclaimed, "What in hell is going on?"

Just then there was a loud crash in the lavatory.

Tuesday, July 16, 2014, 07:27 GMT — Lab

Since the emergency equipment cabinet was at the other end of the module, Karl had to make his unsteady way 8 meters to get to the oxygen masks and anything else he thought they might need. By then, the shaking was so violent Karl was having great difficulty staying on his feet, even with the chair to steady him. After just a few halting steps, Karl was thrown hard against the edge of the counter. As he hit, he heard the disconcerting snap as three of his ribs broke and his face twisted in agony in reaction to the intense stabbing pain in his lower right rib cage. Gasping for air as the intense pain took his breath away — so he couldn't even utter a cry of pain — Karl fell slowly to the floor under the Moon's low gravity.

Seeing Karl's plight and hearing his gasping for air mixed in with all the noise, Maria screamed, "Karl, Karl, estás gravemente herido?" and then repeated in an even louder scream, "Are you badly hurt?"

Fighting off the pain, Karl grunted in a voice that was barely audible above the din, "Nein, I'm ok," and continued haltingly, between short, shallow breaths, "I just broke . . . some ribs. . . . I've broken them . . . twice before . . . back on the farm. . . . The pain . . . will pass in . . . a few minutes." But, as anyone who has broken ribs knows, Karl knew that in 2 or 3 days, when the inflammation had had time to set in, his ribs would hurt — wie der Teufel[1] — and said in such a soft voice that Maria could not hear, "Ja . . . it'll pass . . . for now."

Holding his breath against the intense pain, Karl pulled himself up, using the chair for leverage, and again started pushing it towards the emergency equipment cabinet, whose glass door had already shattered. Finally he made it and grabbed 2 oxygen masks and the oxygen bottles, the First Aid kit, and 2 flashlights. He piled everything on the chair seat and started shoving it back towards Maria.

Halfway there, a violent vertical movement of the module threw Karl to the floor and simultaneously shattered the glass of the glove box, which — though cut off from the vacuum outside, was still under a vacuum — imploded violently with a deafening, thunder-like report. As he hit the floor, his face again twisted in agony as the impact made his broken ribs hurt even more than they did when he had broken them less than 2 minutes earlier. The pain in his ribs was so excruciating he did not even notice he had cut his left hand and both knees on broken glass.

Maria screamed again and tried to come out of the cubbyhole on her hands and knees to help Karl, but she was thrown hard against the counter, bruising and scraping her right arm and leg.

Karl grunted as loud as he could, "Go back. . . . Go back . . . before you . . . get hurt. . . . I'm ok," and with fear in her eyes, she reluctantly followed Karl's urgent orders and jammed herself into the cubbyhole as tightly as she could.

The shaking was so strong, Karl could no longer stand even with the help of the chair, let alone walk, so he grabbed the oxygen masks and bottles, the First Aid kit, and the 1 flashlight that had somehow stayed on the chair and put them on the shaking floor in front of him. He looked around for a few brief seconds, trying to locate the second flashlight, but gave up trying to find it in the mess of accumulating debris covering the floor.

Note: [1]like the devil

Crawling on his hands and knees — still not noticing the blood flowing from his left hand and knees — Karl inched his way towards Maria, pushing the emergency supplies ahead of him and leaving a trail of blood behind him.

After what seemed like an eternity to both of them, Karl finally reached Maria, several minutes after leaving the comparative safety of the cubbyhole. He shouted, "Shove this stuff . . . under your legs . . . to keep it from . . . being thrown around . . . and getting damaged."

Tuesday, July 16, 2014, 07:32 GMT

Instead of sliding in next to her as she had expected, Karl slid into the cubbyhole facing her, grabbed her with both arms, despite the resulting pain in his right side as he pressed his Schatz tightly to him, holding her head tightly against his with his right hand to prevent their heads from being violently snapped back and forth and from side to side.

Maria, immediately understanding why he had grabbed her head as he did, grabbed Karl, wrapping her left arm around his waist and held his head against hers with her right hand. Both of them pushed against the sides of the cubbyhole with their feet as hard as they could. Also, with their heads pressed together, they could better hear each other shout above the moonquake's very loud rumbling, which by then, overshadowed the noise of falling and breaking equipment, in part, because almost everything that could fall and/or break, had fallen and broken and, in part, because the rumbling was so loud.

As Karl rested to catch his shallow breath and to wait for the pain of his broken ribs to subside a little, he could smell Maria's sweet perfumed scent mixed with the smell of fear as she shouted again, "Are you hurt badly, mi amado?"

Karl, catching his breath and still speaking in short bursts to lessen the pain in his lower right chest, shouted back, "Nein . . . it's just the ribs . . . that's all."

But then Maria noticed a warm wetness where Karl's left hand was pressed to her right side and said, "I think your hand is bleeding. Take a look at it."

Karl released his hold on Maria for a couple of seconds and saw his hand was indeed bleeding, and quite a bit. As he began to wipe the blood on his lederhosen, he noticed that both of his knees were also bleeding from several cuts, but he did not say anything to Maria about that.

As Karl again grabbed Maria, he felt the wet stickiness of the trickle of blood dribbling from Maria's head and shouted, full of concern, "Liebling . . . you've got . . . a cut . . . on your head."

Maria shouted back, "Oh, I must have done it when my head banged against the wall when you first left. I knew it was bruised, but I didn't think it was bleeding."

Karl shouted, "If you hit it . . . that hard, you might . . . have a concussion."

Maria shouted, "There's nothing we can do about any of this until the shaking stops. How much longer do you think it will last?"

Karl shouted back, "At least an hour . . . if not a lot longer . . . this is a big one. The ones detected by . . . the Apollo network were all . . . less than magnitude 6 . . . and they lasted an hour. . . . So this could last . . . a lot longer."

Tuesday, July 16, 2014, 07:35 GMT

Though they had not noticed it, just after Karl had gotten back to the cubbyhole and while Karl and Maria were comforting and protecting each other, the moonquake's shaking had reached its maximum and was slowly, ever so slowly, beginning to subside. Nevertheless, the shaking was still so violent, the strain of trying to hold on tightly in their cubbyhole so intense, and the fear they felt so strong, that Maria began to get nauseous.

She covered her mouth tightly with her hand and got a panicked look on her face as she fought the powerful urge to vomit, fighting hard so she would not vomit on herself and Karl in their confined space. She suddenly shouted, "I'm going to be sick," and then she was.

Not to be out done, and adding the sour smell of Maria's breakfast coming up to everything else, Karl also vomited. Though vomiting was bad enough by itself, the strain of vomiting on his tortured rib cage caused him to again writhe in pain. All Maria could do was to hold him tight. And then slowly, despite the powerful shaking and noise, they began to recover from their vomiting.

As they sat in muck and misery, the pain in Karl's ribs subsided to a tolerable level and then the lights flickered a second time and went out. A few seconds later, the much dimmer glow of Lab's emergency lights illuminated its shattered interior.

Karl exclaimed loudly, "Scheisse, und das noch zu allem Überfluss[1]. I hope we're on the main emergency batteries in Utility and not just on Lab's tertiary backup batteries. This better not get any worse. Mensch, I wonder how the others are doing?"

Maria shouted, "Did you leave the intercom on?"

Karl shouted back, "Ja, I didn't take time to shut it off, but there's too much noise in here to hear anything, unless you're standing right next to it, even if the thing still works."

Maria shouted, "As soon as we can, we need to try to contact the others," and Karl agreed.

Maria shouted, "I can't tell if air is still blowing in, can you?"

Karl shouted back, "I don't know either, we'll just have to wait and see. The main thing is that the module hasn't been breached."

Tuesday, July 16, 2014, 07:46 GMT

Then, exhausted from the horrific events of the past 22 some minutes, they just quietly held each other tightly, trying not to be further injured or sickened by the constant and still not noticeably abated shaking and listened to the very loud rumbling of humankind's first destructive moonquake.

Tuesday, July 16, 2014, 08:01 GMT

After another 15 terrifying minutes, Maria shouted hopefully, "I think the vibrations are getting a little less violent."

Karl shouted back, "I think you're right Schatz. I've been watching that piece of debris hanging from the ceiling by that wire over there and the amplitude of its swings seems to be a little less than it was when I first noticed it."

Note: [1]Crap, and now that, too

Despite the grimness of their situation, Maria let out a little laugh and shouted, "Leave it to a seismologist to try to make a seismometer out of a piece of junk hanging from the ceiling during a major moonquake."

Her comment made Karl smile and he shouted, "If you can laugh when we're in this much Scheisse, you're the best Fräulein[1] in the world and I'm going to make you marry me the minute we get out of this mess."

For the first time since the quake hit, Maria smiled.

Note: [1]young woman

Chapter 3-2
Looking for Survivors

Tuesday, July 16, 2014, 08:55 GMT

Some 90 minutes after Karl had noticed the first seismic motions, the shaking had dropped to a low enough level so both Maria and he felt they could safely get out of their cramped and foul-smelling cubbyhole and determine what had happened to the others and the condition of the Base.

As they crawled out from their life-saving refuge, their arms and legs were severely cramped and it took them several minutes to get the full use of their limbs and finally stand up.

Though the subsiding seismic vibrations still made walking difficult, it seemed they were no longer in immediate danger and Karl said, "I think the worst is over and I hope we don't have to worry about the kind of aftershocks that follow big earthquakes. None of the tectonic moonquakes detected by the Apollo seismic array had any aftershocks. But the biggest detected was only magnitude 5.8, so it's possible some aftershocks might occur after a big quake like this one, but I sure hope not."

Maria said, "We had better use the intercom to check on the others and then, if everyone else is ok, have Isabel fix us up, or at least do some First Aid on each other."

Being careful not to further injure themselves on any of the debris or to trip over any of it, they gingerly made their way 4 meters through the debris to the intercom at the front of Lab. Though the intercom was still on, it just hissed at them. After a few tries to make it work, it was clear they had lost their electronic connection with the other 3 modules, a fact that was very worrisome.

Maria reached up and put her hand in front of the air vent above the intercom and said, "We are getting fresh air from Utility. What a relief."

As Maria was checking on the inflow of air, Karl looked at the pressure status light for Lab, which was glowing bright green, then at the pressure gauge to the left of the module's main door and said, "Great, the pressure in here is still 0.3 bars," but shouted as he looked to the right side of the door and saw the bright red glow of the tunnel status light, "Scheisse, East Access Tunnel is under a hard vacuum — the main tunnel has been breached."

Pondering the implications of that fact for a moment, Karl added, "The emergency valves in the air delivery system must have successfully sealed it off, or all the modules would have been evacuated and we would be dead."

In light of that fact, Karl exclaimed, "Mensch, I hope the emergency valves can use power from both the primary and the emergency power supplies, because if there are any further breaches and we're still on emergency power, the valves had better shut."

Very worried, they carefully made their way to the back of the module where the pressure gauge for West Utility Tunnel was located. The status light was flickering green and when he looked at the gauge, Karl said in dismay, "It has just over 0.01 bars of pressure — it has lost almost all of its air, but it apparently lost it slowly over the last hour-and-a-half."

Thinking for a moment, Karl noted, "It's possible East Access Tunnel also has a slow leak, but the leak is big enough, so it lost all of its air by now. But, it's just as possible East Tunnel had a major rupture and lost all its air very quickly. Regardless of which is the case, West Utility Tunnel offers us the best chance of getting to the other modules, in order to determine who else is alive."

Having found out the conditions of Lab and the tunnels, they knew they were safe in Lab for the time being, safe enough to attend to their injuries and to try to figure out how to improve their dire situation and get to the others.

Since Maria had advance First Aid training for the times when she, Karl, Bill, and Jim were doing fieldwork in the Traverse Vehicle, she insisted on washing their several cuts and scrapes before applying antiseptic and bandages, despite Karl's warning they needed to conserve the bottled drinking water in what was left of Lab. She also insisted they wash off some of the vomit from their clothes and bodies and only then did they rinse their mouths out and finally take long and somewhat refreshing drinks of the tepid water in the dim, emergency light.

Remembering that Maria had hit her head hard against the wall, Karl said, "Do you have a headache from hitting your head so hard?"

Maria answered, "No, my head is ok."

But Karl wanted to be sure she did not have a concussion and said, "Let me see if your pupils are both dilated the same or not, just to be sure."

Maria held her head up to Karl and looked at him with her eyes wide open. Karl carefully looked at her pupils and, since they seemed to have exactly the same diameters, said, "Good, your pupils look the same. You don't seem to have a concussion," and being somewhat giddy about just being alive after their harrowing experience, he added, "and did I ever tell you that you have the most beautiful brown eyes?"

Maria laughed and asked, "Is that any way for a doctor to talk to his patient?"

Tuesday, July 16, 2014, 09:11 GMT

Having finished attending to their injuries, they turned to their next task — figuring out how to get out of Lab and to the other modules, given the state of the tunnels.

With his background in physics, Karl quickly grasped the situation and said, "Schau mal[1], the volume of air in here and the volume in the tunnel are about the same, if I remember correctly. If the tunnel leak is small, when we open the door, about half of the air in here will rush into the tunnel and the pressure in here and in the tunnel will equilibrate at about 0.15 bars, too low to be able to stand for very long, but high enough so I can get to Utility with the aid of an oxygen mask. If Utility is not breached — and I think that is the case, since we're still getting air from it — when I open Utility's door, the new equilibrium pressure will be — um — ach ja[2], the pressure should be about 0.2 bars. If the tunnel is not leaking too fast, I can easily get to the soft suits, get in one, and bring the

---

Notes: [1]Look here; [2]oh, yeah

other one in here for you. Then we can close off both Utility and Lab to let the air supply bring them back up to 0.3 bars, get you into your soft suit, and then we can go look for the others, even though West Tunnel is losing air."

Maria nodded, but asked, "What if Utility is breached?"

"Ach, ja, a good question. Let me think — ok, in that case, when I open Utility's door — hey, you must close Lab's door behind me in any case and keep your oxygen mask on, regardless of what happens. As soon as you seal Lab's door, the pressure in here will start to increase back to normal — I don't know how long that will take — but it will, if central air is ok, as it appears to be.

"Jetzt lass mich denken[1] — ok, if Utility is breached and has a hard vacuum, but has a slow leak like West Tunnel and you have closed Lab's door, then, when I open Utility's door, the pressure in the tunnel will drop down to 0.07 or 0.08 bars and the pressure in Utility will rise to that value and then it will slowly drop. If Utility is badly breached, the pressure in both Utility and the tunnel will go to zero — very fast."

Despite the latter possibility, Karl continued with the rather optimistic conclusion, "Either way, it's ok. I can still get some oxygen from the mask and get into a soft suit before I run into trouble. Remember, Arthur C. Clark has several stories in which his heroes survive hard-vacuum exposures for a couple of minutes or so. Remember that was in his movie, *Space Odyssey 2001*?"

"Sí, I hope he's right. Ok, what should I do?"

Karl answered, "We have to hyperventilate just before we get started, so we get a lot of oxygen in our blood. Then, just before we open the door, we have to exhale as deeply as we can to get as much air out of our lungs as possible to keep the rupturing of our alveoli to a minimum, we keep our mouths open when we open the door, so our eardrums don't break as the pressure drops, and stand back from the door, so we don't get sucked through it. Then, you help me close and seal the door as soon as I get into the tunnel. Also, I want you to note the equilibrium pressure in Lab and the tunnel just

---

Note: [1]Now let me think

before we close the door, as well as the time it takes Lab to get back to normal pressure after we close the door."

Karl did not know the emergency valves had a time delay of a few tens of seconds before they closed off a module or a tunnel if it was breached and its pressure was dropping fast towards a hard vacuum, so he could only hope the emergency valves would not close immediately and keep Lab from being repressurized after they had closed Lab's door. But very clearly that possibility was worrying him, since he again said — with great emphasis, "Remember, keep your oxygen mask on all the time I'm gone, no matter what, ok?" and Maria nodded.

Maria thought a few seconds and asked, "Are you sure we can get the door open? The big pressure difference will keep the door closed, won't it?"

"Ja, you're right as usual. How did you get so smart and so beautiful, too?"

Maria answered humorously, "Good Mexican genes and good Mexican food."

Karl replied, "Don't talk about good Mexican food, I'm hungry enough after losing breakfast like that and breakfast was over 3 hours ago.

"But back to the door, let's see — ja, the door has about 2 square meters of surface area and the pressure difference is $1/3$ of an atmosphere, so — verdammt noch a'mal[1], the door has 8 or so tons of force holding it closed. I'll have to use the emergency submarine door to get out. That will work, because it opens outwards and the air pressure in here will blast it open. The submarine door is the answer."

Karl thought a second and said, "Oh — we have to be careful the escape door doesn't blast open too hard and get damaged and we're not so close to it, or, as I said, we could get sucked through it. See that electrical wire hanging down from the collapsed part of the ceiling over there? We can use it as a trip-wire to open the door and fasten another piece to the door and to some heavy debris, so the door will have to drag the debris along as it opens. That will slow the door down as it blasts open."

Note: [1]damn it

Tuesday, July 16, 2014, 09:15 GMT

Having attached some of the wire to some heavy debris and the door, they were ready to start the door opening process. They gingerly turned the locking wheel of the escape door, until they heard a slight hiss that indicated the door's seal was very slightly breached, though the door was still latched. Karl fastened some of the wire to the wheel, so he could give it a good counterclockwise tug and unlatch the door from a safe distance.

Getting their oxygen masks ready, hyperventilating, exhaling deeply, and opening their mouths, Karl gave the trip-wire a hard tug — the wire was ripped from his hand, cutting it slightly. There was a loud bang and a loud whoosh as Lab's air rushed into the nearly evacuated tunnel, sucking out half of the air from Lab. Along with the air, papers and small to medium sized objects became airborne and were sucked into the tunnel. Karl and Maria held tightly to a sturdy support as the rapidly escaping air tugged at them. Despite their having their mouths open, pain stabbed at their tortured eardrums as they instinctively swallowed a couple of times to relieve the pressure and the pain. Also, the air became extremely cold and ice fog formed as the air expanded and rapidly cooled adiabatically.

The blowout was over in a few seconds. Karl and Maria quickly put on their oxygen masks. Karl grabbed another length of wire and, despite the pain of his broken ribs and the still significant shaking of the slowly dying moonquake, Karl leaped to — and through — the small submarine door, banging his suffering ribs as he did. As soon as he was through the door, he stood up and started to close it and Maria grabbed the locking wheel to help him. Just before they got the door closed, he could see a mixture of love, concern, and terror in Maria's lovely dark eyes.

Seeing that the latching wheel had stopped turning and neglecting the stabbing pain in the lower right side of his rib cage when he gulped short breaths of oxygen from his oxygen mask, Karl bounded across the 6 meters to Utility's door in 2 giant leaps under the low lunar gravity. Not noticing the hiss the air made as it slowly escaped from the breached tunnel, he grabbed Utility's door handle and looked in utter dismay at the status light which was glowing bright red in front of him, in the dim shimmer of the emergency lights.

Karl exclaimed in near panic, "Scheisse, could this get any worse?" Knowing there was a hard vacuum on the other side of the door and having no choice but to open Utility's main door, knowing the door would then violently swing inward as the air in the tunnel forced the door open and blew into the evacuated module, and knowing in the process, the vacuum might suck him into the module, Karl unlatched Utility's door to the point where, with his head pressed against the door, he could just hear the faint hiss of air leaking into Utility. He quickly attached the wire to the locking wheel and backed off as far from the door as the trip-wire would allow — less than 2 meters. Since there was nothing to hold on to on the smooth wall and floor of the tunnel, he crouched down to minimize his cross-section to the coming hurricane. He tried to hyperventilate, blew the air out of his lungs — and then he let all hell break loose.

Tuesday, July 16, 2014, 09:18 GMT

Immediately upon being fully unlatched, the main door blasted inwards. For the second time in the same number of minutes, there was a loud bang, a loud whoosh, the air got intensely cold, there was pain in his ears, and he rapidly slid along the tunnel to the door and was violently sucked into the evacuated module.

There was a loud hiss, telling Karl the breach in the module was rapidly letting the precious air escape. Despite the swirling ice fog, the cold, and the dim emergency lighting, Karl painfully picked himself up from the debris-covered floor, got his mask back on straight, and took a couple of shallow gasps of oxygen, as best he could, fighting against the low, 0.07 bars of atmospheric pressure.

With no time to spare and feeling dizzy and nauseous from the pain, the near vacuum, and the lack of oxygen, Karl quickly made his way through the debris to the front of the module, where the suits were stored; opened the slightly jammed door of the soft suit storage cabinet; dragged the first one out — not knowing if it was damaged or not, but having no choice — he clumsily started to put it on.

After 2 eternally long minutes, during which the pressure dropped to 0.05 bars and while trying to get as much oxygen as possible from the mask — though most of the oxygen he was trying to breath was sucked out of the mask and into the near vacuum, since there was no way to make an airtight seal between the mask and his face — Karl got his legs, body, and arms into the loose fitting soft suit.

Rather than attaching the gloves next, which was the standard, "nominal" procedure — there was nothing "nominal" about putting on a soft vacuum suit *in a vacuum* — Karl took as big a gasp of oxygen as he could from the mask, took the mask off, grabbed the helmet and the suit's oxygen supply, put the former on, locked it in place, and turned the latter on.

Though most of the precious oxygen escaped through the suit's open wrists — freezing his hands and wrists as it adiabatically expanded into the, by then, 0.04 bar "atmosphere" and cooled drastically — he was still getting more oxygen than he had gotten from the mask. Swaying from dizziness and fighting nausea, but less so than during the past few minutes, Karl slipped the left glove on and sealed it in about a minute, thereby lessening his loss of the suit's life giving oxygen.

Then, very clumsily, because of his gloved left hand and because he was right-handed, Karl struggled to get the right glove on and had an even harder time getting it sealed, due to the force of the oxygen that was whooshing out the suit's one remaining open wrist and that, as a consequence, was nearly causing his right wrist to get frostbitten.

Finally, after an agonizing 7 minutes since opening the door and at a pressure of just over 0.03 bars, the right glove was sealed and Karl just stood there, trying to get enough oxygen into his oxygen starved body to stop being dizzy and nauseated, trying to get some strength back, and waiting for his cold hands, especially the very cold right hand and wrist, to start to warm up a little.

Feeling better after several minutes of recuperating, Karl knew his soft suit was in good working order — or he would be dead. Checking his 4-hour oxygen supply, he found it had been depleted by more than half while he was trying to get his gloves on, so he would have to take extra oxygen bottles back to Lab, in addition to the second soft suit for Maria.

Gathering up Maria's suit and the extra oxygen bottles, he looked around the sorry looking Utility module; clearly only Bill — if he were still alive — could make sense out of the rubble. Then he made his way to the back of the module, stepped into West Tunnel, closed and sealed Utility's back door, and went to the back door of Lab.

Tuesday, July 16, 2014, 09:36 GMT

With a very concerned look on his face, Karl banged on the door with one of the oxygen bottles and pressed his helmet against the door to hear if Maria was alive and would answer.

A second later he heard her muffled voice, "Are you ok? Did everything go ok?"

Immensely relieved, Karl answered, "Ja und nein. Utility is breached, but the central air system must be sealed, since you're getting air ok. I'm in a soft suit, which is not damaged, and I got yours, which looks ok. The tunnel is under a hard vacuum, so you're going to have to rig up the brake-wire and the trip-wire again to open the submarine door — when the pressure has equalized, we can open the main door, because I can't get through the escape door in the suit. Do everything we did the first time. You'll again be at 0.15 bars with just the breathing mask to help you until we get the door closed, but I did it in a near vacuum for several minutes in Utility and I'm ok. Understand? Hey, what was the equilibrium pressure when we closed the door and how long did it take for the air pressure to get back up to 0.3 bars?"

Karl heard a muffled "Sí, I understand everything. I'll get started getting the wires ready. Oh, it took only 2 or 3 minutes for the pressure to normalize and the equilibrium pressure was 0.16 bars, just about what you calculated."

Karl shouted, "Hey, wrap something around your hand when you pull the trip-wire or the wire will cut you hand like it did mine. Also, while you're getting the wires ready, I'm going to check the other modules to see if everybody is ok.

I'll bang on the door when I get back. Understand everything?"

Again came a muffled, "Sí," from inside Lab.

Tuesday, July 16, 2014, 09:38 GMT

Karl left Maria's suit and the oxygen bottles on the floor
of the tunnel, except for the one he needed to bang on doors
with. He walked the 6 meters to Kitchen's back door, which
actually opened into the back of Hospital, where he stopped
in horror, as he saw the door's red status light glaring at him.
He cried out, "Nein," and, with great trepidation, unlatched
and opened the door and made his way quickly through
Hospital to the door that opened into Kitchen.

Though he knew intellectually what to expect, the scene
hit him like a ton of bricks.

Upon opening the door, he first saw Isabel lying under
the table with her oxygen mask on and one in her hand, dead
from asphyxiation.

Then Karl noticed that the door would not open all the
way. So he stepped into the demolished kitchen and looked
behind the door, only to find Jim slumped against the wall,
also with his mask on and also dead from asphyxiation.

Karl went further into Kitchen to look for Pam, but she
was nowhere to be found. Karl pled in desperation, "Please
Pam, please be back in Dorm for some reason and be spared
the death that visited here."

But then he saw a hand and an arm protruding out from
under a heavy, upright freezer that had fallen over and his
plea turned into a curse. "Scheisse, verdammt noch a'mal."

At first, Karl thought Pam had also asphyxiated, since even
a heavy freezer would not tip over with much force under the
Moon's $\frac{1}{6}$-g. Then he saw the coagulated and vacuum dried
puddle of blood next to Pam's arm and remembered that during
the peak of the quake, things were being thrown around with
accelerations well in excess of 1-g. And even if the freezer had
not killed her outright, she would have died of asphyxiation,
trapped under the freezer, when the module breached.

There was nothing to do but to leave Kitchen and his
dead friends, close and seal the module door, and see if Maria

was ready to let him into Lab — his manner clearly indicated he did not have the heart to check Dorm at that moment, fearing he would find another red status light glaring at him with unconcerned indifference to the human tragedy that had befallen them.

Tuesday, July 16, 2014, 09:41 GMT

Shaken from what he had just found, Karl went back to Lab's door and banged on it to let Maria know he was back, pressed his helmet against the door, and asked, "Are you ready?"

She answered in a muffled voice, "I need a few more minutes. Is everybody ok?"

Karl hesitated several seconds, but finally said, "Nein. Kitchen was breached, Isabel, Pam, and Jim are dead, and I have yet to check Dorm."

As Karl spoke those terrible words, he heard Maria cry a muffled, "Oh no. Oh no, it can't be." And then he heard her sobbing.

He waited a couple of minutes to let her begin to get over the shock and said, in a tone that held both sorrow and the sternness the dire situation required, "Schatz, there's nothing we can do for them, but we might be able to help Tom, John, and Bill. Get the door ready and I'll go to Dorm to see what happened there. I'll bang again when I'm back. Ok? Ich liebe Dich. Ich liebe Dich so sehr[1]."

Maria answered, "I'm sorry. I'm ok. I'll get the door ready. Te quiero, también[2]."

Tuesday, July 16, 2014, 09:44 GMT

With fear painted on his face, Karl slowly walked past Kitchen's back door and the additional 6 meters to Dorm's door. Reluctantly, he forced himself to look at the status light — it was green — a steady, beautiful, wonderful green; there was 0.3 bars of air in Dorm.

Karl quickly and gleefully banged on the door, though just because there was air in Dorm, it did not necessarily

---

Notes: [1]I love you. I love you very much; [2]I love you, too

mean anyone was alive in there — but that thought apparently never crossed his mind.

Karl pressed his helmet to the door and his knocking was rewarded with a muffled, "This is Bill, who's there?"

Karl shouted, "It's me, Karl. I'm in a soft suit and Maria is waiting for me in Lab. Are you guys ok?"

Bill's muffled answer was, "Except for minor cuts and bruises, I'm ok. Tom has a broken leg, but John was in the shower when you called and didn't hear your warning. He was thrown around a lot and an overhead storage cabinet broke loose and smashed into him, he's in pretty bad shape. He's bleeding from his nose and mouth and clearly has some internal injuries. So we need Isabel's help as soon as you can get us to Hospital — and the sooner the better."

Once again, within a few minutes, Karl fought against saying what he had to say, but he did, "Bill, I got very terrible news, Kitchen is breached, Isabel, Pam, and Jim are dead and Hospital is wrecked."

"Goddamn it. Goddamn NASA, the sons-of-bitches have killed 3 more," was Bill's muffled reply, followed shortly by, "Can you get us out of here? We have no power. Shortly after the primary power went out, so did the secondary and the module's tertiary, battery power system never came on line. So we're in here with no heat or light, except for a couple of flashlights, so please hurry."

Karl answered, "Ja, we can get you out, but it will be 10 or 20 minutes before I can get back into Lab, get Maria into a soft suit, and then figure out how to get you guys to Lab, where we can figure out what we should do next. Maybe you can get some of this mess straightened out before we all die. I've got to get back to Lab now."

Tuesday, July 16, 2014, 09:46 GMT

Visibly relieved, especially because Bill was ok and because Bill knew the Base and the external equipment inside and out, Karl headed back to Lab. When he banged on the door, Maria asked anxiously, "Are the rest of the crew alive?" and added before Karl could speak, "I'm ready to open the door."

Karl answered, "Ja, they're alive, John is badly hurt and Tom has a broken leg, but that's it. Let's get this door opened. Are you ready — hyperventilated and everything?"

"Sí, on the count of three — uno, dos, tres."

Since Karl was in a vacuum, there was no sound as the escape door blasted open, though he could feel the vibrations come through the floor and he saw debris and ice crystal fog come blasting out. Then, as the pressure quickly reached 0.1 bars on it rapid climb to 0.16 bars, the familiar whooshing sound of air rushing into the tunnel became evident. When the whooshing subsided, Karl quickly unlatched the main door, pushed it open, jumped inside, and slammed both it and the submarine escape door closed, as Maria leapt toward him. Despite her breathing mask and his soft suit, she hugged him as hard as she could, forgetting about his broken ribs, and he yelped in pain.

"Cariño, I'm so sorry, but I'm just so glad to see you I forgot about your poor ribs."

Karl groaned, "It's ok, I love you, too. Just wait until the pressure is a little bit higher and I can take off this helmet."

A minute later, Karl took off his helmet and Maria took off her oxygen mask and the held each other as tightly as Karl's ribs would allow and kissed each other several times, saying, "I love you," in English, German, or Spanish between each kiss.

They stood there, quietly holding each other for another minute, finally — finally able to relax a little and let the tension of the past $2\frac{1}{3}$ hours subside. Having done so, Maria became aware of the stillness and she suddenly exclaimed, "Karl, I don't feel any vibrations any more, do you?"

Startled out of the private, comfortable world of their embrace, Karl answered, "Nein, Du hast recht[1]. Even the low level vibrations have finally died off — Mensch, they took nearly $2\frac{1}{2}$ hours to damp out completely."

Having the moonquake completely behind them, having relieved some of the anxiety they had felt for each other's safety, and ignoring both the sorrow over the deaths of their

---

Note: [1]No, you are correct

friends and the terror of the quake, they responded to the
dire needs of Tom, John, and Bill in Dorm. Karl helped Maria
get into her soft suit and they checked it out. Then Karl had
Maria attach a full oxygen bottle to his life support unit, so
they each had a full 4-hour supply.

Chapter 3-3
Rescuing Tom, John, and Bill

Tuesday, July 16, 2014, 09:54 GMT

With both of them in their soft suits, but with their helmets off, Maria and Karl started discussing how best to get Tom, John, and Jim to the relative safety of Lab.

Karl said, "I'm getting worried about opening and closing Lab's doors the way we have been doing. We're wasting a lot of air, though I don't know if that's a problem or not — Bill will know for sure — but we could be damaging the seals or the hinges, banging them around the way we're doing during the explosive decompressions. So whatever we do, I think we had better find a plan that minimizes our doing that," and Maria agreed.

Karl continued, "My first thought was to get the hard suits, assuming some of them are ok — take 3 of them to Dorm, and get the guys into them. But that would require decompressing Lab and the tunnel again to get into Utility and then decompressing Dorm twice — once to get in and once to get out — to rescue the guys and then decompressing Lab again to get everybody into it — that's a lot of wasted air."

Maria added, "Sí, since John has internal injuries and bleeding, the decompression of Dorm might hurt him internally even more. My lungs still hurt from the decompressions we've had to do, so that might even kill him. I don't think we can do that."

Karl replied, "Ja, you're right — my lungs hurt, too, and I can taste a little blood in my mouth when I cough. I agree — that's out. Also, I don't see how we could get John into a hard suit, or even into one of these soft suits, without causing more damage to his insides, given how hard it is to get into these things."

Maria continued with, "Sí, Sí, and I think we could make Tom's broken leg worse by trying to get him into a suit. Is the break simple or compound?"

"Bill just said it was broken, but you're right, if it's just a simple break, we could turn it into compound fracture trying to shove his leg into the suit leg. Worse, the bone might puncture an aorta or something and he could bleed to death. We agree that that's out, nicht wahr[1]?" and Maria nodded.

Maria said, "The only thing left to do is to flood the tunnel with air, and hope the tunnel leak isn't so big that the pressure won't hold until we get them in here?"

Karl answered, "That seems to be our only chance. Let's check the tunnel pressure to see how fast it's losing air. I didn't look at the pressure in Lab and the tunnel after you let me in and just before we closed Lab's door several minutes ago — did you?"

"No, that was the last thing on my mind."

Karl replied, "That's ok, I had other things on my mind, too. But the pressure was probably the same as it was the first time and you said it was 0.16 bars, nicht wahr?"

"Sí."

They went to the door to West Tunnel and found that the tunnel pressure had dropped to 0.11 bars.

Karl said, deep in thought, "We closed the door about 10 minutes ago, nicht wahr?" and Maria nodded.

Karl continued, "The pressure in the tunnel has to drop as an e-folding function, but I can't do natural logarithms in my head. So extrapolating linearly, it would take 30 minutes for the pressure to drop to zero and twice as long when the pressure started at 0.3 bars. Schau mal, that's consistent with the pressure having bled down to 0.01 bars when we first looked at it an hour-and-a-half after the quake — assuming the leak started around the maximum of the quake. So I can't be too far off. That should mean we can open Lab's door, leave it fully open, and let central air bring the pressure in Lab and the tunnel up to normal pressure. You said it took only 2 or 3 minutes to bring Lab's pressure up to 0.3 bars, nicht wahr?" and Maria nodded.

"So the tunnel and Lab should be back to normal pressure in maybe 6 or 7 minutes, allowing for the leak, and the

---

Note: [1]correct

slow leak should not cause us any problem — at least, for as long as we need to use the tunnel."

Satisfied, Maria said, "Then we can just open Dorm's door and bring them here and then figure out what to do next."

Karl replied, "Richtig[1] — ," but added in a worried tone, "— assuming the air supply in Utility doesn't run out. But we'll just have to chance it. That also means we really don't need these suits — but, for safety's sake, we had better wear them and close the helmets, too, just in case something goes wrong."

Maria said calmly, "I couldn't agree more. Let's get going."

Maria and Karl put their helmets on and checked to see that the suits, the inter-suit radios, and the air supplies were working properly and then they proceeded to get the escape door wires ready for the third opening of Lab's doors.

Tuesday, July 16, 2014, 10:03 GMT

Protected by the soft suits and since there was still 0.09 bars of atmosphere in the tunnel, the third decompression blast was of no consequence to Maria and Karl, though they still had to be careful not to get sucked out through the escape hatch. Once the pressure in Lab and the tunnel had equilibrated at 0.20 bars, Karl opened the main door. They waited several minutes to be sure main air was able to bring the pressure in Lab and the tunnel back up to 0.3 bars — which it did in nearly 7 minutes — and hold it at that pressure — which it also did.

Maria grabbed their flashlight and they bounded the 12 meters to Dorm.

Stopping at Dorm's door, seeing the green status light, and seeing the tunnel and Dorm's pressures were both at 0.3 bars, Karl simply opened Dorm's door and peered into the darkness.

Note: [1]Right

Tuesday, July 16, 2014, 10:14 GMT

From inside the dark and cooling Dorm came shouts of boisterous greetings from Tom and Bill.

Then Bill came bounding out of Dorm, dressed in his pajama top and pajama shorts, blinked at even the dim illumination of the emergency lights in the tunnel and said, "Goddamn, am I glad to see you two," bear-hugged Maria and then Karl, who again yelped in pain as Bill's bear hug set his broken ribs on fire.

Bill immediately let go and asked, startled, "What's wrong?"

Karl grunted, "I've got some broken ribs, that all."

Bill responded with, "Damn, I'm sorry. Why didn't you tell me?"

In order to better hear, and to be heard, both Maria and Karl opened their faceplates and Karl answered, "I didn't think you'd hug me, or I would have. But don't worry, I've survived worse. How are John and Tom doing?"

"Tom's doing ok, but John's not so good. I didn't know how you were planning to get us into Lab, so I just got them on the two beds that were free from debris. We can use the mattresses as stretchers. I also got mattresses freed from the debris for the 3 of us, thinking we might have to stay in Lab, as well as the oxygen masks, clothes, towels, bedding, blankets, soap, toilet paper — just anything and everything I could find that I thought we might need. All that stuff is piled on our 3 mattresses, so we can get everything into Lab fast and seal Dorm, so we don't lose any more air than necessary. I assume the tunnel is still leaking, or did you somehow plug the leak?"

Maria answered, "No, its still leaking — you can hear it whistling — but as Karl calculated, it's leaking at such a slow rate, central air can keep up with it."

That prompted Karl to ask Bill the question he and Maria had worried about much earlier, "Do you think the oxygen reserves will hold out much longer?"

"I don't know for sure, but we had enough for 6 more months, so I suspect we're ok in that department — but I need to get to Utility to see what shape everything is in, to know for sure."

Karl said, "Utility is breached and a total mess. I hope you can make some sense out of it."

Dismayed, Bill exclaimed, "Crap, what in hell else can be wrong? Sorry, I expected — I guess I hoped — Utility would be ok. Do you have any good news? Does Houston know what has happened?"

Karl responded, "Thus far, the only good news is we are alive, the rest is Scheisse. When I was in Utility, I didn't have time to look around the mess to see if the com- and telemetry-equipment was ok or not. Even if it is, there was no way I could have used it — at least not without Tom's help. I suspect Houston only knows we're not talking to them and they don't have a clue as to why."

Disappointed at Karl's answer, Bill swore, "Shit, well, let's get everything into Lab and then figure out what to do next."

The three of them entered the dark and cool Dorm module and Maria held 2 flashlights to supplement the dim emergency light filtering in from the tunnel. Avoiding the debris, they first went to the compartment John was in — ironically it was Isabel's. John, having been in the shower when the quake hit, was naked under the sheet Bill had covered him with. John's face was pale and drawn and there were streaks of dried blood around his mouth and nose where Bill had incompletely washed his face. John greeted them with a weak, "I'm glad you two are ok — thanks for getting to us."

Maria asked in a concerned tone, "How are you feeling — where does it hurt most?"

After a short pause, John answered, with as much cockiness as he could muster, "I'm not so bad I can't tell you all what to do and chase you around, little muchacha[1]" — which annoyed Karl — but then John added, as a little fresh blood trickled from his mouth, "My guts hurt and it really hurts when I breathe."

Annoyed at John's remark about Maria, Karl said sharply, with a double entendre, "You had better keep quiet, you're only making things worse for yourself."

Note: [1]little girl

Maria gave Karl a slight look of disapproval, but said, "Karl's right, you shouldn't talk very much."

John replied, "Ok, but just wait until I can get up . . . ," and then, as his face contorted in pain, he closed his eyes, grunted in pain, and kept quiet.

Responding to John's agony, Maria said, "We need to get into Hospital and get the morphine and medical supplies — I hope none of them are destroyed."

Tom said from another compartment in the shadows, "Yes, I sure could use a little morphine myself."

Tuesday, July 16, 2014, 10:17 GMT

Karl and Bill picked up John with his mattress, an easy task under the low lunar gravity, and started to carry them to Lab. As they did, Maria went to Tom's compartment to see how bad his leg was and to comfort him. Having been caught by the moonquake in bed, Tom, too, was wearing his pajama top and pajama shorts. Maria could easily see that Tom's left leg was bent at an unnatural angle about 15 centimeters below his knee, where it was also badly bruised, scuffed, and swollen. Somehow they would have to set his leg and splint it, but not until Tom was anesthetized or under a good dose of morphine, or both.

Bill and Karl returned to Dorm in a few minutes and carried Tom and his mattress to Lab, while Maria dragged a mattress loaded with clothes and supplies behind them.

Bill and Karl returned to Dorm to get the rest of the clothing, bedding, and the other things Bill had collected, while Maria remained in Lab with John and Tom and began to clean and bandage their cuts and scrapes.

As she was tending to Tom's relatively few minor wounds, Bill and Karl returned, each dragging a mattress loaded with the remaining clothes and supplies. They let go of their loads and went to look at John. Bill drew back the sheet covering John and found that, though John had very few cuts and scrapes, his entire body was very badly bruised, especially his chest and upper abdomen, which carried several large, angry red bruises.

Leaving Tom for the moment, Maria went to see what she could do for John, which was relatively little.

Bill and Karl began to discuss how best to proceed and Maria continued to help Tom and John as best she could using the limited resources of the First Aid kits from Lab and Dorm. The only painkillers in the First Aid kits were aspirin, so she gave Tom a double dose, hoping they would help a little. Tom gratefully accepted the aspirin and the water, even though they would do little to ease the excruciating pain in his broken leg.

Seeing Maria giving Tom the aspirin, Karl said, "Bitte Liebling[1], give me a few of those, too," and she promptly did.

Because of John's internal injuries and since blood was still seeping from John's mouth and nose and coming out faster when he coughed, Maria told John, "I can't give you any aspirin — which would do you little good anyway — or water, since you might vomit and do yourself a lot more harm." She added, "We'll get you some morphine just as soon as we can."

John grunted and tried to show a little stoic humor, but what he really showed was a little of his true feelings towards her, Bill, and especially Karl, "That's right, attend to everyone else and let your real commander lie here in pain."

From the dismayed look on her face, it was clear John's comment did not awaken any strong Florence Nightingale feelings in Maria, who was doing the best she could for her ex-commander, as were Karl and Bill.

While Maria was attending to Tom and John, Karl explained to Bill how he and Maria had gotten out of — and back into — Lab, what he had found in Utility and in Kitchen in more detail, the rough air leak rate of the tunnel, how long it took Lab to get back to full pressure after decompression, and how long it took Lab and the tunnel to come to an equilibrium pressure once Lab's door was opened.

After Karl finished bringing Bill up to speed, Bill said, "Given that you've decompressed Lab 3 times and flooded the tunnel once, there's a good chance the nitrogen reserves are depleted, though I'm still pretty sure the oxygen is ok. If the nitrogen is gone, then we're breathing pure oxygen, as we do in the suits anyway, and I could drop the pressure in Lab to 0.2 bars, which would help reduce the stress on the modules and

---

Note: [1]Please darling

seals. Regardless, we have to be careful we don't start a fire in the pure oxygen atmosphere — remember the Apollo 1 fire back in '67? Maria, did you and Tom hear that, too?"

Maria and Tom replied in the affirmative and Maria added, "We're listening to what you're both saying."

Bill continued, "Good. Ok, Karl, I agree with you, we must limit the number of decompressions of Lab's module, for the reasons you suggest and, because, if there is any structural damage to the module, too many decompressions and compressions might put enough strain on any weakened points to cause the module to start to leak — or even to cause a blowout. "

Karl emphasized, "An excellent point."

Bill nodded and said, "Given that we agree on limiting the number of ingresses and egresses, I suggest I put on Maria's soft suit and you and I go into the tunnel, close and seal Dorm's and Lab's doors, and let the tunnel lose its air again. I need to get into Utility to see what works and what is wrecked. We take all the hard suits, except those that are obviously damaged, and everything else we can find of use and pile them next to Lab's door. Then we go to Kitchen and Hospital and get all the food, water, and the medical supplies we can find and pile them with the suits and stuff. Then we have to find out if it's possible to get to the surface and — "

Immediately understanding what Bill thought, Karl exclaimed, "Scheisse, the thought the airlocks might be blocked or jammed and we couldn't get out never crossed my mind. I've been assuming we would have no trouble getting to the surface, especially since the airlocks serve no purpose when the tunnels are evacuated, except to function as useless doors to the surface."

Bill reassured Karl, "Don't worry, it's very unlikely that both West Tunnel airlocks are blocked, and it's even more unlikely all 4 airlocks are blocked or jammed."

"Ja, ich verstehe — I mean, yes, I understand. I just never thought of that problem."

"Don't feel bad, you thought of a hell of a lot of critical things, especially under these life and death circumstances, and Maria has done one hell of a good job, too."

"Danke[1], Bill," and Karl added, "After we get the suits and supplies collected, we should try to get to the surface to see what is left working out there and try to contact Houston using the Traverse Vehicle's- or Lander crew module's- radio, if either of them still works."

"As you would say — ja — then we come back in, repressurize the tunnel, using the air from Dorm, and then we can enter back into Lab without decompressing it and risking doing John in. Then we should have enough information to decide what we can and cannot do to survive until help comes from Earth — agree?" and Karl nodded in agreement.

Maria was finished doing her First Aid on Tom and John and went to Bill, to tend to his cuts and scrapes.

Having heard most of Karl and Bill's discussion, Maria had already taken her soft suit off and she gave it to Bill before she started her First Aid.

As she attended to Bill, she said softly, so only Bill and Karl could hear, "I don't want to alarm John and Tom, but the medical training NASA gave me was never meant to cover serious injuries, it was just advanced First Aid. Pam got the full nurse's training. NASA always assumed Isabel would take care of any serious emergencies. What I was taught was just enough to keep an injured Traverse Vehicle crewmember alive and comfortable until we could drive back to the Base and get him to Isabel's Hospital. We need expert medical advice, as well as the medical supplies from Hospital. Until I get that advice, I don't even dare to give morphine to Tom or John, or I could do more harm than good. You have got to get the medical supplies and get advice ASAP."

Bill asked Maria, "Except for the pain, Tom is in no immediate danger with just a broken leg, right? Though John is in pretty bad shape, he seems to me to be no worse than he was right after I pulled him from the wrecked bathroom an hour ago, so he is stable, right?

Maria answered hesitantly, "Yes to both questions, I guess."

Bill continued, "Ok then. We must limit our in- and egresses and we must know immediately if Lab is safe and for

---

Note: [1]Thanks

how long, if the Traverse Vehicle is ok, and so forth. Otherwise
we may miss a chance to survive this mess until Houston can
rescue us — if we can even communicate with Houston.
Finding out how bad things are in the Base and outside and
what resources are available is the absolute top priority, otherwise none of us will survive more than a day or two. I'm
sorry Maria, but Tom and John will just have to suffer it out
until Karl and I can survey the damage and get the supplies all
in 1 trip. Our doing that won't cause a delay of more than an
hour or so in getting help to Tom and John. Understand?"

Maria answered quietly, "Yes."

As Bill put Maria's soft suit on, Karl gave Maria a hug and,
as best as he could through the open faceplate, he gave his
Schatz a long kiss and said, "We should be back in a couple of
hours — with good news, I hope. Ich liebe Dich so sehr, mein
Liebling."

Maria responded with a soft, "Te quiero, también, mi
amado[1]."

Then Bill, all suited up, hugged Maria, and the 3 of them
went to where John and Tom were lying and told them they
would have the medical supplies — especially the morphine
— for them in a couple of hours and that everything would
be ok.

Karl and Bill turned and walked towards Lab's door. As
they did, Karl stopped next to a piece of electrical wire hanging from a section of the partially collapsed ceiling, pulled as
much of the wire — about 3 meters — out of the ceiling as he
could and bent it back and forth until it broke off. Bill gave
him a puzzled look, which prompted Karl to laugh and say,
"Just wait and see," as Maria smiled.

Equipped with the mystery wire, Karl caught up with Bill
and they stepped into the still pressurized, but leaking West
Tunnel and turned to close the door. As they did, Maria blew
Karl a kiss and then waved them both a weak goodbye, with
a sad, tired, and concerned look on her face. They closed
Lab's door and sealed it.

Note: [1] I love you, too, my darling

Chapter 3-4
Surveying the Damage

Tuesday, July 16, 2014, 10:39 GMT

Wasting no time, and hearing the clearly audible whistle of the air escaping from the tunnel, Bill went to Dorm and closed and sealed it's door. At the same time, Karl went to the door of the evacuated Utility module. He again expertly unlatched Utility's door to the point where it just remained latched and to where he could, with his helmet pressed against the door, just hear the hiss of air escaping into the breached module.

Bill rejoined Karl as he was splicing the 3-meter piece of wire to the trip-wire already attached to the door's locking wheel from Karl's first entry into Utility over an hour earlier. A light bulb lit up in Bill's head and he said, "Now I understand — very smart."

To which Karl replied, "Well, I've had a lot of practice lately with this verdammt[1] little game — a hell of a lot more than I like."

Bill and Karl went as far from Utility's door as the spliced trip-wire would allow — a little less than 5 meters — Bill crouched down behind Karl, minimizing their total cross-section to nearly that of Karl's alone, braced themselves as best they could against the tunnel's smooth wall and floor and Karl said, "On three — eins, zwei, drei," and pulled the trip-wire.

Though Karl was far too used to it, Bill experienced for the first time the loud bang as the door burst open, the loud whoosh as the tunnel's air rushed into the module and then right out of the module's breach into the vacuum of space, the formation of ice fog in the air, and he even felt the drop in the air temperature, despite the insulating effects of his soft suit. Of more concern, he felt the strong tug of the air rushing out of the tunnel and into Utility, and since he and Karl had noth-

---

Note: [1]damned

ing they could securely hold on to, they began to slide along the smooth floor towards Utility's door. Luckily, by the time they arrived there, the air pressure had dropped low enough so they were not pulled into Utility against their will.

As they got up, Bill said to Karl, over the suit radios, "Well, that was a nice little ride — at least we didn't have to walk all the way to the door."

Though there was no way they could have known it right then, the tunnel leak rate had increased significantly as a result of the latest decompression.

Tuesday, July 16, 2014, 10:42 GMT

Bill took a look inside Utility and groaned, "Man, I'm surprised anything still works in here at all — what a mess."

Stepping into Utility, Bill immediately noticed the heat exchanger had shifted about half-a-meter and the pipes that carried its working fluid to the radiator on the lunar surface were snapped off.

Pointing to the broken pipes, Bill said, "Well, those pipes are probably part of the breach, but there may be more leaks. So we've lost the heat exchanger — that means it should start to get hot in Lab. I'm surprised it hasn't already."

Karl replied, "But, Lab's air has undergone drastic adiabatic cooling 3 times in the last 1½ hours, that would keep it cool for a while. Also, not much is running in there, except the emergency lights, so there should be little heat generated in there, except for our body heat — and that can't be too much, can it?"

"I don't know offhand, Karl, but you're probably right. If you are right, Lab will cool down — like Dorm has been doing — to the temperature of the regolith. You're the selenophysist, what is the ambient temperature a few meters down in the regolith?"

"The Apollo heat-flow probes and the one I emplaced at the Fra Mauro Station 10 weeks ago show the temperature at 1 meter depth is about $-20°$ C and then it rises at 1½ to $2°$ C/m with increasing depth. So ambient around the modules is about $-10°$, a lot colder than I would like it in Lab."

"Well, don't worry about it Karl, the emergency batteries will last only a day or maybe two at most, while it should take the modules several days to cool down to that low a temperature. If we don't find a solution to our predicament within a day or two, we won't have to worry about freezing to death."

They worked their way to the front of the module where the surface exploration suits were stored, moved some debris out of the way, and opened their lockers. A quick inspection showed that 2 suits had sustained obvious damage. But the other 6 looked ok, though only a careful inspection would tell for sure.

Then they checked the PLSSs, 3 of which were obviously useless. Each took a suit and a PLSS out into the tunnel and carefully placed them adjacent to Lab's door. After two more trips, they had the vital surface, or hard suits ready to take into Lab, when their surface work was done.

Tuesday, July 16, 2014, 10:58 GMT

Bill said, "I want to look at the central air control unit and the oxygen and nitrogen tanks next." They went back to Utility and Bill looked at the air control unit. Many of its gauges were broken and he said, "I suspect even the unbroken gauges are inaccurate. So, I'll just use man's simplest method of determining the amount of fluid in the tanks."

He got a hammer from the adjacent workshop, went to the first liquid oxygen tank, pressed his helmet against it so he could hear in the vacuum, and banged on the side of the tank.

Happily, he reported to Karl, "Tank 1 seems to be about half full." Bill tested Tank 2 and said, "About the same here."

After banging on Tank 3, Bill got a concerned look on his face and banged it again. "Number 3 seems to be empty." Then Bill noticed a large crack near the bottom of the tank, where one part of its support structure was welded to it, and said, "Well, the LOX just leaked out and boiled way in the vacuum. It's a good thing the automatic shut off valve between the tank and the common feed line to the central unit worked, or we wouldn't be here to look around."

Then Bill went to Tank 4, did his little musical number again, and was rewarded with a sound that he said, ". . . means the tank has about a quarter of its oxygen left." Bill added, "I guess we have somewhere between 2½ and 3 months of oxygen left — actually, 4 or 5 months, since, unfortunately, there are only 5 of us left to breathe it. Well, at least, we won't die from the lack of oxygen."

Bill went to the nitrogen resupply tank and smacked it with the hammer. "Just as I expected — dry as a bone. No matter, breathing pure oxygen won't hurt us — though I would like to reduce the pressure to 0.2 bars. But given the condition of the control unit, I'm afraid to try doing that, for fear of totally screwing our air supply up. It's a case of — 'if it ain't broke, don't fix it'."

Karl added, "If that saying ever applied, it sure applies to our air supply right now."

Bill went to the tank that held the hydrogen for the fuel cells and tapped on it. Looking very concerned, Bill hit it a couple of more times and then exclaimed, "Shit, the hydrogen has leaked out, too. This means we can't refill the fuel cells."

Resigned to that fact, Bill said, "Ok, let's check the main water tank under the floor," which they quickly found was nearly ¾ full.

Satisfied, Bill said, "Let's take a look at Tom's com-cubicle."

Tuesday, July 16, 2014, 11:06 GMT

They opened the slightly jammed door to Tom's cubicle, looked inside, and knew immediately what the prognosis was. Part of the ceiling had fallen on the main com-console. That would not have caused a problem under lunar gravity, but at the high levels of acceleration during the peak of the quake, the falling ceiling had hit the console with a great deal of force. The console's frame was distorted out of shape. Though the blow probably did not damage the console's individual solid-state electronic boards, the boards themselves were certainly disengaged from their connectors.

Just to be sure of that, Bill pushed the debris away and flipped the switch of the radio on a couple of times — to no avail. "Well it was worth a try. I don't know enough about it to see if it can be fixed. We'll just have to get Tom to look at it. Until he can, there's nothing we can do about it, so let's not waste any more time in here."

Having found out what little was working in Utility and what was not, Bill said, "Let's gather up some tools and whatever else might be useful and add them to our pile of stuff next to Lab's door, shut the emergency lights off to conserve battery power, and get the hell out of here."

"Donnerwetter[1], I should have turned off the lights the first time I was in here."

"Don't give it another thought Karl, you were trying to survive and save the rest of us. Don't blame yourself for not turning off the lights. The hour or so they were on doesn't amount to anything — forget it."

Tuesday, July 16, 2014, 11:08 GMT

After they carefully piled the salvage from Utility next to Lab's door, Karl grabbed Bill's trusty hammer and banged on the door, pressed his helmet against it, and shouted, "Schatz, we're done in Utility and we're now going to Kitchen and Hospital, hast Du verstanden[2]?" He heard Maria's muffled confirmation and he said to Bill, "Let's go."

As they took the few strides to Kitchen's back door, Karl said, "Just so you know what to expect when we get into Kitchen, Isabel is under the table — dead from asphyxiation — Jim is behind the door between Hospital and Kitchen, also dead from asphyxiation, and Pam is under the big freezer which apparently crushed her. It's not a pleasant sight in there." Bill silently nodded. Karl opened the door and they stepped into Hospital.

Though Karl had hardly taken notice of the condition of Hospital during his first trip into the module, there was surprisingly little damage in the little hospital, though the examination table had tipped over. They immediately went to the locked drug and medicine cabinet, whose glass doors were not even shattered. Not knowing where the key to the cabinet was hidden — though Isabel probably had it with her — and not hesitating even a second, Bill simply and effectively smashed each of the glass doors with his hammer, saying, "There's nothing like breaking and entering when you are in

---

Notes: [1]Damn; [2]did you understand

a hurry," and added, "Get Isabel's lab coat over there, so we can bundle up all this stuff in it."

Though Hospital was in fairly good shape, the contents of the cabinet were in total disarray. Some of the vials of morphine and other fluids, as well as some of the bottles of pills and hypodermic needles, were broken.

Karl set the examination table upright, spread out Isabel's lab coat on it, and they carefully loaded the coat with the intact items, especially the morphine, bags of saline solution, anesthetic, and antibiotics.

They went to the bandage closet, took all the bandages, and added them to their growing pile of medical treasures. They even took some of Isabel's medical instruments, though they did not know quite how to use them, but Maria might know.

Suddenly Karl noted, "Hey, we need to find a splint for Tom's leg — or at least something that can serve as one."

They were looking around for a classic wooden splint, when Bill happened upon a set of inflatable plastic splints, exclaiming, "Look what I just found."

With that, they had everything they could conceivably need, and, having agreed they needed to get everything useful out of Hospital during that trip, they took a lot of things they would probably never use.

They took the bundle of medical supplies and carried it to the stack of salvage next to Lab and returned to the module to enter Kitchen proper.

Karl opened the door between Hospital and Kitchen and they stepped inside the tomb of their friends. Despite having discovered his dead companions just over an hour-and-a-half earlier, it again hit Karl hard to see their lifeless bodies in that devastated module, especially seeing Isabel's once immaculately groomed clothes and body despoiled with dust and bits of debris. Karl said, sorrowfully and uncharacteristically eloquently, "How quickly and indifferently a random act of nature, aided by NASA's arrogance and stupidity, can end life."

Bill, unable to say anything, just absorbed the shock of actually seeing his dead companions and thus having first-hand knowledge they were really dead and worse, they had

died violent deaths — the first victims of the human exploration of the Moon since the Apollo 1 fire in 1967.

Recovering quickly, since there would be time to grieve
later and forced into action by their own need to survive —
and especially John and Tom's desperate need for the medical supplies they had already collected — Bill and Karl went
further into Kitchen to look for food and drink.

Since most, but not all of the frozen food was in the
freezer that had crushed Pam and since the door-side of the
freezer was on Pam, it was apparent they would have to set
the freezer upright, uncovering Pam's body in the process, to
get to the frozen food. But some of the debris on top of the
freezer was supporting a large portion of the ceiling, so Bill
said, "I'm worried the entire ceiling might come crashing
down on our heads if we try to remove the debris to get to
the freezer, we had better leave it where it is. There should be
quite a bit of frozen food in the freezer compartment of the
refrigerator, as well as other cooled eatables and juice in the
refrigerator itself. Then there's all the dehydrated food. All
that should last us a few weeks, at least."

They began collecting all the food they could find and
piled it on the food cart to take to Lab. They made three trips
before they had exhausted all the food and juice they could
find.

Karl asked rhetorically, "What about drinking water?
There's no way we can run the water tap to fill any contain-
ers, the water will simply boil away in the vacuum."

Bill answered, "We'll just have to find some way to transfer
water from Utility into Lab — if we stay in Lab. I'll have to think
about that after we see what the condition of the equipment on
the surface is. We're finished in here, let's get to the surface."

Karl objected, saying, "Bill, we just can't leave them like
this. I know there's not much we can do right now. But out
of respect, let's at least lay Isabel and Jim on the table, clean
them up a little, get their breathing masks off, and cover
them, even if we can't do the same for Pam."

Bill thought for a second and replied, "I'm sorry, you're
right. The few minutes we'll need to care for them, won't
make any difference to our chances of surviving this mess."

They quickly took off Isabel's breathing mask, closed her eyes, put her on the table, and straightened her clothes and hair a little. Then they brushed off most of the bits of debris and dust that were on her clothing, face, and hair and covered her with a tablecloth.

They went to Jim, carried him to the table, and did him the same honors.

After they finished their last, sad tasks of respect for their fallen friends, they shut the emergency lights off and closed and sealed Kitchen's back door.

They went to Lab's door and Karl banged on it with Bill's hammer and shouted, "Maria, we're done in Kitchen. Now we're going to the surface. We should be back in a couple of hours, three at most, ok?"

Maria's muffled answer was, "Ok, but be careful."

Tuesday, July 16, 2014, 11:39 GMT

Bill and Karl proceeded to the NW airlock, since it was the closest accessible exit to where the Traverse Vehicle and the Rovers were parked near the mouth of NE exit. Upon arriving at the inner door of the lock, the status light was glowing green, indicating the lock had 0.3 bars of atmospheric pressure in it. Bill opened the manual, emergency release valve to the lock's interior and they could see air rushing out via the little jet of ice fog that instantly formed as the escaping air and water vapor adiabatically expanded and cooled drastically. Slowly, the red status light came on and the green one blinked out. Bill said, "That'll stop the door from blasting open in our faces when I hit its open button," and added after a short pause, "Apparently the airlock's integrity has not been compromised."

Then he hit the open button, the door came open with ease and Bill said cautiously, "So far, so good."

Bill stepped in the airlock and deactivated the interlocking mechanism that prevented both doors of the airlock from being open at the same time. He pushed the open button for the outer door, but nothing happened. He pushed it again, with the same result. Bill unlocked the outer door manually and tried to push it open, but it would not budge, not even when Karl helped push.

Bill cycled the interlocking mechanism on and off a couple of times and they tried to push the door open again. Bill looked at Karl and said, "It's no use — the door is jammed. Let's try the south lock."

As they left the useless NW airlock, the ever-mindful Bill turned the lock's emergency lights off and then closed and sealed the door, saying, "We don't want any air leaking out through the lock when we repressurize the tunnel to get back into Lab."

Karl nodded approvingly at Bill's foresight and added, "Good idea, there are more than enough leaks in here already."

They walked the 24 meters to the SW airlock and were relieved to find its green status lighting burning brightly. Bill opened the manual, emergency release valve and they both saw the reassuring ice fog plume form as the air escaped from the airlock's interior and the status lights slowly turned from green to red.

Bill hit the open button — and nothing happened. Bill hit the button again, and again the door remained motionless.

Bill said forcefully — willing the damned door to open, "We'll do it manually." and Bill tugged on the manual wheel which began to turn, but it was clearly resisting his efforts.

Karl said loudly, "Lass mich helfen — ah, I mean, let me help," and together they managed to get the door unlatched. Then they both pulled on it — it budged a few centimeters. In frustration, Karl, enabled by the low lunar gravity, put both feet against the wall and pulled on the door with his entire body strength, along with Bill.

As Karl strained against the door, his face twisted in pain and he again became acutely aware he had broken his ribs earlier — a painful fact he had almost forgotten in all the turmoil.

Suddenly, the jammed door gave way and Karl was flung several meters down the tunnel, where he landed hard on his back and bounced a couple of meters further. Groaning in pain from his newly aggravated broken ribs, Karl started to get up as Bill arrived and helped him to his feet.

Bill asked very concerned, "Did you hurt yourself badly?"

"Nein, but my ribs did not like that at all — give me a minute to catch my breath and I'll be ok."

Bill replied in a slightly reprimanding tone, "Ok, but the next time, let me do the aerobatics."

"Ja, I sure will."

After a couple more minutes, when the pain had subsided a little, Karl grunted, "I'm ready, let's see if we can get out of this rattrap."

Karl and Bill walked into the airlock; Bill deactivated the interlocking mechanism, paused, and said, "Here goes — cross your fingers." Karl looked puzzled for a few seconds, having forgotten in all the excitement and confusion that an American crosses his fingers for good luck, while a German holds his thumbs. Karl tried to cross his fingers, an impossible task in the gloves of the soft suit, but he could hold his thumbs — so he did.

Bill punched the open button and, as Karl and Bill held their breaths, the outer door opened effortlessly.

Tuesday, July 16, 2014, 11:47 GMT

As soon as the outer door finished swinging open, Karl and Bill walked out of the airlock into the exit tunnel and, as Bill turned to hit the close button, Karl said urgently, "Don't close it, if we can't get it open again, then we'll all die."

Bill responded, "If we leave the door open, it could prove fatal to Maria, Tom, and John if Lab begins to leak."

Karl shook his head and said, "That's unlikely. It's more likely the door could jam closed for some reason — ah, because of an aftershock — and then we would not be able to get back in."

Bill thought several seconds and replied, "I guess you're probably right, but the difference between the two probabilities has to be small — ok, I agree."

They turned and walked up the inclined exit tunnel towards the lunar surface. When they reached the surface, it was bathed in the harsh light of the Sun, which was about 5° above the western horizon and hence about 10 hours from setting. They immediately noted the long, coal black shadows cast by the low rolling, cratered topography — topography that appeared highly exaggerated under the very low angle of illumination.

They also immediately felt the effects of the low surface temperature, which was already at $-67°$ C and was falling rapidly towards a sunset temperature of about $-140°$ C.

Karl, being used to the sturdy surface exploration suits, became concerned and asked, "Are these soft suits going to handle the surface environment very well? I already feel cold — though my sun-facing side is still warm?"

Bill answered, "The only good thing about your moonquake, is it happened several hours before sunset. These soft suits were designed for use in the modules in case there were air leaks to repair and they are of only limited use on the surface. They are too poorly insulated to protect us against the $-170°$ of the nighttime cold or against the $+100°$ of the midday heat for even an hour. Also, they can't take the abrasion of the lunar dust. So we're very lucky — there are only a few hours during the lunar day/night cycle when these suits can protect us before it gets — in our case — too cold for us to use them. And that's now, so we had better hurry."

With that to urge them on even more, and despite the reinvigorated pain in Karl's ribs, they bounded around the west side of the mound of regolith, which covered the habitation modules, and simultaneously saw the destruction the moonquake had caused to 3 vital pieces of equipment.

The 50-meter tall antenna mast had collapsed and lay twisted and bent on the surface. Karl said, "For some strange reason, that twisted antenna reminds me of the rattlesnakes I saw on the training fieldtrips to the Malpais lava flows near Grants in northern New Mexico, the volcanic fields around Flagstaff in northern Arizona, and the Pinacate lava fields in northern Sonora, Mexico."

The 5-meter diameter, parabolic antenna that served as the high data rate communication link between the Base and the Earth had been ripped from its mount, was lying on its side, and its shape was certainly no longer that of a parabola.

Next to the destroyed high-gain antenna was the Base heat exchanger's radiator. It was broken into three unequal pieces. Not surprisingly, the pipes leading to Utility below the mound of protective regolith had been severed, as they were in the module itself, as Bill had found out a little over an hour earlier. Bill said, "These broken heat exchanger pipes are certainly part of Utility's breach. Let's go on top of the mound to see what other evidence of the breaches we can find, so we can get some idea of how safe — or unsafe — the intact parts of the Base are."

They found 2 funnel-shaped, blowout craters in the regolith just above the west end of the buried Utility module and 3 coalescing funnel-shaped, blowout craters that were situated just above East Access Tunnel and its NE airlock.

Karl said, "These blowout craters sure tell us where the air came rushing out of Utility and East Tunnel. I suppose the tunnel breached at the junction between the airlock and the tunnel."

Bill said, full of rage, "Goddamn those stupid, arrogant NASA bastards. I told the Administrator, and anyone who would listen, we couldn't put the Base together tele-robotical-ly, that it wouldn't be safe, because it's hard to align and secure big pieces of hardware, even with humans doing the work. But no, NASA had spent money on tele-operated research and it's better to kill people than to admit to Congress that NASA had wasted money on useless programs. Damn it — it's just like Challenger, Columbia, and Atlantis all over again! Except this screw up is on the Moon and we're in the middle of it. I hope to hell Congress and the President finally get rid of NASA, before it kills any more people with its stupidity!"

Bill paused a minute to let his anger ebb and finally said, "I'm sorry Karl, but I just had to let that out. I guess I feel par-tially responsible for this — I let them bully me into using tele-robots when I was convinced it was unsafe. "

Karl replied, "Bill, don't blame yourself. What choice did you have? If you had refused to do it their way, you would have been fired, and some ass-kissing NASA bozo would have totally screwed it up. Besides, die Hurensöhne[1] wouldn't

Note: [1]the sons-of-bitches

listen to Nakamura, Binder, and me about the possible danger of moonquakes either. NASA won't listen to anybody who disagrees with their plans. So forget it for now. We'll deal with those bastards when we get back to Earth."

Bill replied, "Yeah, you're right — let's go. We have more important things to do."

They walked south along the top of the mound; from that vantage point they could see the crane, bulldozer, and trailer, which were parked 50 to 60 meters to the east of the mound. The crane had tipped over, but the bulldozer and trailer seemed to be ok. When they got to the part of the mound above Kitchen, they found 4 blowout craters, 1 very big one and 3 medium sized ones all in a row, and Bill said, "With those 4 breaches, the Kitchen decompression must have been hell on them — though poor Pam might have already been dead. From the blowout pattern, a welded seam must have given away."

Turning north, they carefully looked for blowout craters along the entire length of the West Tunnel, but they did not find any. Karl remarked, "The West Tunnel leak must be so slow the air can diffuse out through the regolith without disturbing it enough to make a crater."

Bill answered, "Yeah, I guess that's right. You're the selenologist, you know about craters and all. We're done up here, let's get to the Traverse Vehicle."

Tuesday, July 16, 2014, 12:04 GMT

Bill bounded down the NE side of the mound, towards the Traverse Vehicle that was parked some 15 meters to the NE of the NE Access Tunnel's exit. But because of the pain in his aggravated ribs and since only one person could go into the Traverse Vehicle at a time via its small airlock, Karl started gingerly walking down the side of the mound and over to the Traverse Vehicle.

When Bill arrived, he saw two things. First, the vehicle's tracks in the regolith showed it had danced around by a meter or more during the moonquake and second, the airlock's red status light was on, showing it was evacuated, as it should have been. When no one was inside the Traverse

Vehicle, the last person to leave evacuated the airlock and when there were people inside, the airlock was pressurized by the last one to go in.

The first observation was expected. The Traverse Vehicle was built with big, springy wheels and big, shock absorbers, so it could take the bouncy rides over the rough and cratered lunar surface. Bill radioed Karl, who had just finished coming down the mound, "Hopefully, these wheel tracks mean the Traverse Vehicle just bounced around during the worst of the moonquake and didn't suffer any damage and since everything inside is securely lashed down, most everything inside should be ok, too."

His second observation showed that the airlock was probably ok, but that did not necessarily indicate whether the Traverse Vehicle was breached.

Bills went to the Traverse Vehicle's external display panel. He opened the panel's door and was greeted by a number of green lights and illuminated dials — there were no red lights showing anywhere.

He scanned the panel and found the atmospheric pressure was standard at 0.2 bars of pure oxygen. He checked the main electrical bus load current and voltage and the fuel cell current and voltage and several other parameters — all of which were normal. However, though the Traverse Vehicle was still connected to the Base via the electrical umbilical to provide power and to recharge its reversible fuel cells, which were 2/3 depleted during the Copernicus Traverse, the fuel cells did not show a reversed current. They were getting no power from the Base's nuclear reactor.

Since the Base had also lost its primary power, it was clear they would have to live off the little battery power they could muster up and the juice that was left in the Traverse Vehicle's fuel cells at the end of the Copernicus Traverse. Registering all that, Bill said thoughtfully, "When I have more time, I have to figure out a power budget, but right now, the main thing is, the Traverse Vehicle is in good condition."

Karl arrived at the vehicle just as Bill stepped into its small airlock.

Tuesday, July 16, 2014, 12:08 GMT

As soon as Bill got out of the airlock, and without waiting for Karl to cycle through it, he opened his faceplate, sat down at the com-console, switched it on, and switched to the omni-antenna, since the gimbaled high-gain antenna was not pointing towards Earth as a result of the moonquake-dance the Traverse Vehicle had performed, and said, "Houston, Fra Mauro Base here. Do you read me?" Not waiting for the 2.5 second delayed reply, he repeated, "Houston, Fra Mauro Base here. Do you read me?" Then he paused and waited.

Then, clear as a bell, came, "Fra Mauro, we copy you — where in hell have you been? We lost contact with you over 4½ hours ago."

Bill answered quickly, "We had a catastrophic moonquake, just like Karl warned NASA about. The Base is in shambles, just as I was afraid it would be if it were built tele-robotically. Pam, Isabel, and Jim are dead. John has serious internal injuries and Tom has a broken leg. We need medical advice about what to do to help them. Except for minor cuts and scrapes, Maria, Karl, and I are ok, though Karl has some broken ribs. Karl and I are out surveying the damage right now. The Traverse Vehicle is ok and we'll probably have to use it as a lifeboat until you come and get us. The nuke seems to be out, but we haven't checked that yet, nor the Landers. We'll do that as soon as we leave here. The only livable module is Lab, but only until the emergency batteries run out in a day or so. Maria, John, and Tom are in it waiting for us to get back and bring medical supplies and advice, food, and the hard surface suits from the other modules. Oh, East Tunnel is breached and West has a slow leak, so we have been doing some fancy maneuvering to get in and out of Lab. That's about it for now. We'll call back in about an hour or so, after Karl and I have checked on the Landers and the nuke. When we get back, have an internist and a broken leg MD there, so we can ask them what to do for Tom and John."

Just then Karl came in through the airlock's inner door and Bill asked, "Do you want talk about the moonquake?"

Karl answered, "No, I can tell them what little I know when we're safe."

Houston started to ask Bill a question in response to his disastrous report, but Bill, who had worked himself up in a lather, interrupted, "I don't have time for your NASA bullshit now. I'm signing off until we get back," and said to Karl, "Let's go see if we have the first part of the ride back home."

Tuesday, July 16, 2014, 12:11 GMT

With that, Karl turned around and started to cycle back out the airlock, having been in the Traverse Vehicle for less than thirty seconds, and Bill followed him immediately. They walked the few meters to the Rovers and found that both had danced around during the moonquake like crazy and one had tipped over.

Bill and Karl quickly righted the Rover, checked them both out, and found their fuel cells were fully fuelled. They seemed to be in good condition and Bill said, "Let's take this one and get out to the Landers pronto, before we get too much colder."

Karl responded, "Nein, let's take both — they may have damage we can't see and if one breaks down, we can both ride back on the good one."

Bill smiled and said, "A particularly good thought. You take this one."

They sped off to the north and moved along at an average speed of about 12 km/hr. It would take them a good 25 minutes to reach the Landers.

Tuesday, July 16, 2014, 12:36 GMT

Twenty minutes after leaving the Base, when they were about a kilometer from the South Landing Pad crater, Bill said cautiously, "The Lander with the crew module doesn't look right to me. What do you say?"

"Mensch, I've been thinking the same thing. We'll know in a few minutes if it's ok or not, but I'm worried."

Three minutes later, they were 400 meters from South Landing Pad and it was abundantly clear that the Lander with the crew module had tipped over.

Two minutes later they drove into the landing pad crater and could finally see that 2 of the Lander's 4 legs had snapped off and the whole stack had pitched forward and smashed the front of the crew module. The Lander's 2 liquid hydrogen tanks and 1 of the 2 liquid oxygen tanks had broken open and their contents had rapidly boiled away.

Bill said, concerned and hastily, "Let's not waste time here. We need to checkout the other Lander before we get too cold."

Tuesday, July 16, 2014, 12:42 GMT

They started the 1-kilometer drive to North Landing Pad. The Lander at that pad had last carried the Traverse Vehicle down from the 200-kilometer altitude, rendezvous orbit and had nothing sitting on it.

As they approached the pad's crater, they could see the Lander was standing upright. Worried after seeing what had happened to the first Lander, neither Karl nor Bill said a word, even after they had entered the landing pad crater and pulled up beside the Lander.

Tuesday, July 16, 2014, 12:47 GMT

They climbed off their Rovers and went to inspect the seemingly intact Lander.

Bill said, "You give it a good visual inspection and I'll go look at the instrument panel."

Saying, "Will do," Karl started to carefully look at the landing gear, the fuel tanks, the main- and steering-engines, and the structural elements of the Lander. He saw the Lander had hopped around a lot during the moonquake, but had suffered no visible damage. Puzzled, Karl said, more to himself than to Bill, "Lass mich denken — ok, compared to the other Lander with the heavy crew module, this one is lighter and has a much lower center of gravity. Ach ja, so it just bounced around without exceeding the breaking loads of the legs and was stable enough so it didn't tip over. Right Bill?"

Bill answered a noncommittal, "I guess so," and continued looking at the instrument panel.

It took Karl 10 minutes to walk completely around the Lander and carefully inspect it. By that time, Bill had finished reading all the gauges and had checked the Lander's avionics. Bill said, "The fuel tanks are about a third full, as they should be after landing. Power system is ok. Fuel cells are ok. And the avionics are ok. Unless you found some structural damage, this thing is good to go."

Karl said, "That's great and no, I found no obvious structural damage. However, I'm getting verdammt cold in this flimsy suit."

"Me too. The only problem is, like the Traverse Vehicle and the Base, the Lander is getting no power from the nuke. The monitoring systems are running on standby, using fuel cell power, but they draw so little power, they are of no consequence. The problem is the cryogenic refrigerators that re-liquefy the hydrogen and oxygen boil-off need power from the nuke and there is none. That's not much of a problem for the oxygen, since the nighttime temperature gets down to within 10 to 20° of its boiling point, so the oxygen boil-off rate will be low. Even now, just before sunset, the temperature here is only a little more than 100° above oxygen's boiling point. The problem is, hydrogen's boiling point is 80 to 90° below the minimum nighttime temperature. So we're going to lose a good fraction of the Lander's hydrogen.

If Houston can't get the new Lander with the new crew module down here, we'll have to ride this thing up to lunar orbit strapped to its structure. If so, the payload would be next to nothing — just us and our suits — so the remaining hydrogen might be enough, if Houston can get the OTV to the rendezvous orbit during the coming night or very shortly after sunrise. If they don't get it here within 3 or 4 days after sunrise, I suspect we will have lost all the hydrogen. Anyway, that's my best guess."

That all sounded pretty glum, but Karl said, "Well, we'll have to make the best of it. Let's get the hell out of here, before we freeze, and take a look at the nuke."

"Yeah, let's roll," and they both climbed onto their Rovers and took off to the SE to drive the 4 kilometers to the nuke, their teeth chattering.

Tuesday, July 16, 2014, 12:59 GMT

The drive to the vicinity of the nuclear power generator took a little over 20 minutes and as they started driving up the rim of the 50-meter diameter, 7-meter deep crater in which the reactor sat. Bill said, "We can't stay very long in the reactor's line-of-sight, because of the radiation, but we have to know if it is damaged or not. Though I doubt it, it's possible the nuke is ok and the loss of power is just due to breaks in the surface lines between the reactor and the Base and the Landers, breaks we can easily repair."

As they reached the rim crest, Karl exclaimed, "Scheisse, look at that mess. I guess you've got your answer."

Bill replied in disgust, "You're right with your Scheisse. Don't stop, just keep going, so we can get to hell out of the radiation."

Hastily, they turned their Rovers to the SW to escape the radiation and to start on the last, 4-kilometer leg of their inspection tour.

The surface temperature had dropped 8 more degrees C, to –75° C, during the hour-and-a-half since they left the Base. As Bill and Karl drove to the Traverse Vehicle to report to Houston before they went back into the Base, they became hypothermic and found it hard to control their limbs and bodies due to their strong shivering.

Halfway there, Karl swore loudly in exasperation and with his teeth chattering, "Scheisse, I ju-ju-just peed in my su-su-suit — I couldn't con-con-control myself."

Bill laughed and stuttered, "Don't fret, I di-di-did it just a-a-after leaving the nu-nu-nuke. When you're as c-c-cold as we a-a-are, you lose co-co-control of your ba-ba-bladder and pee in-in-involuntarily. My gr-gr-grandfather was a gu-gu-gun-ner on a B-17 in WWII a-a-and on bo-bo-bombing runs o-o-over Germany — aha, I so-so-sorry, I didn't me-me-mean to be in-in-insensitive — "

"Don't wo-wo-worry, that's ancient hi-hi-history to me — be-be-besides, my grandfather wa-wa-was a fighter pi-pi-pilot who flew Me 109s a-a-and later the Me 262 je-je-jet fighter — so our gra-gra-grandfathers probably s-s-shot at each o-o-other and since th-th-they both lived to te-te-tell about it, they mu-mu-must have both be-be-been bad s-s-shots. Go on wi-wi-with your pee st-st-story."

"Ok — well, an-an-anyway, be-be-because the B-17's fl-fl-flew in the icy st-st-stratosphere, the crews fr-fr-froze — like we a-a-are — despite their sh-sh-sheep's skin, fleece-lined, fl-fl-flight suits, and every o-o-one of them in-in-involuntarily pe-pe-peed in their fl-fl-fleeced suits. He sa-sa-said, wh-wh-when they got ba-ba-back to the warm de-de-debriefing ro-ro-rooms, the st-st-stench was unbearable.

Also, when A-A-Alan Shepard ma-ma-made America's f-f-first, 15 minute, su-su-sub-orbital flight ba-ba-back in '61, he wa-wa-was sitting on the launch pa-pa-pad so long, wa-wa-waiting to be la-la-launched, he had t-t-to pee in his sp-sp-spacesuit. He was ly-ly-lying on his ba-ba-back with his le-le-legs elevated, so the p-p-pee ran d-d-down his ba-ba-back and shorted ou-ou-out all the me-me-medical sensors. S-S-So we just j-j-joined the Alan S-S-Shepard Spacesuit P-P-Pee Club, that's a-a-all," and Bill chuckled loudly, as his teeth continued to chatter.

Karl, however, with his limited, German sense of humor and because his initially warm pee had gotten very cold in the right leg of his soft suit, said, "S-S-Somehow, that do-do-doesn't seem ve-ve-very funny right n-n-now."

Finally, 23 minutes after leaving the nuke crater, they reached the Traverse Vehicle. Shivering, they staggered off their Rovers and, one at a time, climbed into the airlock and into the warmth of the Traverse Vehicle. The surface temperature had dropped another 4° C, to −79° C.

Tuesday, July 16, 2014, 13:44 GMT

It took them several minutes to stop shivering enough to start discussing their developing survival plan.

Bill said, "Roughly, the emergency batteries in the Base would normally last about 24 hours, of which 6 hours are already gone. But, with power on only in Lab and in East Access Tunnel, the batteries could last up to 3 times longer, or another 50 to 60 hours — if they are not damaged and if the main emergency batteries in Utility don't get too cold as the module cools down to ambient. In short, I don't trust the emergency power beyond another 24 to 36 hours.

I'm also worried about the integrity of the Lab module, given all it has been through. If there are aftershocks, and you said there could be, Lab could easily be breached. So, I think we should get everybody out of there and in here before we get into even more trouble."

Regarding the Traverse Vehicle's life support capabilities, Bill said, "Though I want to do a better analysis after we get back in Lab, the vehicle came back with 9 days of power and life support reserves and the reversible fuel cells had about 10 hours of charge time before the quake hit. With a charge to discharge ratio of about 5, that would give us another 2 days of power. Then we have 1 day of power in the Traverse Vehicle's emergency batteries. All together, we have power for 12 days. In the emergency power mode, which uses power at 80% the normal rate, we can stretch that to 15 days or maybe a little more. Also, if we can get some of the batteries out of Utility, we can add another couple of days of power to that.

"We got plenty of food from Kitchen and there is enough oxygen in Utility's tanks for a few months. Drinking water will be a little scarce, but the fruit juices will help there.

"So, we should be able to last 2½ weeks — and with a lot of luck — maybe almost 3 in the Traverse Vehicle, though the lack of adequate power to run the Traverse Vehicle's heat exchanger to keep the cabin cool, starting a day or so after sunrise, might limit us to 16 or 17 days. If Houston hasn't gotten us out of here by then, well — what can I say?"

Karl said, "That all sounds good to me. We've made it this far. We'll make it the rest of the way."

Having agreed on the tentative plan, Bill flipped the radio switch on and called, "Houston, Fra Mauro here. Do you copy?" and waited.

"Fra Mauro, Houston here, we copy you. Bill, this is off the record — we know you guys are pissed, and you have every right to be, but the guys and gals in the trenches want you to know we will do everything possible to get you home safely. We won't let anybody or anything get in our way. This will not be another Columbia — I think you know what I mean. Now back to business. What is your status?"

The comments of the controller brought tired smiles to Bill and Karl's faces and they visibly relaxed. Reassured, Bill gave Houston a brief report on their findings at the Landers and the nuke and the details of their plan to abandon Lab and get everyone into the Traverse Vehicle.

Houston concurred with their survival plan and said, "We'll check, but I doubt we can get the new Lander with the new crew module to the Moon in 3 weeks, but we should be able to get the OTV to the lunar rendezvous orbit in 15 to 18 days. If so, as you suggest, the 5 of you can ride to orbit strapped to the Lander and the OTV can rendezvous with the Lander and pick you up."

Bill said, "Copy, but try to get here in 15 days. I'm worried about the boil-off of the hydrogen and the power in the Traverse Vehicle. Though possible, I don't think we will last 18 days."

Houston said, "Copy. We'll look into the hydrogen boil-off rate and advise you as to what we find."

Bill asked, "Do you have the MD's there for us to ask what we can do for John and Tom?"

"Yes, here's the internist, Dr. Maxwell."

After listening to Bill's description of John's condition, Dr. Maxwell said, "There's little you can do for John, except keep him comfortable, sedated, on an IV, and hope he makes it back to Earth where we can operate on him." Then Dr. Maxwell told them what dosages of morphine they should give John and how to do the IV.

When he was finished, Dr. Jacobson came on line and told them how to set Tom's leg and what else they could do for him.

Bill replied, "We'll do all that and keep you posted on their conditions. Maria will probably have more and better questions when we're all in the Traverse Vehicle." Bill asked Karl, "Do you want to tell Houston anything about the moonquake?"

Karl declined, saying, "We need to get back to Lab. I can tell Houston what I know about it when we are all safely in .here. Besides, I'm still too pissed to give them a civil report."

Bill replied, "Yeah, I know what you mean," and then told Houston, "I expect it will be 3 or 4 hours before we're back in the Traverse Vehicle," and signed off.

Chapter 3-5
Back Inside the Base

Tuesday, July 16, 2014, 13:59 GMT

As Bill, and then a couple of minutes later, Karl, stepped out of the Traverse Vehicle's airlock, the Sun was less than 4° above the western horizon and the surface temperature was –82° C and falling rapidly. They hurried to the south entrance of West Utility Tunnel and went down the ramp to the open airlock door. Bill shut the outer door, but left the inner door open, since Karl had said, "Don't close it Bill. We barely got it opened earlier, if we closed it now, we might never get it open again."

Bill replied, "Good idea, but it's risky having just one airlock door closed, instead of both, but we'll just have to accept it."

As soon as they were finished at the airlock, they went to Lab's door and Karl pounded on it. Pushing his helmet against the door, he shouted, "Maria, we're back and we're going to flood the tunnel now. See you in 10 minutes."

Karl heard Maria say in a muffled voice, "See you in a little bit."

As Karl talked to Maria, Bill went to Utility and got some of the electrical wire Karl had use to open Utility's door just over 3¼ hours earlier and both of them went back to Dorm. The green status light and pressure gauge showed Dorm still had its normal 0.3 bars of pressure.

With the skill acquired by so much practice during the past 4¾ hours, Karl pressed his helmet against the door and unlatched the emergency submarine door to the point where he could just hear the hiss of air escaping from Dorm. He rigged the trip-wire and went off to the side, where Bill was waiting, and pulled the trip-wire.

They saw the emergency door swing violently — but for them silently — open. Debris and ice fog came shooting out the opened door and, as the pressure quickly built up to the expected 0.16 bars, they began to hear the whooshing of the air entering the tunnel. All they had to do was to wait the expected 6 or 7 minutes it would take for central air to bring the pressure in Dorm and the tunnel from 0.16 bars back up to 0.3 bars. Then they could enter Lab, get the hard suits and supplies inside, close Dorm's and Lab's doors, take care of John and Tom, and then get the hell out of the Base and into the relative safety of the Traverse Vehicle.

Tuesday, July 16, 2014, 14:12 GMT

Karl and Bill waited 10 minutes, but the pressure rose rather slowly to only 0.21 bars and would not budge any higher. Disconcertingly, the tunnel displays at all 4 module doors showed just 0.21 bars. Even so, Karl had asked Maria twice what the pressure reading was on Lab's inside display and it was always 0.21 bars.

In addition to that conundrum, they had been on their suits' life support oxygen for nearly 3½ hours, so they had only about thirty minutes of oxygen left in the main tanks and another 15 minutes in their emergency tanks. Noting that, Karl suggested, "Since we're already breathing 0.2 bars of oxygen in our suits, why don't we just open our faceplates and breathe the tunnel's 0.21 bars of oxygen?"

Bill replied, "I don't think we should risk it. The last decompression clearly increased the tunnel's leak rate, so there's a good possibility there could be a blowout when we open the door. We had better keep using our suit oxygen until we're safely inside Lab."

"Ja, you're right and you were sure right — we need to get the hell out of here before the whole thing comes collapsing down on our heads."

Karl banged on Lab's door and, with his helmet pressed against the door, said, "Liebling, the tunnel is leaking faster. So the pressure out here won't get any higher than it is now. Rig the escape door with the wires, but tie the brake-wire to something solid, so the door can only open a few centimeters and hopefully the air in Lab will come out over a period of a few minutes, instead of in just a few seconds. That way, there won't be an explosive decompression that could hurt John.

You won't need your breathing masks at 0.25 bars, but put them on anyway, just in case the decompression increases the leak rate or causes a blowout."

Maria's muffled answered was, "Sí, I understand. Give me a few minutes while I tell John and Tom what is going to happen, put oxygen masks on them, and rig the break- and trip-wires. I assume, since the pressure difference is only 0.09 bars, the decompression won't be too bad, even if the door did open all the way fast, right?"

Karl answered, "Ja, you're right, but tie the brake-wire as taut as you can. There will be a lot of give in it, so if it's not really taut, the door will open too far, ok?"

Maria answered, "Sí," and tied the brake-wire to a cabinet support, rigged the trip-wire, moved John and Tom as far from the door as possible, told them what to expect, put oxygen masks on them, and finally put her own on. She banged on the door and shouted to Karl, "I'm ready — get back away from the door."

Maria waited 30 seconds and jerked the trip-wire. Instead of a loud bang, she, John, and Tom just heard a loud pop, a loud twang as the brake-wire went taut, and the whoosh of air exiting the Lab.

Karl and Bill heard the pop, saw the door open about 2 centimeters and just a little ice fog formed, but no debris came flying out the cracked open door.

The pressure rose quickly to 0.26 bars as the air from Lab rushed into the tunnel, but rose no further and slowly started to fall towards the tunnel's previous value of 0.21 bars, as central air unsuccessfully struggled against the leak trying to bring the pressure back up to 0.3 bars.

Just before the pressure dropped to 0.21 bars, Karl said to Maria, "You had better wait a few minutes after the pressure equilibrates at 0.21 before taking off your oxygen mask, just in case the leak rate has again increased and the pressure drops further. But after you take it off, keep it with you just in case, ok?"

"Sí."

After waiting impatiently the extra few minutes Karl said, "The pressure seems to be holding at 0.21 — ok, let's go."

Maria took off her oxygen mask, unfastened the brake-wire from the partially opened escape door, closed that door, and opened the main door.

While they were waiting for Maria to open the main door, Karl and Bill took off their helmets and as soon as Maria had opened the door, Karl rushed into Lab, hugged Maria with desperation, and gave her a long, fierce kiss. "Kindlein[1], I'm so glad to see you."

Maria replied, "Me too, querido."

Tuesday, July 16, 2014, 14:26 GMT

After giving Karl and Maria a few moments to themselves, Bill said, "Let's get the hard suits and PLSSs in first, then the medical supplies, a few of my tools, and just enough food and drink to last a few hours. We don't need it all in here, since we will be taking it to the Traverse Vehicle soon."

Karl and Maria let go of each other and began to help Bill bring in the suits and supplies. In their absence, Maria had gotten some of the debris out of the way, so they had room to work and places to store the supplies.

She had also found some of her clean clothes among those Bill had put on the mattresses, found a quasi-private corner of Lab, and put on a plain cotton bra, panties, blouse, and shorts. She carefully laid her vomit- and blood-stained clothes aside, hoping she could, at least, save the blouse her mother had so lovingly embroidered with colorful flowers, when they were rescued.

Between the three of them, it took only a few minutes to get everything in Lab they needed for the short time they expected to remain there.

Bill went to Dorm and closed and sealed its door. When he came back to Lab, Karl closed and sealed Lab's main door behind him and Lab's pressure began to climb from 0.21 bars back to its normal 0.30 bars. They were safe in Lab — for the time being.

Note: [1]Baby

Tuesday, July 16, 2014, 14:31 GMT

While Karl was closing the door, Maria took the oxygen masks off of John and Tom and then sorted out the medical supplies. She asked, "Should I go ahead and give John and Tom some morphine and, if so, how much?"

Bill answered, "Dr. Maxwell said to give John 4 milligrams right away, then get him on a saline solution IV. Set the drip rate at 165 grams per hour — the bag will last about 6 hours. After that, he gets morphine, via the IV, whenever the pain gets too much. Tom gets 4 milligrams, too. Go ahead and give them the morphine shots while Karl and I get out of these suits and then we'll help you with the IV and set Tom's leg."

As Bill was telling Maria what to do, he and Karl were getting out of their soft suits and as they peeled their suits down to where their legs were exposed, the stench of warm urine filled Lab's air.

Maria smelled the urine just after she finished giving John his morphine shot and she turned around just as Bill and Karl stepped out of their suits. She saw that Karl's right leg was wet, as were both of Bill's legs, starting from just above the crotches of their shorts and running all the way down to their urine soaked socks. Putting two and two together, she exclaimed, trying to suppress the smile that was forcing its way across her lips, "Did you two wet your pants?"

Bill was not even a little bit embarrassed by the situation and answered, "It was damned cold out there and, like anyone who goes hypothermic, we peed in our spacesuits."

However, unlike Bill, Karl was embarrassed to have his Schatz know he had, in her word, "wet" his pants. Seeing Karl's face turn red, Maria just could not help from laughing and could not resist saying, with a sly smile and a little chuckle, "You mean my macho man needed a bebecito[1] diaper?" and burst out laughing as Karl got redder and redder.

Bill thought Maria's question and Karl's increasing embarrassment were uproariously funny and doubled over in laughter. Karl, trying in vain to save face, said to Bill, some-

---

Note: [1]little baby

what annoyed, "What are you laughing at, you peed down both legs."

With that comment, even Tom, who was still in pain and who would never, ever laugh at someone's embarrassment, could not hold back and started to laugh.

John, who was already feeling the effects of the dose of morphine said, "It's worth getting my guts all busted up just to see the Kraut pee his pants," and did not regret his effort that then caused him to go into a fit of coughing and spitting up blood.

Though Karl's lack of a real sense of humor and his embarrassment hindered him from seeing the humor in the situation, it was obvious even to him that the laughter had done everyone some good, except perhaps John, and seeing his beloved Maria's tired eyes light up was worth his embarrassment. Knowing, "if you can't lick'em, join'em," Karl said, referring to John and Tom, "Besides, you two are going to have to wear these pee filled suits to get to the Traverse Vehicle." Though not bad for Karl, his attempt at humor fell well short of Maria's, and resulted in a few just groans. With that failure, Karl looked like he desperately wanted to change the subject to anything else possible and it was Maria who saved the day.

"Ok, enough is enough. You two go find some dry clothes. I sorted out our clothes while you were gone. They're in piles on that mattress over there. Then help me with John and Tom."

Tuesday, July 16, 2014, 14:49 GMT

After Bill and Karl had toweled themselves off and put on clean underwear, shirts, shorts, socks, and sneakers, they went over to help Maria with John, whose face was ashen and drawn. Maria had an IV bag ready and Karl found something in the rubble to hang it on. Then Maria inserted the intravenous needle into John's right arm and John said, "Thanks beautiful, you're an angel," to Karl's annoyance.

Then, all three turned their attention to Tom. Bill explained to Tom and Maria, "Following Dr. Jacobson's instructions, we'll give you some morphine, anesthetize you, set your leg, and splint it with the inflatable splint."

Maria said, "But the inflatable will be too big to fit into the leg of the soft suit."

Karl said, "Ja, as usual, you're right Liebling. We'll have to make a temporary splint out of something else and replace it with the inflatable one after we get to the Traverse Vehicle. Let's look around to see if we can find anything suitable in the debris."

Almost, immediately, Bill's practiced eye for finding usable construction materials from the junk bin of a workshop, located long pieces of aluminum L-bar that had been part of the ceiling. He dug out a piece nearly 2 meters long and said triumphantly, "This should do nicely. I'll get my hacksaw and file — now I know why I wanted my tools from Utility — and have the splints cut and filed smooth in a jiffy."

As Bill attacked the aluminum L-bar with gusto, Maria said, as she finally gave Tom his shot of morphine, "We should take the old bandages off the cuts and scrapes on his leg, clean them, put more antiseptic on them, and then re-bandage them. Then we should wrap his leg in a clean towel to protect his skin from being chaffed by the aluminum, no matter how smooth Bill files it. Tape the 4 — Bill, you are cutting 4 splints, aren't you?"

"Yes."

Maria continued, "Tape the 4 splints firmly to his wrapped leg and then tape another towel over the aluminum splints to protect the soft suit from chafing and maybe puncturing."

Bill stopped his work for a moment and said, with admiration, "Sounds like a good plan, señorita." Tom agreed and Karl smiled at Maria.

Karl said, "Given how my ribs feel, I'm not sure I can pull hard on Tom's leg. Bill, you're going to have to do most of the pulling. Maria can help you and I'll hold Tom by his shoulders and take care of the anesthetic, ok?" Everyone agreed.

"But first you're going to have to help me start the anesthetic, Schatz. Dr. Jacobson said it would be easiest to give Tom the shot in the butt — which I could do — but it would take an hour or so to knock him out. If we give it to him in a vein, he'll be out in few minutes and you're the only one who knows how to get a needle into a vein. I don't think we should wait around an hour . . . ," and everyone nodded, including Tom. ". . . ok, if you start the shot, I can slowly give him the 1 to 5 milligrams of Versed Dr. Jacobson said would take to put Tom under, while you're in position to help Bill pull the second he is out, ok?"

Maria replied, "Sí."

Bill was ready with the 4 splints, Maria had the towels, tape, antiseptic, and bandages ready, and Karl had the 5-milligram shot of Versed ready.

Tom said politely, "The morphine has really begun to work — I'm ready."

Maria proceeded to take the old bandages off Tom's leg, clean the wounds, put new antiseptic on them, and re-bandaged the leg.

When she was finished, she took the needle from Karl and inserted it into a vein in Tom's left arm and handed it back to Karl, who asked, "Are you ready Tom?"

Tom answered, with his usual politeness, "Yes, let's go."

Karl began slowly pushing in the plunger of the hypodermic needle — very slowly increasing the dose of Versed. Tom began to show the effect of the anesthetic within 2 minutes and slid into a semi-unconscious state in a little more than 3 minutes. As he did, Karl said softly to him, "Schlaf schön Kindlein. Schlaf schön[1]. The next time you see my handsome face, your leg will be all fixed and we'll all be in the Traverse Vehicle."

As Karl finished his inspired soliloquy, Tom went completely under the influence of the Versed and Karl nodded to Maria and Bill. Following Dr. Jacobson's instructions, Karl had given Tom enough Versed to insure Tom's leg muscles would be totally relaxed and would not resist Bill and Maria's pulling on the leg to set the broken bones. Also, they had to be sure Tom was out long enough for them to get him into a soft suit, into the Traverse Vehicle, and back out of his suit, before he began to wake up. That was necessary because it would probably be very painful for Tom when they stuffed his splinted leg into the suit's leg and — and far worse — Tom

---

Note: [1]Sleep well little child. Sleep well

might vomit when coming out of the anesthetic and that could prove fatal, via choking, if he were in a soft suit.

Next came a delicate procedural issue. Bill said, "In order to get enough leverage to pull hard enough on Tom's leg to set it, I'll have to put my left foot in Tom's crotch — and someone has to reach into Tom's pajama shorts and move his private parts out of harm's way."

Maria looked uncomfortable with the topic and as far as Karl was concerned, her doing that task was completely out of the question. Bill could not do it from his position at Tom's feet with Maria, so Karl bit the bullet and swore, "Oh, zum Teufel[1], I'll do it — but you two had better never tell anyone about this, or else." Both Bill and Maria nodded and by their expression, neither dared to even crack a smile.

Being the chosen one, Karl quickly did his duty and Bill put his left foot firmly in Tom's crotch and said, "Pull everybody — pull like hell."

Slowly, Tom's muscles yielded and suddenly the bones slid into place. Bill, Maria, and Karl slowly released most of the tension on Tom's body — his leg remained straight and all three smiled with satisfaction.

Bill said, "Well, it looks like we did it. I'll keep a little tension on the leg and you two start getting it splinted."

Maria wrapped the still swollen, but straight leg in a towel and as she held the towel securely, Karl wrapped some tape around it to secure it and then taped the towel to Tom's skin above and below the ends of the towel, so it would not slip up or down. Karl took 2 of the aluminum splints, put one on top and one on the bottom of Tom's leg, and Maria secured both ends of the splints to the towel with tape. Karl put the 2 remaining splints on the sides of Tom's leg and Maria secured both of them with tape. Finally, Karl helped her wrap tape around and around the leg until the splints were covered from top to bottom. At that point, Bill relaxed his grip on Tom's leg. All that remained was to wrap the second towel around the taped splint and secure it with more tape. When that was done, Bill, Maria, and Karl sat back, relaxed,

---

Note: [1]what the devil

and admired their work. They had done a good job and they were pleased with themselves.

Maria went over to John, who had fallen asleep under the influence of the morphine. John's face was not as drawn as it had been and he seemed to have regained a smidgen of color.

Having finished with John and Tom, Maria asked Karl, "Do your ribs still hurt?"

Karl, answered, "Not too much, except when I bang them or strain hard or breathe too deeply. But, I could use some more aspirin or something stronger if you can find anything in the medical supplies."

Maria searched a minute or two, found the Percoset pain pills and gave two tablets and a bottle of water to Karl, who gratefully took the pills with a gulp of water.

Done with their immediate medical duties and knowing they had done the best they could for their injured crewmates, Bill, Maria, and Karl turned to their own bodily needs — they were hungry as wolves.

Tuesday, July 16, 2014, 15:23 GMT

Bill had not eaten since the previous evening and though Maria and Karl had had breakfast nearly 9 hours earlier, they had lost it during the quake. Thus, none of them had had any real nourishment during the previous 20 hours. They hungrily searched through the food supplies and quickly found some vacuum packed hard salami, cheddar cheese, Melba toast, dried fruit, and several cans of apple and grape juice.

They took their treasures to a cleared spot on the floor, sat down, and enjoyed their gourmet meal. After the first few ravenous bites, they slowed down and completely relaxed for the first time since the moonquake had struck 8 hours earlier.

Once satiated, they rested and let the tension of the past hours drain from their bodies and, as their adrenaline levels decreased, "Bill asked, "Are you guys as tired as I am?"

Both Karl and Maria answered, "Yes," simultaneously.

Nevertheless, they still had to get John, Tom, and the supplies to the Traverse Vehicle, before they could totally crash.

Tuesday, July 16, 2014, 16:06 GMT

After resting for about 30 minutes, Bill, Maria, and Karl began the task of very carefully inspecting and testing the 6 hard suits and the 5 PLSSs.

Two of the suits were no longer airtight, but all the PLSSs were working properly. So they had a hard suit and a PLSS for the 3 of them, plus a spare suit and 2 spare PLSSs.

They checked the 2 soft suits they would have to use to transfer John and Tom to the Traverse Vehicle and they were both still ok — though their legs were still soaked with urine. They replaced the nearly depleted oxygen bottles of each suit; so, the soft suits were good for another 4 hours, far more than enough time for John and Tom to be safely taken to the Traverse Vehicle.

Tuesday, July 16, 2014, 17:21 GMT

The crucial inspections of the hard and soft suits had lasted 1¼ hours, during which Maria had checked on John and Tom twice, and when they were finished, Bill, Maria, and Karl began discussing their next step — getting everyone and their supplies into the Traverse Vehicle.

Bill said, "We need to completely shut the Base down — turn off the emergency power so we can use the emergency batteries to supplement the fuel cells in the Traverse Vehicle, shut central air off, and open all the module doors and air-locks to evacuate the entire Base. That way we'll have easy access to everything in the Base in our hard suits. We can leave most of the supplies, including the spare suit and PLSSs, exactly where they are and we can readily get to other things in the Base we might need, but have not already collected."

Maria added, "We can put most of the frozen food in the mouth of the SW exit tunnel. There it will be exposed to the low nighttime temperatures and remain frozen — rock solid."

As Bill and Karl anticipated, the temperature in the Base had already dropped from its standard 21° C to a cool 12° C. Karl said, "Soon it will be cold enough in the tunnel for the cooled food we collected from Kitchen's refrigerator to remain edible. All that means is we only have to take a little extra food and drink to the Traverse Vehicle to supplement what was left after the Copernicus Traverse."

They agreed they would need to use the 2 Rovers to transfer John and Tom the 50 meters from the SW exit tunnel's mouth to the Traverse Vehicle and they worked out exactly who would do what and when, to minimize the time John and Tom would have to spend in the soft suits — ever mindful of the fact that Tom must not be allowed to wake up and possibly vomit in his suit.

Concluding they had everything properly planned, they were ready to start the dangerous task of getting their injured crewmates to the Traverse Vehicle, as well as the extra supplies they would need for the next day or so.

Tuesday, July 16, 2014, 17:37 GMT

Maria said, "Let's put Tom in his soft suit first. He's not as critically injured as John and is considerably smaller, so we won't have as hard a time getting him suited up as we will with John. That way, we'll have some practice before we tackle John," both Karl and Bill agreed.

Maria thought a second and quickly added, "Hey, we have to use the soft suit Karl wore for Tom. First, it would be difficult, or perhaps impossible, to slide Tom's bulky, bandaged left leg into the wet, tight leg of a soft suit and second, if we succeeded, the outer towel would get soaked with urine — and we can't have that. Luckily, you only wet the right leg of you suit and luckily — so to speak — Tom broke his left leg.

Despite the embarrassment caused by his Schatz bringing up his "wetting his pants" again, Karl said, "Mensch Schatz, I would have never through of that, no wonder I love you so much," and Bill nodded in complete agreement.

Taking the soft suits with them, they went to Tom's bed. Before starting on Tom, they took a quick look at John. Maria took his pulse, which was weak, but steady, and they agreed he looked slightly better and was breathing slightly easier.

Turning their attention back to Tom, Maria checked his pulse, which was strong. Karl prodded him to see if the effects of the anesthetic had begun to lessen. However, Tom did not respond to Karl's poke in any way and Karl said, "Gut[1], he's still out like a light."

Lifting Tom's right leg, they slid it effortlessly into the wet right leg of the suit. They gingerly lifted his bandaged and splinted left leg and began, very carefully, sliding it into the suit's dry leg. When they reached the point where the suit leg had to start going over the thick wad of taped splints and towels, they had to slowly tease it over the bulky obstruction, a task that took them a good 5 minutes, but which was accomplished without causing injury to Tom or to the suit.

Bill said, "Boy Maria, you were right. That was tough enough. If the suit leg had been wet, I doubt we would have succeeded in getting his leg in there."

After that, the job became very easy. They lifted Tom's light body, pulled the suit up over his trunk, slid his hands and arms unceremoniously into the suit's sleeves, zipped the front of the suit up, put the gloves on — with some difficulty, because it was hard to get Tom's limp fingers into the glove fingers — sealed them, and finally, put the helmet on and sealed it.

Bill quickly checked to see if Tom was getting oxygen and then opened Tom's faceplate, just in case he woke up and vomited.

They were finished with the whole process in 12 minutes, which was a relief, since during their discussion, they had assumed the process was going to be very difficult and take a long time.

Turning to John, Maria quickly withdrew the IV needle from John's arm and said, "The IV bag is still half full. Should we try to salvage it? We don't have a lot of them."

Bill answered, "Just seal it as best you can. We'll deal with it later, if it doesn't leak out into the vacuum when we open the doors."

They started the delicate task of sliding their second, semi-unconscious patient into his soft suit. John made no response as they slid his legs into the suit's wet legs, but when they started to lift his trunk to slide the suit over it,

---

Note: [1]Good

John's eyes fluttered open in pain for a split second or two; he groaned and began coughing and spitting up blood. Maria exclaimed, "We're killing him."

Bill replied in a cold voice, "Maybe, but we have no choice. We either get him into this suit and into the Traverse Vehicle, or he's dead in a day or two anyway."

After his coughing stopped and a little fresh blood appeared on his lips, John seemed to completely lose consciousness.

Biting their lips, Bill, Maria, and Karl finished getting John suited up, checked his air supply, and opened his faceplate.

Tuesday, July 16, 2014, 18:02 GMT

Bill, Maria, and Karl immediately started getting into their hard suits, checking them before sealing their helmets and gloves. Karl and Maria quickly rigged the escape door wires in preparation for opening Lab's door to the evacuated tunnel, which had leaked all of its air away and whose gauge was showing a hard vacuum. While Karl and Maria were busy with the door wires, Bill shut John and Tom's faceplates, checked their oxygen supplies, and gave Maria and Karl a thumbs up. They were ready in 20 minutes flat. Karl jerked the trip-wire.

Chapter 3-6
In the Traverse Vehicle
Safe Haven

Tuesday, July 16, 2014, 18:22 GMT

Immediately after the accustomed blowout, they opened the main door and Bill and Karl, taking some new wire with them, went to Utility's door, which they quickly rigged for opening.

Karl bounded the 21 meters to the SW airlock, turned, and waved to Bill, who, immediately pulled on the trip-wire. Not even waiting for the 0.16 bars of air in the tunnel and Lab to finish rushing into Utility and out to space, Bill half slid and half scrambled the 5 meters to Utility's main door and through it. He quickly got to his feet and went to the main air control unit and shut it off. He bounded back to Lab and helped Maria carry John on his mattress to the SW airlock exit tunnel.

When Karl saw Bill open Utility's door, he waited a few moments as the tunnel pressure dropped rapidly towards zero and hit the open button of the airlock's outer door. With a push from the residual air escaping from the tunnel, Karl bounded out of the exit tunnel onto the lunar surface, whose temperature was −116° C. The Sun was just 1½° above the horizon and would set in 3 hours.

Karl bounded the 50 meters to the Rovers. He hopped in the driver's seat of the closest one and, with wheels spinning and throwing up rooster tails, he drove as fast as he could back to the SW exit tunnel, where Bill and Maria arrived carrying John on his mattress. They lifted John off his mattress and loaded him onto the back of the Rover. Maria jumped in the right seat and they drove off to the Traverse Vehicle; with Bill loping along behind them, moving almost as fast as they were driving.

As soon as they got to the Traverse Vehicle, Bill went into the airlock, cycled it, and stepped into the cabin. Karl and Maria carried John to the airlock, opened its outer door, stood John up in the narrow airlock as best they could, closed the door, and pressurized the airlock.

Bill opened the airlock door as soon as the green status light came on and caught John as he slowly fell out of the narrow airlock, laid him on the left lower bunk in the sleeping quarters, and exited the Traverse Vehicle.

While Bill was doing that, Karl and Maria drove back to the SW exit tunnel and went inside the Base to get Tom.

Bill jumped in the driver's seat of the second Rover and drove hell-bent to the SW exit tunnel.

When Bill arrived, he met Karl and Maria carrying Tom, on his mattress, out of the exit tunnel and he proceeded into the Base to get the bundle of medical supplies and the extra food they had decided to take to the Traverse Vehicle.

While Bill loaded the food and medical supplies on his Rover and drove to the Traverse Vehicle, Maria and Karl drove to the Traverse Vehicle, put Tom in it, and laid him on the right lower bunk across the aisle from John.

Shortly thereafter, they heard Bill place the supplies in the airlock, shut the outer door, and start its pressurization cycle. When the status lights turned from red to green, they opened the inner door, took the supplies out, and closed the door, so Bill could get in — which he did a minute later.

Finally, and barely 11 minutes after they had started their escape from the Base, they were all in the relative safety of the Traverse Vehicle.

Tuesday, July 16, 2014, 18:33 GMT

Without pausing to even catch their breath, but after taking off their helmets and gloves, they quickly opened Tom and John's faceplates. Both were still out cold and though Tom looked like he was sleeping peacefully and had good color, John looked like death warmed over.

John's face was so pale and drawn it prompted Karl to say, "Though we didn't kill him, we sure tried — das arme Schwein[1]. If he makes it back to Earth, I'll be verdammt surprised."

Note: [1] the poor bastard

Bill nodded, but Maria said quietly, "No, he'll make it — he has to. I can't lose another crewmate," and Karl tried to hug her to comfort her, an impossible feat in their hard suits.

Bill said, "Let's get out of these suits, get them out of theirs, and get John back on the IV."

After de-suiting, they took off John's suit and Maria immediately got a new IV bag ready and soon had the needle in John's arm. She got a wet washcloth and wiped the blood off his face that had trickled from his nose and mouth. She rinsed the washcloth out and wiped the urine off his legs. After rinsing the washcloth again, she wiped off the rest of his naked body. After asking Karl and Bill, "Would you two lift his body for me?" she placed a square meter piece of thin plastic sheeting under John's buttocks and thighs and used a towel to make a diaper for him.

Apparently, neither Bill nor Karl had thought of the fact that John would eventually urinate, especially since he was getting fluid intravenously, and Bill said, full of admiration, "Boy, you really do think of everything. If I ever need a beautiful, smart, Hispanic nurse, I'm going to call on you," and Karl beamed with pride at his sweetheart.

Smiling at Bill's complement, Maria took John's pulse, which was very weak and looked at Karl and Bill with worried eyes. She covered John's unconscious and battered body with a clean sheet and a light blanket.

They eased Tom's suit off and left him lying on his bunk in his pajama top and shorts, looking none the worse for all the wear and tear the transfer had caused him. His pulse was strong and he was still sleeping soundly from the anesthetic.

Maria then wiped the urine off Tom's right leg.

Finally, after Maria, Karl, and Bill had rested a few minutes and collected their thoughts, Bill went to the radio, switched it on and said, "Houston, Fra Mauro Traverse Vehicle here. Do you copy?"

"Houston here, we copy you. What's your status?"

Tuesday, July 16, 2014, 18:54 GMT

Bill proceeded to give Houston a detailed report on what had happened during the 5 hours since they had last reported, what their plans were, and asked to talk to Drs. Maxwell and Jacobson.

When the MD's came on line, Maria described John's poor condition and how they had set and splinted Tom's leg. She asked, "Should we replace the aluminum splints with one of the inflatable ones we have from Isabel's hospital?"

Dr. Jacobson answered, "No, the job you did setting and splinting his leg sounds good. The splints you have on will do the job nicely and you could do more harm by replacing them, especially since you would have to put them back on when you transfer him to the rescue vehicles. Just keep me informed about how he's doing."

Unfortunately, Dr. Maxwell had little advice about John, except, "Keep him comfortable, on the IV, and, when necessary, give him more morphine."

Houston said, "We would like some information about the moonquake from Karl."

Karl responded, "Look, we're exhausted and there's nothing I know about the quake that will help you figure out how to get us out of this mess. I'll tell you all I know tomorrow."

Bill signed off.

July 16, 2014, 19:19 GMT

Looking at the GMT clock on the instrument panel, Karl said, "Schau mal, it's almost exactly 12 hours since the quake hit. That quake sure changed a hell of a lot of things in a short time. Mensch, am I tired," and both Bill and Maria agreed.

Maria said, "Tom's been out for over 4 hours already, and should be coming around soon. If you two want to get some rest, I'll stay up until he's come out of it. You guys get some sleep."

Karl responded, "Nein, you've done enough alone already. I'll stay up with you, besides, I'm hungry — that little snack we had was 4 hours ago."

Bill chimed in with, "Yeah, I'm hungry, too. Besides, the three of us have seen this through to this point together, so I say we all stick it out until we know Tom's ok. Remember the three musketeers? All for one and one for all? Well, we're the three lunar rocketeers, ok?" Corny as that was, Maria and Karl laughed and nodded.

Bill added, "I'll go find us something to eat and pop it in the magic microwave, while you two relax and make out a little."

Maria was a little embarrassed at Bill's last suggestion, but Karl's eyes brightened considerably at the thought — though Bill's idea was rather academic, given that he would never be more than 3 meters away from them at all times. But as always, it is the thought that counts.

As Bill began to look for the appropriate repasts for their first hot meal in 24 hours, Maria and Karl did relax and, at least, cuddled a little bit.

Ten minutes later and with great fanfare, Bill came with three piping hot, TV-type dinners and some fruit juice. He said, in the best French accent he could muster, "The chef has prepared international cuisine appropriate for this multicultural gathering."

Setting Maria's dinner in front of her, he said with his best Mexican accent, "For la señorita bonita[1], I have chosen a delicious Mexican dinner consisting of tamales, enchiladas, and refried beans, served with an aged red grape juice."

Maria smiled sweetly and countered with, "Muchas gracias, señor. Usted es muy simpatico[2]."

To which Bill replied, "I got the muchas gracias, but I'll assume the rest was something about how handsome I am."

Then, placing a hot dinner before Karl, Bill said with a very good fake German accent, "Und für Herr Doktor[3], I have chosen sour-braten, spaetzla, und red cabbage, with a white grape juice von der Rhein[4]."

Karl played it to the hilt, "Vielen Dank, Herr Oberkellner. Sauerbraten, Spätzla, und Rotkohl, mit Rheinwein ist meine lieblings Speise. Ich muss mich beim Koch bedanken[5]."

Defeated, Bill said "Whatever," but perked up considerably as he said, again with his French accent, about his own

---

Notes: [1]the lovely young lady; [2]Many thanks, sir. You are very nice; [3]And for Mr. Doctor; [4]from the Rhine; [5]Many thanks, sir headwaiter. Sour-braten, spaetzla, and red cabbage, with Rhine wine is my favorite meal. I must give my compliments to the chef.

dinner, "And for the handsome and dashing Chief Engineer, I have prepared a delicious chopped steak, mashed potatoes with brown gravy, and buttered corn, along with a fine apple juice."

After Bill's grand formalities were done, they began to sup. Despite her hunger, Maria retained her ladylike manner, while Karl and Bill tended to gobble — though, at least, Karl tried to eat in a more civilized manner when Maria caught his eye and politely tilted her head and frowned in a way that told Karl to stop eating like a pig.

Tuesday, July 16, 2014, 19:58 GMT

After having supped, Maria and Karl checked on John, who still looked very bad, who had a weak pulse, and who was breathing very shallowly.

Tom continued to look good, and when Karl shook him slightly, Tom stirred a little. Karl said, "Gut, he seems to be coming out of it — it's been 5 hours since he went under. Jacobson said he should come around in 5 to 6 hours, so I guess he's about on schedule."

Fifteen minutes later, Tom opened his eyes for a few seconds and said weakly, "I don't feel good," and appeared to go to sleep again.

Ten minutes later, Tom seemed to wake up a little more and said urgently, "I'm going to be sick."

Maria had a container ready and as Tom lurched up to vomit, Karl grabbed Tom around the shoulders and held his head to steady him. Tom retched several times with the dry heaves. Exhausted after his unsuccessful efforts to vomit and still under the influence of the Versed, anesthetic, Tom laid back, closed his eyes, and fell asleep again; but within 5 minutes, he bolted upright, retched several times, and then slurred, "May I have some water, please."

Maria had a bottle of water ready and allowed Tom to take a couple of modest swallows of cold water, which Tom promptly threw-up. However, having something to throw-up made him feel better and after his was finished, he asked for more water, which Maria gave him. Tom said groggily, "I feel better now," and succeeded in keeping the water down. He again slipped back asleep, but awoke after several minutes and asked, "Can I have something more than water?"

Karl got him some apple juice, which Tom drank greedily and then he said groggily, "I do not feel so sick now, but my leg hurts a lot," and appeared to drift away, but suddenly said, quite lucidly, "Thanks for all you have done for me. I will never forget it," and promptly started to fall asleep again.

Maria immediately shook him awake, and, following Dr. Jacobson's instructions, gave him a couple of Percoset pills for the pain and Ambien, a sedative. As soon as he had taken them, Tom fell fast asleep. Maria noted, "He'll sleep-off the rest of the effects of the Versed during the night."

As Maria was finishing tending to Tom, Bill checked on John again and shook his head. Maria and Karl looked at John and Maria said, "I wish there was more we could do for him," and checked the IV.

Karl asked Maria, "Can I have a couple more Percoset tablets? My ribs still hurt. I'm sure I'll have a hard time sleeping, unless the pain is deadened."

Maria gave him two tablets, which he downed with a swig of grape juice.

Tuesday, July 16, 2014, 21:04 GMT

Bill said, "There's nothing more we can do for either of them tonight and we need to get some rest so we can function tomorrow. You two take the upper bunks and I'll sleep on the floor."

Karl said, "Nein, Maria and I can share one bunk and you take the other one."

There was not really enough room for two people on the narrow bunk, but it was clear Maria and Karl wanted to be close after the tragic day they had all endured. So Bill just said, "Good idea — good night," and he dimmed the cabin lights and climbed into the bunk above Tom.

Karl helped Maria up on the bunk above John and climbed up with her. The bunk was so narrow they had to lie on their sides — with Karl on his left side to protect his painful ribs — facing each other and holding on to one another, but they would have done that even if they had been in a king-sized bed.

As Karl kissed Maria tenderly, he could smell, very faintly, the White Diamonds perfume she had put on, what seemed like a century ago. He whispered, "Liebling, I'm so proud of you. You thought of things and did things today that few people, men or women, could have done under such circumstances. I love you so much, ich liebe Dich so sehr," and tenderly kissed her again and added, "You mean the world to me and always will."

Maria said softly, "Karl, I love you just as much. I have loved you ever since we met and I will always love you. You mean so much to me, and I know without your having figured out how to get to Utility and having risked your life to get to the soft suits in the vacuum, none of us would be alive tonight — or, at least, we wouldn't have a chance to survive more than a day or so." She added with great tenderness and admiration, "You're the hero — certainly my hero — for the rest of my life, te amo mi amado[1]. Hold me tight, very tight tonight," and Karl did — an act of intimacy that was far easier to do all night on the Moon than on Earth, because of the low lunar gravity.

Holding each other in their tender embrace, they slowly relaxed enough to fall asleep. Thus ending a day that had started with so much promise and that had ended in a way no one could have ever dreamed.

It was 21:24 GMT, exactly 14 hours after the first sensible tremor hit the Fra Mauro Base. Outside the Traverse Vehicle, the Sun had just set behind the low, rolling hills of the Fra Mauro Formation and the surface, whose temperature had already dropped to $-143°$ C, was bathed in the bright, blue light of the slightly gibbous Earth that hung motionless $16°$ due east of the zenith.

Note: [1] I love you my darling

Part Four

SURVIVING THE LONG LUNAR NIGHT

Chapter 4-1
Taking Stock

Wednesday, July 17, 2014, During the Night

Despite their desire to hold one another the entire night, the bunk on which Maria and Karl were sleeping, was far too narrow for two people to get a good night's rest. Karl woke up twice, as he was about to fall off of the bunk. While the 1.7-meter drop to the floor — which was equivalent to only a 28-centimeter fall on Earth — would have caused neither him nor his tortured ribs any harm, if he dragged Maria with him and she fell on his rib cage — well, that would have been a different story.

Each time Karl felt himself slipping off the bunk, his struggle to keep from falling woke Maria up and she suggested they take a look at John and Tom.

The first time, both were sleeping soundly, but John looked very bad.

The second time, John had urinated in his towel diaper and he woke up when they dried him and put on a new diaper. John said, "Man, my guts hurt like hell."

Maria took his pulse, which was very weak, gave him another 4 milligrams of morphine via the IV, and exchanged the empty saline bag for a new one.

Within 15 minutes, John was sleeping again. Maria and Karl got back in their bunk and fell asleep in each other's arms.

Wednesday, July 17, 2014, 06:40 GMT

Tom woke suddenly after a restful night's sleep. He was in pain and needing to urinate badly. The throbbing in his leg was caused by both the damage done to the muscle tissue around the broken bones and the pressure caused by his swollen leg pushing against the tightly taped splints. However, having been properly set and splinted, it did not hurt him half as much as it did when he had lain for 3 hours in the dark in Dorm waiting and hoping to be rescued and more than 4 hours in Lab, while waiting for Karl and Bill to get back with the medical supplies.

In an effort to be quiet, so he would not wake up Maria, Karl, or Bill, who were exhausted from their efforts of the previous day, and in spite of the pain, but aided by the ⅙ gravity, Tom gingerly got out of his bunk and tried to quietly hobble to the tiny lavatory. He was not successful.

Tom was weak and wobbly and, in the dim light, he stumbled a step or two after successfully getting out of his bunk. Though his fall did not damage his leg, his mild exclamation woke up Maria, whose questions, "Tom, is that you? Are you alright?" woke Karl up with a start and he promptly fell off the bunk.

As he hit the floor, after his 1.5 second fall, Karl's loud, "Scheisse, verdammt noch a'mal," woke Bill up.

Bill demanded, in a sleepy, but loud voice, "What in hell is going on in here?"

Tom responded, "Oh, I'm very, very sorry. I did not mean to wake you all up, but I have to go to the bathroom very badly," an explanation that made Maria, Karl, and Bill chuckle — despite their rude awakenings.

Karl got up off the floor, helped Tom up, and escorted him to the lavatory door. Tom said, "Thank you very much. I can handle it from here."

Karl, having had to "help" Tom the day before by getting his penis and testicles out of harm's way when they were setting his leg, replied very seriously and with great emphasis, "I have absolutely no intension of helping you in there," at which, both Maria and Bill burst out laughing — to Tom's bewilderment and to Karl's very great embarrassment.

Tom asked, in all innocence, "What is so funny?"

Karl answered sourly, "You don't want to know — and don't ask again," which set Maria and Bill off again, so much so they both had tears in their eyes.

Mystified, Tom shook his head and went into the lavatory to attend to his bodily needs.

Karl turned and gave Maria and Bill a pleading look. Maria, seeing her amado was so embarrassed, said, "We're sorry, but you have to admit, that was funny."

Karl did not agree and Bill was clearly and absolutely not sorry.

While Tom was in the lavatory, Maria checked on John and his IV; though the IV was fine, but getting low, John was not — and there was nothing she could do about it.

When Tom came out of the lavatory, he said, "My leg hurts quite a bit. May I have some more pain pills?"

Maria gave him two Percoset pills and then she, Karl, and Bill, in turn, took care of their bodily needs and freshened up a bit, but did so very sparingly with the limited water that was available.

Tom said, "Do we have anything to eat? I am very hungry."

Bill answered, "Yes, we do. I'll get something to eat for all of us," and proceeded to get some frozen breakfasts of scrambled eggs, bacon, and biscuits from the mini-freezer, put them in the microwave, and found some bags of juices to go along with the meal — Tom's first in 31 hours.

When Karl heard what Bill had put in to the microwave, he groaned to Maria, "Mensch, doesn't he know I hate eggs, especially verdamnt scrambled eggs? I wish I had a real breakfast — a sweet roll or a couple of donuts." While Karl liked American pastries, especially pies, very much, he said further, "I wish I had some good German pastries from the Herrieden Bäckerie[1] or from the Konditorien[2] in Ansbach or Feuchtwangen. When I get back to Earth, I'm going to eat my way through an American bakery and then fly to Germany for a second course."

Maria just laughed at Karl's pastry fantasy, which came to an abrupt end when Bill brought the hot breakfasts.

While serving the hot meals, Bill said, "Enjoy these hot breakfasts. They're going to be the last hot food we have, since we can't afford to use the little power we have running the microwave. Similarly, we need to keep the lights low and off, whenever possible, and forsake hot water in the lavatory."

Despite those depressing, but necessary remarks, or perhaps because of them, everyone dug into the scrambled eggs and bacon with relish — even Karl.

Notes: [1]bakery; [2]pastry shops

After Tom had stilled his hunger enough so he could join the breakfast conversation, he said, "You all have done everything so far and I really appreciate everything you have done to save us, but I'm ok now and I want to help. Though I am a little clumsy and I cannot move around very well, I can sit at the console and monitor the Traverse Vehicle's systems and do my real job of handling communications and the onboard computer — and maybe even help look after John."

Since Tom could not hurt his leg further by doing those light duties and the activity would help keep his mind off the pain and their situation, as well as allow the rest of them to attend to the more serious matters concerning their survival through the long lunar night, Maria, Karl, and Bill agreed that Tom's suggestion was a very good one. Tom smiled.

Wednesday, July 17, 2014, 07:26 GMT

After breakfast, Tom took up his duties as the Traverse Vehicle's Communication Officer and called Houston.

Bill reported on the status of the equipment and said, "We're going to work out a detailed power budget over the next couple of hours to determine exactly how long we can last. We have abundant food and oxygen, but water might be a problem. Once we've gotten all the details worked out, we'll call to tell you what we've found, but, in order to conserve power, we'll call no more than once per day, once we've gotten everything worked out and you guys have agreed with the plan."

Bill asked, "Have you worked out the hydrogen boil-off rate for the intact Lander? What equipment will be available to rescue us — specifically, will you have the new Lander and the new crew module ready? And, most importantly, what is the timetable of the rescue? Can you get here in 16 or 17 days?"

After considerably more than the 2½ second light-time delay, Houston cautiously replied, "The new Lander with the new crew module is out. Lockheed Martin and Boeing say there is no way the hardware will be flight ready for another 45 to 50 days, assuming nothing goes wrong with the final preparations of the new equipment for launch, there are no launch delays, and the on-orbit-assembly of the hardware keeps on schedule — and you know what the chances of all that happening are. You're just going to have to ride the remaining Lander to the rendezvous orbit in your spacesuits.

"The boil-off rate is uncertain, but sufficiently high, even with the 5 of you plus 3 hard suits and 2 soft suits as the payload, the Lander cannot achieve the elliptical transfer orbit, let alone circularize at 200 kilometers, after 14½ more days, with an uncertainty of about ½ of a day.

"However, with such a small payload, the Lander won't need all the LOX in its tanks. If you can dump the excess LOX, the critical time is extended by 36 to 42 hours, or about 16 days from now.

"There is another thing you can do to help. Once sunrise occurs and sunlight hits the hydrogen tanks, they will heat up fast and the boil-off rate will increase rapidly. If you can make a sunshield and keep the hydrogen tanks in the shade, that will give you another 24 to 30 hours for a total of 16½ to 18 days."

Bill replied, "We can find enough of the lightweight ceiling panels in the Base to make an excellent sunshield, so you can count on that. And I'm sure we can find a way of dumping the excess oxygen. So those two things shouldn't be a problem, but how soon can you get the OTV here? I think we can stretch our power out to 17 days. We'll know for sure when we call back in a few hours — but it can't be much more than that."

After a long pause, Houston again answered cautiously, "The earliest we can launch the OTV is in 15 days and the fastest trajectory we can use is the old Apollo free-return-trajectory with a transit time of 2.6 days.

"If you guys can stretch your power out another half a day, if you can get the hydrogen boil-off rate way down, and if you launch a couple of orbits before the OTV burns into lunar orbit, you should just make it under the wire.

"Also, the 2 orbits would give us enough tracking data on your Lander to get a good determination of your orbit, so we can make a quick rendezvous and get you guys safely home.

"But, as you see, there is no positive margin."

Concerned about the lack of margin and mistrustful about the coincidence that the earliest rendezvous time was

17½ days and their latest launch time from the Moon was, with a lot of ifs, close to 17½ days, Bill asked, sarcastically, "Tell me, did you guys find the latest time we might be able to launch and then push the rendezvous time back to match it or the other way around?"

Again, after another long pause, Houston answered, "Look Bill, we are clearly pushing the envelope in both directions, but our back room boys are certain the launch and rendezvous calculation are correct. But I don't have to tell you, there is absolutely no wiggle room for anything to go wrong — with your getting the boil-off rate way low after sunrise and dumping the oxygen, or for any delays in our getting the OTV on its way to pick you up."

Resigned to the uncertainties, Bill replied, "Ok, I know you're doing your best, and we will, too. We'll get you our power estimate ASAP. Here's Maria to tell you about John. Tom can tell you about his condition himself."

Maria told Dr. Maxwell about John's condition and asked, "Are you sure there's nothing else I can do to help him?"

Dr. Maxwell told her, "By keeping him stable, you are doing everything you can do to help him. But until John is back on Earth, there is little that can be done to improve his condition."

Dr. Jacobson came on line to talk with Tom, but first, Maria asked him, "Is there anything we can do for Karl's ribs — tape them or anything like that?"

Jacobson answered, "No, don't tape them, it won't do him any good and could do some harm. In addition to the Percoset, you might start giving him Ibuprofen, to help reduce the inflammation which will soon set in," and Karl nodded, knowing from past experience what to expect in another day or two.

Maria handed the mike to Tom.

"Hello, Dr. Jacobson. I am feeling quite good, thanks to Maria, Karl, and Bill. My leg is swollen and the pressure against the splints and bandages hurts, but the Percoset is keeping that in check. So I think I am ok."

Dr. Jacobson asked Tom a couple of other questions and said, "It sounds like you're doing fine. The pain will start to

lessen as the swelling goes down over the next few days. Have
Maria give you some Ibuprofen, too, and you'll do just fine.
When you get back, we'll x-ray your leg to see just how good
a job they did setting it and to see if it's healing properly."

The Houston communicator came back on, "Headquarters wants Karl to finally report on the moonquake and
they want to talk to Bill about the Base." The last comment
made Bill turn red with anger and he motioned to Karl to
take the mike without saying a word.

By avoiding reporting on the moonquake earlier, Karl
had cooled down to the point where he could keep his anger
at NASA's arrogance and incompetence in check. Karl said
calmly but sternly, "I have no data from the seismometers at
the Copernicus and Fra Mauro Stations, but this was probably the magnitude 9 or 10 moonquake Nakamura, Binder,
and I had warned you about, and it killed 3 people already
and, before this is finished, it might kill 5 more. I assume the
downlinked telemetry data recorded the first few seconds of
the quake and then the seismometers saturated and the stations went off the air, nicht wahr, ah, I mean, correct?"

Karl waited the 2.5 seconds to see if he got a response to
his assertions, which he did. To Karl's surprise, the Associate
Administrator for Science from Headquarters was on line and
said, "That's correct, both stations recorded the arrival of a
strong P-wave and, within a couple of seconds, the seismometers were off scale high and in less than a minute, both stations stopped transmitting. What you couldn't have surmised
is the P-wave arrived at the Fra Mauro Station 32 seconds
before it arrived at the Copernicus Station. So that puts the
quake somewhere in the southern hemisphere and probably
not too far from the Base, given the damage it caused."

Karl responded, "From the tracks left in the regolith by
the Traverse Vehicle's wheels and the Lander's feet, the later-
al ground movement was a meter or more and the way we
were being thrown around in the modules, I would guess
there was a meter of vertical movement, too, and the accelerations were way, way above that of lunar gravity and I would
guess way above 1-g. Also, from the time we first felt the
quake to the time we could walk again without being thrown

around was a good hour-and-a-half and the vibrations didn't completely die down until 2½ hours had passed. It was a killer quake and the 5 of us are lucky to be alive. That's all I can tell you." His anger having returned to the boiling point, Karl did not say he was handing the mike to Bill — he just did it.

Bill said, in a carefully measured tone, "This is Bill again, who am I talking to?"

Several seconds later, a familiar voice came over the radio, "Bill, this is the Administrator. I can't tell you how sorry I am about this unfortunate accident. But, the engineers need to know the condition of the Base, what failed, and why it failed, so we can correct the problems and move forward. And I want to assure you, and the others, I have ordered everyone to do everything possible to get you all home safely."

Bill went apoplectic; the blood vessels in his forehead bulged out so much they looked like they would burst. He waited several second and finally said slowly and in a voice so cold it could have made hell freeze over, "You stupid — arrogant — self-serving — son-of-a-bitch. How dare you say 'unfortunate accident' and the rest of the bullshit you just laid on me. You and the rest of the NASA upper-management pricks were warned often enough about the possibility of dangerous moonquakes and I told you, in your own goddamned private meeting room, not to build the Base tele-robotically, but. . . ." Bill stopped a couple of seconds and then said, "Screw it, I'm wasting my time talking to a bastard like you. When I get ba——, if I get back, I'll talk to the President and Congress and they can deal with you. Until then, do me a favor and go straight to hell." Bill unceremoniously shut the radio off.

Wednesday, July 17, 2014, 07:49 GMT

Having vented his anger, and since there were more pressing issues at hand, Bill immediately said, "To hell with them, let's see if we can last 17½ days or not. As of last night, the Traverse Vehicle had 11 days of power at its normal usage rate — 9 days of reserve left after the Copernicus Traverse plus 2-day's worth of recharge before the quake hit. Then we have the 1-day's worth of power from the emergency batteries — but that is at the reduced, emergency power consumption rate of 80% normal. By going to the emergency power rate all the time, the 11 days stretches out to — ah, I'm never good at doing arithmetic in my head."

Karl said, "13¾ days plus the batteries, makes 14¾ days."

"Ok, thanks Karl. Since last night, we've used somewhat less than a ½ day's worth of power, since most of the time we were asleep with the lights low. So we're shy by 3¼ days. If we can get all the emergency batteries from the Base and if they are all in good shape, then that's another 2, maybe — with a lot of luck — maybe 3 days of power. That's getting us close. Anybody got any suggestions?"

Maria answered, "What about getting the fuel cells from the wrecked Lander and crew module, if they're ok?"

Karl added, "And what about the Rovers' fuel cells?"

Bill replied, "Good ideas, but if we use the power from the Rovers, then we'll have to walk the 5 to 6 kilometers to the Lander sites."

Maria said, "That's ok, the three of us can walk out there to put up the sunshield and get the fuel cells and when we go to take off, Tom and John can ride out — all we have to do is to make sure we leave enough power in one of them to get Tom and John out there just once."

Tom reacted quickly, "No we won't. Remember, we are sitting in the Traverse Vehicle. We can drive it out there when we are ready to leave."

Bill replied, "Good point Tom. I forgot about it. I guess I'm used to thinking about the Traverse Vehicle in terms of long traverses, not using it to get to and from the Landers, which is the job of the Rovers.

"Ok, continuing, in the emergency mode, we have to limit the number of ingresses and egresses from the airlock — which take a lot of power each time — and limit the usage of the hard suits — since recharging them with oxygen and power also takes a lot of power. We can work out the most economical plan for the external activities. But I think we can stretch our power reserves an extra 1 or 2 days with the fuel cells for a grand total of 17 to as much as 19 days — long enough to survive until they can get the OTV in orbit to pick us up."

Karl said, "But Bill, won't the Traverse Vehicle use a lot of extra power during the nighttime to keep us warm — after all, its easily 150 below out there now and it will get down to –170 before the night is over?"

Bill answered, "Don't forget, during the heat of the day, when we usually use the Traverse Vehicle, this thing uses a lot of power keeping cool. I'll have to check with Houston, but I suspect it's a wash — we probably use as much power during the night as during the day to keep the temperature livable in here."

Tom asked, "Is there any way we can get electrical power or heat by running the Traverse Vehicle's drive motor?"

Bill answered in disgust, "No, thanks to NASA's brilliant management, they decided to keep the drive motor, which uses diesel fuel and 100% hydrogen peroxide as the oxidizer, and the electrical system, which uses the fuel cells, totally separate — except the diesel uses power from the fuel cells to get started, but once the motor is running, they are disengaged. NASA didn't want to have a generator hooked up to the diesel, since it would be more complicated and less efficient power-wise. It was cheaper, easier, and more efficient to carry enough fuel cells to provide the Traverse Vehicle with its electrical needs. The water in the diesel exhaust is condensed and used as an expendable working fluid in the heat exchanger and the CO_2 is just expelled immediately into the vacuum —

"Hey, it just occurred to me, we could shunt the water from the exhaust condenser into the water supply and solve part of our water problem. However, that stuff is not potable, but we could use it for washing and the like and it would be hot — or, at least, warm. First, we would need to get all the potable water out of the tank — store it in anything we can find — and then we could use the condensed hot water.

"The only problem is, it takes quite a bit of power to start the diesel engine, and even more when the engine is at night-time temperatures — and that power comes from the fuel cells. So that is something we could not do very often, or perhaps ever. That might also eliminate the possibility that we drive out to the landing site when it comes time to be rescued. But both possibilities are worth keeping in mind."

Maria, Karl, and Tom all perked up at the thought of having hot water once in a while, to try to stay somewhat clean during the next 17 days. Maria said, "That's great — no wonder they pay you the big bucks," a comment that was way off the mark, since, as a civil servant and NASA engineer, Bill did not make anywhere near the amount of money he did when he worked in his engineering consulting company before rejoining NASA.

Bill continued, "As to heating the vehicle with its engine — that's out. Again, since the Traverse Vehicle was meant to be used mainly during the hot lunar day, the engine heat goes directly to the heat exchanger radiator and is radiated to space. Speaking of heat, in order to conserve power, we are going to have to drop the temperature in here from 21° to as low as we can stand it — we'll have to put on extra clothes to. . . ."

Maria interrupted, "I'm sure we can't do that. We have to keep John warm and even with extra blankets, he's not going to generate enough body heat in his condition to keep warm. I'm pretty sure of that, but we can check with Dr. Maxwell."

Bill replied, "You're probably right. We'll check with the Doc and set the temperature as low as we can without hurting John, ok?"

Maria answered, "Ok," and since she was speaking about John, that reminded her to go to his bunk to check on him and the IV — both needed changing. She said, "We have another problem. We have only a few more clean towels. How are we going to keep John dry? We can't let him lie in a puddle of urine and it would smell to high heaven in here in just a short time if we did."

Karl suggested, "We could take the wet towels outside and freeze dry them. That would make them dry, though it would leave the uric acid crystals in the towels — but it would be better than nothing."

Bill injected, "We can't do that. It would require us using the airlock and a suit too often."

Tom quickly said, "I've got a better idea. Since you have to go to the Lander to put the sunshield up and to try to get the fuel cells from the crew module and wrecked Lander, can't you get one of the male-urination-hoses out of the crew module? Then we could put the condom-like-end on John and the other end of the hose in a plastic bottle we could easily empty in the lavatory."

Karl, fearing he would be asked to "put the condom-like-end on John", said quickly, "An excellent idea Tom, but I'm not volunteering for that duty. Bill it's your turn," at which both Maria and Bill burst out into nearly uncontrolled laughter. Karl turned red and Tom looked totally bewildered.

Tom asked politely, "Why are you two laughing like that? This is serious business," which only induced Maria and Bill to laugh even more, while Karl just looked stone-faced at them.

Finally, Bill stopped laughing long enough to say, "Tom, you do not want to know. Believe me, you do not want to know."

Maria, clearly feeling guilty about laughing at Karl and clearly feeling sorry for him, hugged him and whispered in his ear, "Querido, te amo[1]. I'm sorry. I'm not laughing at you, just at the situation — pardoname, por favor[2]?"

Karl, not really being able to be mad at Maria and certainly not being able to resist her feminine charms, whispered back — lying just a little bit, "Don't worry, my feelings are not hurt und ich amo te auch[3]," which made Maria laugh a little, since Karl never mixed Spanish and German together like that, except when he was flustered.

Bill then said, "Getting back to business, can anyone think of anything else?"

Maria answered, "Nothing I can think of, other than getting our extra clothes, your tools, the extra oxygen we need, and the food we left in the Base. And if we are going to limit the number of in- and egresses, we had better get everything we need in 1 trip, rather than leaving it in the Base and getting it when we need it, as we decided yesterday."

Karl agreed, "Ja, we better do everything — get the stuff from the Base, hookup the LOX hose from the tanks in Utility to the Traverse Vehicle, and go to the Landers — just do everything in 1 trip outside. Also, we had better scour the

---

Notes: [1]Darling, I love you; [2]forgive me, please; [3]I love you, too

Base for anything we overlooked when we were in a rush yesterday. Let's do it all in 1 long trip and then cocoon ourselves in the Traverse Vehicle, like hibernating bears. And, the sooner the better — today or tomorrow, at the latest — since my ribs are going to start hurting wie der Teufel once the inflammation sets in, and after that, I'm not sure how well I'll be able to get around in a hard suit."

Maria, ready to defend Karl's well being, said, "Bill, I should go with you instead of Karl."

Karl interjected, just as ready to keep his Schatz out of any harms way, "I know you can do it, Liebling," and used the paper-thin excuse, "But I'm all right and you're needed here to keep an eye on John," but did not dare say he was stronger and therefore more capable then his delicate señorita pequeña.

Maria knew full well what Karl really meant, but would not hurt her man's feelings and knowing he was not a male chauvinist pig, rather just a young man who loved her very much and wanted to protect her, she acquiesced. She said to Bill, whose expression indicated he was worried about Karl's ability to go out again in a hard suit, "I know Karl well enough to know if he were really in pain and could not perform his duties, he would not risk our lives just to prove he can take it. But you must go now and not wait."

Bill said, "Ok, that's fine with me and I agree with going now. Though my first thought was to delay going out to the Lander to put up the sunshield until just before sunrise, but since we need the urination device for John and the fuel cells from the wrecked crew module, we should do everything now. I also thought of saving suit resources by breaking the safety rule and going out alone, but going into the wrecked crew module in its condition, and even into the Base to get the ceiling panels for the sunshield, let alone getting the emergency batteries out, is a two-man — or a man and a woman — job. So, yeah, let's get everything done in 1 trip and do it today. Then we'll finally know if everything will work the way we hope, or not. Any more comments or suggestions?"

Tom said politely, "Yes, I have a question. Why do you want to take the emergency batteries out of the Base? Can't you hook them up to the primary electrical system, so the Traverse Vehicle can get the power through the umbilical?"

Bill answered, "Man, I completely overlooked that simple solution. Since the backup power systems are wired independently from the primary power system, I just assumed I would have to get the secondary, emergency power batteries out of Utility and the tertiary batteries in Dorm, Kitchen, Lab, and Utility, set them up next to the Traverse Vehicle, cover them with insulation and regolith — to protect them from the nighttime temperatures — and connect them to the Traverse Vehicle via the umbilical port. But you're right Tom, that's brilliant." Tom smiled.

Bill added, "I'll have to call Houston to find out if your suggestion will work — though I see no reason why it won't. I also need to find out how to hook up the emergency systems' wiring to the primary system, without shorting out the whole mess and losing the batteries."

After a thoughtful pause, he added, "I'll bet I can also hook up the Rovers' fuel cells directly to the Traverse Vehicle via the umbilical port, too, and not have to mess around trying to dismount them from the Rovers and mount them in the Traverse Vehicle in some way."

Bill asked, "Any other brilliant ideas I didn't think of?"

Tom thought a few more seconds and said, "Yes. You said the exhaust water is not drinkable, but what about the water produced by the fuel cells? If I remember correctly, the Gemini, Apollo, and Shuttle Astronauts got some of their drinking water from their fuel cells."

Bill answered, "Yeah, you're right again. The fuel cells we have are rechargeable, that is, the water produced when the fuel cells are making electricity for the Traverse Vehicle is stored in a tank and when the Traverse Vehicle is at the Base, power from the nuke is — or was — used to break the water back down into oxygen and hydrogen, via electrolysis, to recharge the fuel cells. So I can easily tap the fuel cell water tank and get the rest of the drinking water we need. Sorry guys, there goes the hot water, but I assume you would rather be a little dirty than very thirsty, right?" Everyone agreed, but they were a little disappointed.

After a moment, Bill finally said, "Good thinking Tom. Ok, any more suggestions, Tom — Maria — Karl? — No? Ok, let's call Houston and let them know what we've decided. Also, I have a few questions about how to hook up the emergency batteries and the fuel cells to the Traverse Vehicle."

Wednesday, July 17, 2014, 08:18 GMT

Tom called Houston and Bill laid out their plan and asked the engineers a number of questions regarding the hookup of the external batteries and fuel cells to supply the extra power they so desperately needed. The chief engineer replied, "We'll have the answers in an hour or two, at most."

Bill said, "Good, we'll be ready to go out in about 2 hours, so don't take any longer.

"Regarding our power situation, if everything works well, we should have enough power to keep us going for another 17 days." Bill cut off the mike and said to Maria, Karl, and Tom, "I'm not going to tell Houston the power might even last for 19 days. First, because NASA might rely on the higher number and stretch out the launch of the rescue OTV another 2 days. Second, because I didn't really know how much power we can get from the external sources — if any. And third, because I want some margin in case we can't keep the cabin heating to a minimum, because of John and other unforeseen things. As far as I'm concerned, NASA has to believe they just have 17 days to get the rescue vehicle in lunar orbit, period. Everybody understand?" All three nodded.

Bill continued, "Sorry for the break, but the 17 day estimate assumes the Traverse Vehicle uses no more power to keep warm during the lunar night than it needs to keep cool during the lunar day. I need you to check that assumption," and then he asked a couple of other, less important questions. He told Houston, "We'll check with you just before we go out and again after Karl and I are done outside, and then we'll report only once a day, giving you a very brief update."

Houston concurred with everything Bill said and then Bill added, "We have some questions for Dr. Maxwell."

Dr. Maxwell came on the line and Bill asked, "How low can we set the cabin temperature without causing John harm?"

Dr. Maxwell answered, "I wouldn't go any lower than 17°, and even that's pushing it."

Bill replied, "That small a decrease is hardly worth risking John's life for, so we will leave it as it is at 21°," and Maxwell agreed that would be best for John.

Tom signed off.

Chapter 4-2
Carrying Out the Plan

Wednesday, July 17, 2014, 10:23 GMT

Two hours after their discussions with Houston, Bill and Karl were in their hard suits and, armed with the information Bill had requested 2 hours earlier, but which the engineers had ready for them in just 45 minutes, were ready to leave the Traverse Vehicle and carry out their plan.

The Sun had set over 14 hours earlier and the surface temperature had dropped to −153° C. In the bright, bluish light of the waxing gibbous Earth, light that was already 40 times brighter than moonlight at full Moon, Bill and Karl could see their surroundings without any help from the flashlights they carried for use in the dark Base.

Prior to leaving the Traverse Vehicle, they agreed to save power by having Maria and Tom call them only once an hour for a very short status check, except when they were out of radio contact in the Base. Because of the latter problem, when Bill and Karl came out of the Base, they would bang on the hull of the Traverse Vehicle to let Maria and Tom know they were again in radio contact and they would give them a status report.

Immediately after egressing the Traverse Vehicle's airlock, Bill went to the umbilical port and unplugged the electrical umbilical to insure the Traverse Vehicle's fuel cells would not short out if he made a mistake while wiring the batteries and the fuel cells into the umbilical. He then went to the back of the Traverse Vehicle and opened a panel to gain access to the fuel cell water tank and the main water tank. He checked to be absolutely certain the information was correct the Houston engineers had given him about the length and diameter of the plastic hose he would need to shunt the fuel cell water to the main water tank. Satisfied, Bill radioed Karl, just as the latter emerged from the airlock, and said, "Ok, let's go."

Not even aware of the beautiful, Earth-lit scene, they loped off to the SW exit tunnel, entered the base, and went directly to Utility, since Bill needed a voltmeter, wire cutters, heavy insulated wire, plastic tubing, and some clamps.

By the time they entered the Base, the temperature inside had dropped to $3°$ C — just above freezing.

As Bill cleared away some debris from the floor panels covering the secondary and tertiary emergency batteries in Utility, Karl took the tubing and other supplies they would need for the Traverse Vehicle to the mouth of the SW exit tunnel, where they had stored the frozen food the day before.

When Karl got back to Utility, he went to the emergency supply cabinet and got the 2 flashlights stored there to supplement the 2 they had from the Traverse Vehicle and the one he had from Lab, one of which was already illuminating Bill's work.

Once the emergency batteries were exposed, Bill quickly checked the terminal voltages of each of the batteries and said, "Good, they all read between 25 to 26 volts. They have between 50 and 70% of their charge left, a little less than I had hoped, but about what I had expected."

Bill went to the central electrical distribution box, selected the heavy wires leading in from the dead nuke, and cut both wires. Quickly finding the primary power terminals to all 4 modules, the 2 access tunnels, and the 4 airlocks, he cut their wires in rapid succession, being careful to leave the wires to the Traverse Vehicle umbilical intact. After giving his destructive work a final, careful once-over, Bill said, "Ok, I've isolated the umbilical from all the other primary wiring. Now we can start hooking up the secondary emergency batteries to the umbilical and then do the same for the tertiary batteries in all the modules."

Bill cut two, 30-centimeter long pieces from his spool of heavy electrical wire, quickly found the terminals for the wires from the secondary emergency batteries, and shunted those terminals to the primary circuit terminals — saying, as he checked the voltage across the latter terminals, "Ok, we have the secondary emergency batteries hooked up to the umbilical and — yep, the voltage is 26 volts. So far, so good.

Now let's get the tertiary batteries in here and in the other modules hooked up."

They lifted the adjacent floor panel. Bill checked the voltage of the tertiary batteries, and swore, "Shit, they're dead. They must have been damaged internally and shorted out. I sure hope they're the only ones."

Next Bill cut two, 30-meter long pieces of wire from his spool and connected each one to a terminal of the last battery in the row of secondary batteries, paying close attention to the need to keep all the batteries in a parallel circuit.

Illuminating the way with the flashlight, Karl led Bill, who was stringing out 8 to 9 meters of wire, to the point in Lab's floor where the tertiary batteries of the module were located. They lifted the floor panel; Bill checked the voltage of the batteries, which was 30.7 volts. Bill said, "Wonderful, fully charged."

Bill quickly connected those batteries into the parallel battery circuit and said, "On to Kitchen."

Playing out another 8 to 9 meters of the pair of wires, and being careful not to confuse which wire was positive and which was negative, they entered Hospital. Bill repeated the performance he had done in Lab and happily found that Kitchen's batteries were also fully charged.

They moved to Dorm. When they lifted the floor panel, Bill exclaimed, "Well, now I know why Dorm's secondary and tertiary power systems failed. Look, the batteries came loose from their mounts, ripped out all the emergency wiring and one cracked open. I'm sure they're all dead, but I'll check just to be sure."

A quick check of the battery voltages showed they were, indeed, all zero and Bill, swore, "Damn. Ok, let's cut the wires off at the terminals of the batteries in Kitchen, just to be tidy and to insure we don't trip over the wires and mess up all our good work."

Wednesday, July 17, 2014, 11:16 GMT

Having finished wiring all the good batteries into their new power system, Bill and Karl went to Lab and collected the rest of the clothes Maria had piled on the mattresses the previous day and took them to the mouth of the SW exit tunnel.

They searched the modules until they found enough intact ceiling panels to make a good sunshield and took them to the exit tunnel.

They returned to each module to carefully look for any useful items they might have missed the day before. They especially looked in Hospital to see if they had missed anything, but concluded they had expertly plundered it the first time.

Since they had more than enough food, they did not bother to look around Kitchen, except to get the First Aid kit and flashlights from the emergency supply cabinet. With the exception of the 1 flashlight Karl lost in Lab during the moonquake, they had all the available flashlights, which would serve them well in the dark Traverse Vehicle. Finally, they had scrounged everything they could think of and could find in the debris of the modules. Satisfied, they got the spare hard suit and PLSSs from Lab and took them and the last of their plunder to the SW exit tunnel.

When they got to the pile of clothes, food, wire, ceiling panels, suit, PLSSs, and what not, Karl said, "We can carry this stuff to the Traverse Vehicle, but there's no way in hell we can carry the panels 6 kilometers to the Lander, they're too big and ungainly. It would take us forever to get there and I am sure we would use more of our power reserves in the suits than we would if we drove one of the Rovers."

Bill thought a minute and replied, "Yeah, I guess you're right. Let me see, the fuel cells were full-up when we started and its 6 kilometers to the Lander and 4 more to the nuke and 4 more back to the Base. So we used 14 of their 100-kilometer range. If we add 12 more kilometers to just one of them — I guess that won't kill us, at least I hope not.

"Ok, let's carry all the rest of this stuff to the Traverse Vehicle and I'll get started shunting the fuel cell water to the main water supply and hooking up the LOX hose from Utility to the vehicle."

As they were carrying the first load of supplies to the Traverse Vehicle, Karl grimaced as the dull pain in his ribs become more intense from the strain of wearing his hard suit.

Wednesday, July 17, 2014, 12:18 GMT

When they arrived back at the Traverse Vehicle with the last load, Bill knocked on its hull and within seconds, Tom was on the radio. Bill explained what they had accomplished and what they were about to do, adding, "We've decided to use one of the Rovers to get out to the Lander with the bulky ceiling panels. We're loading the first load of stuff in the airlock now. You can cycle the airlock and get it in the Traverse Vehicle as soon as we're done and have closed the outer door."

When they were finally finished, Bill went to work on the water tubing. With Karl looking over his shoulder and holding a flashlight to supplement the nearly bright enough earthlight, Bill slipped an end of the plastic tubing over the fill valve of the main water tank, firmly clamped it down, and then cut the aluminum tubing between the fuel cell and its water storage tank. Immediately, ice crystal fog came shooting out of the cut tubing as the water in the tank boiled under the sudden vacuum. Bill quickly slipped the other end of the plastic tubing over the cut end of the aluminum tubing coming from the fuel cell and clamped it down very tightly. Finished, he opened the fill valve, and said, "Ok, now to the LOX."

Bill got the LOX transfer hose, dragged it to the Traverse Vehicle and plugged it into the LOX inlet port of the vehicle, started to walk away, and said, "And that's that. Let's go to the Landers."

Surprised, Karl exclaimed, "Wait, don't we have to somehow pump the LOX into the vehicle? But how are we going to do that without power from the nuke?"

Bill laughed and answered, "Simple, we're not going to pump the LOX into the vehicle's tank." Seeing the puzzled look on Karl's face through his faceplate, Bill continued, "We don't need to. Even at the $-10°$ Utility will eventually get down to, oxygen will boil off the LOX in Utility's tanks fast enough to supply us with the extra oxygen we need and the pressure gradient in the hose will force the gaseous oxygen into the Traverse Vehicle's LOX tank, to the regulator, and from there into the cabin. We don't need the oxygen in liquid form in the tank, just the gas."

Karl said, "Was für ein Dummkopf[1], I should have thought of that — just basic physics," and laughed at himself for not having seen the obvious answer.

Bill knocked on the Traverse Vehicle's hull and Tom was again on the radio in seconds. Bill said, "We're heading out to the Landers — call us in an hour."

Wednesday, July 17, 2014, 12:51 GMT

Karl was right. Even loading and securing the light, but bulky ceiling panels on the back of the Rover was a challenge. After 20 minutes of effort, they were finally ready to make the 30-minute drive to the intact Lander. Less than half of the way there, some of the panels fell off the Rover. They stopped, back tracked, picked them up, and reloaded and re-secured them — all of which took over 15 minutes.

Right on schedule, Tom and Maria called while Bill and Karl were again driving towards the Lander and Karl gave them an update.

When they were about ¾ of the way there, close to the crippled Lander, all the panels fell off the Rover and again, some 15 minutes were wasted reloading and securing them.

Finally, they arrived at the Lander, but the 30-minute drive took them an hour to complete.

As Bill stopped the Rover, he swore, "Let's get these damned things stacked against the Lander before something else happens."

To their relief, it took only 10 minutes to lean and stack the panels against the east facing legs and structure of the Lander. When they were done, they carefully inspected their work of art. Karl shined his flashlight on the sunshield, while Bill looked from behind to see if there were any light leaks, making absolutely certain the vital hydrogen tanks were total-ly shielded from the Sun that would be rising due east in almost exactly 14 days.

After several minutes of careful inspecting, Bill said, "I don't see any holes. But before we go, I want to look at the tanks to see if there is an easy way we can off-load the excess LOX."

Note: [1]What a dummy

When he was finished, Bill said, "I don't see any way we can get rid of the LOX. We'll have to discuss it with Houston. They'll have to come up with a solution or our goose is cooked."

Karl replied, "Mensch, the thought of a nice roasted goose, like we have back on the farm, makes my mouth water — I'm getting hungry and all I can look forward to is a cold supper after we get back, Scheisse."

Bill was amused, clearly Karl didn't have a clue as to what the American expression, "our goose is cooked," meant.

But then Karl, who had a talent for finding the simple solution to a problem, suddenly said, "I'll bet we won't need even half of the oxygen in those 2 tanks. If that's the case — and Houston can tell us if it is — we can just punch a big hole in the bottom of one of the tanks and let the liquid oxygen run out. There is an isolation valve on each tank that would prevent the other tank from losing its oxygen, too, nicht wahr?"

Bill answered, "The answer to your last question is yes, we can isolate the tanks from one another. But if we do that, then with one fuel tank nearly a third full and the other empty, the Lander will be way out of balance and I doubt the steering engines can make up for that."

"Kein Problem[1], we can all sit over the empty tank and our weight will make up for the difference — Houston can tell us exactly where to sit — or better yet, we can figure it out ourselves using the lever rule."

Bill answered slowly, "Yeah, I guess you're right. But to be sure, we'll ask Houston, despite your confidence in your lever rule. Ok, let's go to the other Lander."

Wednesday, July 17, 2014, 14:25 GMT

They jumped on the Rover and took off to the crippled Lander. They covered the 1-kilometer distance in 5 minutes.

After dismounting the Rover, Bill said, "The Lander doesn't look too stable, so why don't we take a look at the fuel cells before we try to go inside."

Note: [1] No problem

Karl countered with, "I doubt it can tip over any farther. The shaking lasted so long and died out so gradually, I'll bet the module settled into a very stable position. Aber ja, let's look at the fuel cells first," and they walked around to the back of the Lander.

When they got to a point where they could see the fuel cells of the Lander and those of the crew module, it was quite apparent there was no use spending any more time on the mess they saw. Disappointed, they started walking back to the front of the tipped over stack.

Again, right on schedule, Tom and Maria called while they were walking around the crippled Lander and Karl gave them an update.

Knowing Bill was worried about the module tipping over, Karl said, "I did a little climbing in the Bayerishe Alpen[1], so I'll climb up to the docking hatch and see if I can get it open."

Bill said, "Ok, but be careful. I still think the thing can tip over."

Though hard suits were definitely not made for climbing, especially on a wrecked spacecraft, Karl managed to climb to the upper docking port and tried to open the hatch, without success. After a couple more fruitless tries, Karl said, "Verdammt noch a'mal. The hatch is jammed. How are we going to get in, with the front hatch buried in the regolith?"

Bill laughed and said, "That's why I brought along my handy tin-snips," — he held them up and made a few short cutting motions. "The walls of the module are hardly more than very heavy-duty aluminum foil. I'll just cut a hole in the side of the module. Come on down and help me."

By the time Karl was on the surface, Bill was going at the wall of the crew module with vengeance. He soon had a hole cut that either one of them could get through in their hard suits, with much room to spare.

As Bill stepped back to admire his work, Karl, without saying a word and with a flashlight in hand, stepped to the hole and started to climb in.

Note: [1]Bavarian Alps

Caught by surprise, Bill exclaimed, "Be careful. Watch out you don't rip your suit on the jagged edges."

But by then, Karl was inside the module and asked, "Where in hell are the pee things. Everything in here is just a jumble."

Bill stuck his head and shoulders into the hole and shined his flashlight upward, towards the back of the module, and answered, "They should be over there somewhere."

Karl climbed up to where Bill was shining his light and said happily, "Ja, I see them. Throw me your handy cutters and I cut a couple of them off, leaving as much hose on them as possible."

Bill gently threw the tin-snips up to Karl in a slow arc and Karl caught them seconds later at the top of their trajectory. The sturdy tin-snips made short work of cutting through the thin walled, small diameter, plastic hoses.

As Karl climbed down with his prizes, he said, very emphatically, "This time, you do the pecker trick."

Bill just laughed and said, "Jawohl, Herr Kapitän[1]."

Their tasks completed, they began their 25-minute drive back to the Traverse Vehicle.

Wednesday, July 17, 2014, 15:27 GMT

Karl and Bill arrived at the Traverse Vehicle and banged on its hull. Tom called almost immediately.

Karl said, "Stay on the line — we'll soon be coming in. All that's left to do is to hookup the Rovers' fuel cells to the umbilical."

While Karl was talking, Bill cut some wire from the wire spool and proceeded to hookup the fuel cells of both Rovers to the umbilical plug. He checked the voltage at the plug and said, "Everything seems to be ok. I'm going to plug in the umbilical." As he did, he was biting his lip.

Having told Maria and Tom what they should see and, hopefully, not see on the panel meters, Tom said jubilantly, "The voltages and currents are close to what you said they should be. Come on in."

Note: [1]Yes indeed, Captain, sir

Chapter 4-3
Back in the Traverse Vehicle

Wednesday, July 17, 2014, 15:41 GMT

Their outing lasted 5 hours and 20 minutes and both Bill and Karl were tired, hungry, and very glad to be back in the Traverse Vehicle.

As soon as they got out of their suits, Maria gave Karl a gentle hug — being careful not to hurt his ribs — and a big kiss, which almost, but not quite, turned his thoughts from food to Maria.

Bill immediately went to the control console and looked at the various gauges. Looking pleased, he announced, "Right now, our external power supplies are recharging the Traverse Vehicle's fuel cells, but that's very inefficient. I'm going to switch the system so we're using the external power as our only source of power, that way, we'll get the most out of the batteries and the Rovers' fuel cells. However, when they run out of juice, we have to switch this switch — see this one — from external power to internal power. Since I don't really know when we'll have to switch over, we're going to have to watch the power panel all the time. I suggest we have two, 12-hour shifts — which is a good idea anyway, given the mess we are in and given John's condition — by the way, how is he doing?"

Maria answered, "He woke up again in pain, but he said he didn't hurt as much as he did before. His color is a little bit better, his pulse is a little stronger, and he's breathing is somewhat better. I think he has gotten over the damage we did to him bringing him here from Lab. I gave him some more morphine and later he urinated again — did you get the . . . ," and Karl nodded. Maria continued, "Good, we can fix that problem."

Karl looked sternly at Bill, but did not say anything — nevertheless, Bill again got the message and nodded.

Bill got one of the urination devices, while Tom got an empty 2-liter plastic bottle. Bill pulled down the sheet and blanket covering John, took off his diaper, and unceremoniously rolled the condom-like end of the device onto John's penis and inserted the other end of the tube into the neck of the bottle, which he sat on the floor next to the bunk and asked, "Will someone get me something to secure the bottle to the wall, so it won't tip over and make a mess."

Tom found some tape, and soon the task was finished.

Karl had a very smug look on his face as he nodded and pointed to Bill, who laughed a little and said, "Ok, ok, we're even."

Tom looked puzzled and shook his head.

Bill continued his previous thought, "Ok, well, as I started to say, until we have switched back to internal power, we should have a 24-hour watch to be sure we make the switchover when the external power supplies go dead. Tom and I can take one watch and you two lovebirds can take the other one. Given what time it is now, I suggest we make the breaks at 2:00 and 14:00 GMT. Any other suggestions? — No, ok, who wants the current watch?"

Karl answered, "I'm tired enough and my ribs hurt enough, so I think I could get some sleep with some more Percoset and be ready for the 2 AM shift. How about you Liebling?"

Maria answered, "Sí, that would be fine with me."

Bill said, "Fine, that's settled — let's eat."

Wednesday, July 17, 2014, 15:57 GMT

Maria and Tom had let some precooked TV dinners thaw out while waiting for Bill and Karl to return, but since they could not use the microwave, they had a cold, and therefore not too appetizing dinner, waiting for them. Nevertheless, as the German saying says, "Hunger ist der beste Koch[1]," so Bill and Karl ate their cold repast with gusto — though neither Maria nor Tom quite shared Bill and Karl's enthusiasm for their cold meals.

After dinner, and after they rested 10 minutes, Bill said, in the very dim emergency light of the Traverse Vehicle, "Ok,

---

Note: [1]Hunger is the best cook

let's see how much power we really have. If I remember correctly, we need 3¼ day's worth of external power. The secondary batteries in Utility have 50 to 70% of their charge. We have 2 sets of tertiary batteries that are full and 2 Rovers' fuel cells that, together, are 80% full.

"The secondary batteries can keep the 4 modules going for a day and each module in the emergency mode takes about ½ as much power as the Traverse Vehicle does in its emergency mode, so that would be 2 day's worth of power, if they were full. But they are not, so they have just 1 to 1½ day's worth of power. But that's at normal temperatures, not at zero, which the Base is now at, and not at the –10° it will soon become. That also assumes the batteries have no internal damage, like the Utility tertiary batteries apparently suffered. So, we can probably count on only 1 day's worth of power from them and hope for a little more.

"Each ternary battery set has a little over 6% of the capacity of the secondary batteries and we have 2 of them with full charges, so that's, at most, ¼ of a day's worth of power — if they are both fully ok.

"Then we've got the Rovers' fuel cells. Those fuel cells together have about a tenth of the capacity of the cells in the Traverse Vehicle, which last 21 days under normal use. So the little cells have 2 days of power and they're 80% full, but our emergency power consumption is 80% normal — so that's a wash.

"Ok, it looks like we have close to 3¼ — and maybe even as much as 3¾ day's worth of external power. If all goes very well, we'll just make it — barely. But Christ, it couldn't be any closer and just like the hydrogen boil-off, there's absolutely no clear positive margin. This is a double case of the cavalry having to arrive just in the nick of time. We need to call Houston and tell them how close it is and see if there's anyway they can launch even ½ a day earlier. If they can't, I'm sorry to say — there's a good chance we won't make it."

Wednesday, July 17, 2014, 16:16 GMT
Tom radioed Houston and Bill told them, "Barring any problems, and if everything goes right with the boil-off and

our stretching the power, we can just — and I repeat — just last until the rescue vehicle makes it into lunar orbit. But, like the hydrogen boil-off, we have no clear positive margin — I repeat again — zero with a capital Z — zero, clear positive margin on the power. Is there any possible way for the OTV to get here even ½ a day earlier?"

Houston answered, "Bill, I'm sorry, but I doubt it. But the back room boys will work it to death to get you every extra minute possible.

"Unfortunately, the thermal engineers finished their calculations and they found if you keep the cabin at 21° during the lunar night, you're going to use more power than during the lunar day. They recommend you drop the temperature to 8° C or lower.

"So we talked to Dr. Maxwell again and he said in your do-or-die situation, John could take a cabin temperature as low as 15° C, if you put extra blankets on him and make some hot water bottles — out of plastic bags and the like — heat them in the microwave as often as you can spare the power, and use them to keep him warm. He also said you could heat the IV fluid in the microwave once in a while. If you can do all that, Dr. Maxwell says John will be — ah — comfortable at 15°.

"Anything else you need to have us look at before I go on?"

"No."

Houston continued cautiously, "Ok — after the Administrator's last attempt to — ah — ah — communicate with you, he thought it would be better if I gave you the following information. Headquarters has consulted not only with Dr. Maxwell, but also with several leading internists at major hospitals. They all agree, it doesn't look good for John — at 15° with the hot water bottles and all, or even at the normal cabin temperature. To be blunt, most think he will die before the OTV gets there no matter what you do and those who give him even a slim chance of surviving until he gets back here think it will be too late to save him. I suspect you guys already know that yourselves.

"Given that, given your power crunch and the fact that, under the most optimistic, but current hydrogen boil-off calculation — the guys are still refining those calculations, but the trends are clear — the Lander has only about a 30% chance of making the 200-kilometer OTV rendezvous orbit with the 5 of you on board and that becomes, maybe, up to 50% with just 4 of you. Headquarters is order—— ah — strongly suggesting you turn down the cabin temperature to the 8° C the engineers calculated and not to use the microwave to heat up hot water bottles and the IVs for John.

"Bill, I know what you're thinking, but Headquarters is right, it'll be a hell of a lot better to get 4 of you back, than having 5 more dead up there, either because you run out of power or because you can't make the rendezvous orbit. Bill, and the rest of you, I know Headquarters — or none of us — can make you do anything you don't want to, but please, give it some serious thought, ok?

Bill asked pensively, "Has NASA told our families — and especially John's — about this? If it hasn't, do not — I repeat — do not let NASA tell them. We don't need our families emotions making our decision more difficult, understand?"

Houston replied, "I understand. I'll do my best to make sure Headquarters keeps quiet, but I'm sure you know they don't want this leaking to the press, so I wouldn't worry about it. That's it from here, anything else?"

Glumly, Bill answered, "No, we'll call you in 24 hours, at 16-hundred, unless something comes up earlier," then Tom signed off.

Bill turned to the others and said slowly, "Unless anyone disagrees, I think we should lower the temperature to 15° as Dr. Maxwell first said, but no more. We can make some hot water bottles and heat the IV, but we'll have to do it sparingly or we will use more power doing it, than just keeping the cabin temperature up. We'll have to see how John reacts to 15° before we do anything else. Also, we need to see how long the external power lasts — then we can re-discuss the temperature issue. Since all our lives depend on this, I think we should vote on it to be fair to everyone. And — I don't mean to be cold hearted about it — but I'm sure they're correct, John will probably die no matter what we do."

Karl immediately said, "I will not intentionally let John, or anyone else, die to save my life. After hearing the calculation about the chances of us making orbit with 4 of us on the Lander instead of 5, I'd walk out the airlock right now, without a hard suit, if I knew it would save Maria and John — and you and Tom, too. My vote — we do what we have to do to keep John alive — no question about it." Maria nodded, with tears in her eyes.

Tom said, "I agree with everything Karl said — no lower than 15°."

Without saying a word, Bill turned back to the control panel and set the thermostat down to 15° C — then said somberly, "You two get some sleep. You have 9 hours before your watch begins. Tom and I will tend to John."

Maria said, "No one will get much sleep in the bunks if the crew on watch has to keep heating John up with hot water bottles and heating them and his IV in the galley. I think we should take the mattresses to the work area in the back of the cabin and sleep on the floor. Also, each team can sleep together to help keep each other warm, so John can have all the blankets he needs."

Karl said, "I'll vote for that, especially the sleeping together part."

Somewhat more reluctantly, but seeing the wisdom in Maria's suggestion, both Bill and Tom agreed.

Wednesday, July 17, 2014, 16:34 GMT

Before going to bed, Maria checked on John — who looked a little better, took his pulse — which was fairly good, saw that his IV bag was still over half full, and noted he had not urinated. She took the covers from the other three bunks, added them to the one already on John, and said to Bill and Tom, "That should hold him until about 20-hundred, when he will need a new IV bag. If you need any help with it, just wake me up — oh, and check his urine bottle once in a while."

Bill replied, "We can handle the IV exchange and the pee. Just go to bed and get some sleep."

Maria and Karl took the mattresses from the top two bunks and a couple of blankets and pillows and placed them in the back work area of the cabin. Karl unscrewed the light bulbs of the dim emergency lighting that were closest to their bed, so it was very dark back there.

Maria, who was used to living and sleeping in the hot, desert climate of Tucson and, more recently, in the hot and muggy climate of Houston, put on a pair of slacks — the only ones she had at the Base — and an extra blouse to keep warm, since to her, 15° C was freezing, and lay down.

In contrast, Karl was used to the cool climate of Germany and was used to sleeping at 15° C or less, so he was content with the thought of sleeping with the cooler cabin temperature and just lay down next to Maria.

They both said, "Good night," to Tom and Bill.

The latter responded with, "We'll be as quiet as possible. Get some sleep."

Maria and Karl snuggled as close together as they could — but not to keep warm, since the cabin temperature had not dropped significantly in the 15 minutes since Bill had turned the temperature down — rather to be as intimate as possible under the circumstances. They kissed several times, whispered endearments in each other's ear and then, because both had slept badly on the narrow bunk the previous night, because Karl was exhausted from the trip outside and the constant pain of his ribs, and because they were emotionally exhausted from the communication with Houston about John, they quickly fell asleep in each other's arms, despite the early hour.

A few hours later, after the cabin temperature dropped to 15° C, Maria awoke for a few seconds, snuggled even closer to Karl, who was sleeping very soundly, to get the welcome warmth of his body heat, and fell back asleep within seconds.

About the same time, after waiting for the cabin temperature to drop, Tom and Bill made sure Maria and Karl were fast asleep and quietly collected the IV bag John was on and all the empty IV bags, filled the latter with water, tightly sealed them, and heated them and the IV bag in the microwave. They put the hot water bags on John and hooked the warm IV bag, which they had wrapped in an insulating towel, to the thin tube, also wrapped in insulating cloth, that led to the needle in John's arm.

When they did, they discovered John had urinated. Thankful they had the urination device on John and the bottle, Bill emptied the bottle in the lavatory, being extremely careful not to disturb Maria and Karl, and put it back in its workplace.

Tom and Bill went back to the front of the cabin, continued to monitor the Traverse Vehicle's systems — especially, its power — and continued to swap stories — big and small, true and false — to pass the time in the dimly lit, cool cabin.

From where they sat, they could look out the Traverse Vehicle's front window to the east and see the blue, Earth-lit lunar surface, whose temperature was $-157°$ C. In the cool earthlight, the low rolling hills of the Fra Mauro formation looked beautiful and serene, even inviting — in stark contrast to the reality that hostile environment had to offer the 5 fragile humans who were trying to survive the icy cold of the lunar night and the deadly vacuum of the airless Moon.

Chapter 4-4
The Survival Routine

Thursday, July 18, 2014, 02:00 GMT

At 02:00 GMT, Bill shook Karl awake. Karl, who almost always woke up quickly, yawned and asked, "Is it 2:00 already? Mensch, it's dark in here."

Bill answered quietly, "Yes, it's 2:00, and yes it's dark. Following your lead, I unscrewed all the emergency light bulbs, except those over the control console and in the galley — we use the flashlights for everything else. Did you sleep well?"

Karl answered quietly, "Jawohl, Maria had an excellent idea when she suggested we sleep back here."

By then, Maria had begun to slowly wake up and said sleepily, "Good morning — or good night, whichever the case might be. How did things go? How's John? Did he get too cold?"

Bill answered, "Things went well. John seems to be doing a little better. The hot water bottles, the warm IV, and all the blankets seem to be keeping him warm enough, though his hands and feet feel a little cold."

Six hours had passed since Bill had last added a new IV bag, so it was time to do that again. Maria got out a new bag from the rapidly dwindling supply. She heated it in the microwave, along with the hot water bottles Bill retrieved from John, and exchanged the warm bag for the empty one and put the hot water bottles back on John.

Maria and Karl used the lavatory and Maria made herself as presentable as she could with the very limited resources available to her — though it was so dark in the Traverse Vehicle, no one could see she was not in peak form anyway.

Several minutes later, Maria and Karl joined Bill and Tom.

Tom said, "We thawed out some precooked breakfasts for you and have some vacuum packed food for suppers for us. We thought it would be nice to eat together before we went to bed."

Both Maria and Karl appreciated their thoughtfulness and they started their combination breakfast/dinner.

Tom had selected French toast, maple syrup, sausage, and juice for Maria and Karl, a meal more to Karl's taste than the scrambled eggs of the previous day. However, cold French toast and sausage did leave a lot to be desired.

After they finished their meals, Bill said, "Wake us no later than 11:00. We can spend the afternoon talking about how we can improve our situation, especially John's. Believe me, I'm looking forward to a little more company than just old Tom here, after sitting at the console in the dark all night swapping war stories with him. We're still running on external power, as I expected, but keep a close eye on it and if you see the batteries are going dead, wake me, ok?"

Maria answered, "Sí, we'll do that. Now go to bed and be sure to put on some extra clothes. This isn't Tucson or even Houston — it's more like Karl's beloved Deutschland[1]."

Bill and Tom went to the rear of the cabin, with flashlight in hand, went to the lavatory, and crawled into bed.

As they disappeared, Karl smiled smugly. Maria, knowing Karl was enjoying the intimate sleeping arrangement Bill and the completely innocent Tom were forced into, poked Karl in the shoulder lightly and said in faked sternness, but with a slight smile on her lips, "Shame on you," which made Karl laugh out loud.

Thursday, July 18, 2014, 02:37 GMT

Like Bill and Tom before them, just after Maria and Karl were alone on their watch, they quickly fell into a dull routine of checking the Traverse Vehicle's subsystem readouts — especially those of the electrical subsystem — checking on John every hour, periodically reheating his hot water bottles and IV bag, and checking his urine bottle. They talked about lunar science in general and specifically about lunar petrology and, of course, moonquakes. Maria practiced her German and Karl practiced his Spanish, but the time dragged on and on in the dimly lit and chilly cabin.

Note: [1]Germany

Since they were just sitting and not generating much body heat, Maria was getting colder and colder. She added a third blouse and she and Karl snuggled to keep warm and to enjoy the comfort of being close to each other. Though Karl was used to a cooler climate than Maria, he, too, began to feel the effects of just sitting around in the cool cabin. But unlike Maria, he did not have any long pants at the Base, so he added a second shirt and wrapped another around his bare legs.

They looked out the window at the blue-lit landscape and admired the stark, desert-like beauty of the ancient surface spread out before them — a 3.8 billion year old landscape that had been violently modified by moonquake induced landslides just 2 days earlier.

While they were enjoying looking at the Moon's stark surface, Karl suddenly said, "Let's turn off all the lights and see if we can see any stars," and they did. Out the window, about 40° above the southeastern horizon, they saw a reddish star and Karl exclaimed, "Look, there's Antares, the brightest star in the Scorpion and just below it is Mars, which is nearing opposition — and over there, just rising in the northeast — see, the blue-white star. That's Vega in the Lyre." They searched in vain for other stars, but little else was visible and Karl remarked, "Well, the earthlight is just too bright for us to see any dimmer stars." Disappointed, they turned the dim cabin lights back on and Mars and those two stars disappeared from view.

Maria went to check on John, who was sleeping rather peacefully. She turned to go back up front, but, on a sudden impulse, she turned and tiptoed to the back of the vehicle, where she saw Tom and Bill were sleeping soundly and were snuggled very close together.

She very quietly tiptoed back to Karl, hugged him from behind as he sat in the chair looking at the console readouts, kissed his right ear softly, and whispered, in a sweet, seemingly innocent, but inviting tone, "John, Tom, and Bill are all fast asleep. If we turn off the lights again and if we are very, very quiet — " but she never got to finish her sentence. Karl, completely forgetting his painful ribs, turned around quickly and smothered her words with a long, hard, passionate kiss. Then, unlike the earlier part of the night, time seemed to pass by far, far too quickly.

After their romantic interlude, Maria and Karl were both relaxed and warm, having finally done some intense physical activity that increased their body heat markedly.

Then, far too quickly, the dull routine of their night watch returned, interrupted mainly by having to change John's IV bag at 8:00 GMT, by having a mid-watch snack shortly thereafter, and by emptying John's urine bottle twice.

Finally it was time to wake Bill and Tom.

Thursday, July 18, 2014, 11:00 GMT

Over their common, breakfast/lunch meal, Maria and Karl told Bill and Tom about the non-events of their watch, leaving out a certain, all too short span of time, and Maria said, "I'm getting more and more concerned about the supply of saline solution bags. We're going to run out of them soon at the rate we're using them. We have to ask Dr. Maxwell what to do when they run out, or if we should slow the drip rate to make them last longer."

Bill said, "Of course. We'll do that on the next scheduled contact this afternoon."

With little to do, except to watch the Traverse Vehicle systems and to take care of John — adding a new IV bag at 14:00 GMT — all four of them sat in the semidarkness, talking and trying to keep as warm as possible.

They called Houston at the agreed upon time of 16:00 GMT and, after reporting their general condition, Maria asked Dr. Maxwell about the problem of the limited supply of IV bags. He responded, "You'll have to slow the drip rate and make each bag last 12 hours, instead of just 6. Once you run out, there's nothing you can do."

Houston reported the good news, "The preparations for getting the fuel loads for the OTV launched are going smoothly and are on schedule. Also, one of the 2-man crew of the rescue vehicle will be one of our astronaut MD's, who can look after John and the rest of you as soon as you're in the crew module."

In addition to the formal reporting, NASA had flown Karl's parents in from Germany and Maria's in from Tucson. They, along with Nancy, Tom's wife, and John's wife, were in Mission Control to talk to their trapped loved ones.

Nancy was stoic and assured Bill, "I know you will all make it Bill. You have never failed at anything and, with companions like Maria, Karl, and Tom to help you, I just know I'll be seeing you in a few days. Then you can raise as much hell about NASA as you want."

Bill found it hard to say anything except, "I love you babe, see you soon," as he tried vainly to choke back the tears, which started slowly streaming down his cheeks under the low lunar gravity.

Karl's parents told him how much they loved him and missed him in German and then, in halting English, his father said, for the benefit of those around him, "Ve know you vill do da right ting, Karl, no matter vhat happens. Ve are fery proud uf you. Auf Wiedersehen, mein Sohn.[1]"

Maria's father, speaking in Spanish, was emotional, but held it together, while her mother completely lost it.

Tom's wife simply said, with quiet dignity, "We love you, we are waiting for you, and we will see you soon."

Last was John's wife, Betty, who said very stoically, "I know how well you're taking care of John and the sacrifices you are all making to keep him alive. I cannot tell you how much that means to me and I know to John, too. If there is anything, anything at all I can do for you, or your families, to repay you, just tell me and I'll do it," but then she added, hinting she knew exactly how deadly serious the situation was — unlike the other family members assembled there, "But please remember, all sacrifices have their limits — next time John is awake, tell him I love him and to hurry on home so I can take care of him."

Thursday, July 18, 2014, 16:43 GMT

Immediately after the emotionally draining tele-con was over, Maria dried her tears and went back to John and

---

Note: [1]Goodbye, my son

changed the IV drip rate — and his urination bottle, saying as she did, in a effort to quell her run-away-emotions and get back into her survival routine, "I'm timing this so the IV bag will be changed at the changing of the watch, at 02:00 and 14:00 GMT. That will simplify things and make sure our sleep is not disturbed."

Thursday, July 18, 2014, 17:12 GMT

Half-an-hour later, after they all had composed themselves and as they were having their evening meal, the dull pain in Karl's lower right rib cage was growing more intense. He grunted, "Well, it's been nearly 2½ days since the quake, so the inflammation has begun to set in right on schedule. Liebling, I'm going to need some more Percoset, and maybe even a sedative, if I'm going to get any sleep tonight."

Maria went to the medical stores and got some Percoset, Ambien, and Ibuprofen. Karl gratefully took all the pills between short, shallow breaths as he tried to control the pain caused simply by taking too deep a breath.

By then, it was their bedtime, so Maria and Karl went to the rear of the cabin. Since it was impossible for Karl to lay in any other position than on his back, without causing great pain in his inflamed and evermore sensitive ribs, he had to forsake sleeping on his left side — his usual position — and forsake cuddling Maria. So she snuggled up to Karl, facing his left side, and held him with her left arm, both for affection and to keep warm — an increasingly difficult task to accomplish.

Despite the pills, Karl spent a restless night and his increasing agony also disturbed Maria's sleep.

Friday, July 19, 2014, The Night Watch

When Bill woke Karl and Maria up at 2:00 GMT, neither was well rested, partly because of the emotional turmoil of the previous day and partially because of Karl's ribs. As a result, they took turns taking naps during their night watch — though Karl's ribs hurt so much, even the naps did not help much. Their watch passed with the same boring routine in the darkness and chill of the cabin as it had the previous night, with one big exception, Karl's ribs hurt so much there was no mention of romance.

John seemed to be holding out well. The slight improvement he had shown the previous day was holding — he was getting neither better nor worse. Maria and Karl were satisfied that the 15° C temperature was not making him worse.

Friday, July 19, 2014, 12:00 GMT

When Bill and Tom woke up, a little before 12:00, they all had a meal.

Tom said, "My leg does not hurt so much today. I think the swelling has gone down a little."

Maria replied, "That's good news. Now we can start dropping your dosage of Percoset."

When Maria changed the IV at 14:00, John was still stable.

After the evening meal, Maria and Karl, the latter with a double dose of Percoset and Ibuprofen, retired for the evening a little before 18:00 GMT, and were soon fast asleep.

Friday, July 19, 2014, 19:33 GMT

A little over an hour-and-a-half after Maria and Karl had gone to bed and 3½ days after John had been badly hurt in the moonquake, Bill shook Maria awake with some urgency, and said, "Maria, I'm sorry to wake you, but John seems to have taken a turn for the worse."

Uncharacteristically, Maria was wide-awake in a split second and Karl woke up immediately. Maria asked, as she jumped out of bed, "What happened?"

Bill answered, "A couple of minutes ago, John began to make some noise and we went back to see what was wrong. He was awake and said he was in excruciating pain. He looks like hell and his stomach is swollen and hard as a rock."

By then, all four were at John's bedside and Maria asked, "Tell me exactly where it hurts."

John answered haltingly, between shallow breaths, "My guts . . . hurt . . . really bad. . . . It feels . . . like they're . . . going to . . . burst. . . . My lungs . . . hurt like . . . hell and . . . I can't . . . seem to get . . . enough air. . . . I keep . . . tasting blood.

Though Maria knew John was getting much worse, her medical knowledge was far too limited for her to make any sense out of what John told her. She gave him an 8-milligram dose of morphine and increased the IV drip rate back to its initial faster rate. When she was done, she said, "John, we talked with Betty yesterday and she said to tell you she loves you and can't wait until you're home where she can take care of you."

"Tell . . . her . . . I . . . love . . . her . . . too." Then John began to slide back into a comatose-like sleep and Maria said, "We've got to talk to Dr. Maxwell. This doesn't look good."

Chapter 4-5
John's Deathwatch

Friday, July 19, 2014, 19:46 GMT

Tom called Houston and said they needed to talk to Dr. Maxwell about John's worsening condition. Houston found Dr. Maxwell at his office and patched him into the radio via the telephone. After Maria described what John had told her, Dr. Maxwell said bluntly, "I'm surprised he's lasted this long. There's nothing you can do for him, except keep him sedated with morphine and as comfortable as possible. It sounds like he is going into shock from internal bleeding. I'd give him 24 to 36 hours, at most. If you haven't done it already, you guys had better really start thinking about yourselves and turn the heat down."

Houston had some questions about the condition of the Traverse Vehicle and said they were on track with the rescue preparations. They signed off after saying, "Keep us posted about John," without asking about the cabin temperature; the downlinked telemetry clearly showed Houston the fact that the cabin temperature was still 15° C.

Maria asked Bill, with tears in her eyes and in a pleading voice, "It won't make any difference — power-wise — if we still keep him warm — as long as he lasts, will it?"

Bill answered somberly, "I don't think so. We'll just drop the temperature down really low after — I mean, later." Then he added, "You two go back to sleep. Maria, why don't you take a sedative, too, and we'll let you two sleep until you wake up by yourselves, ok?"

Maria answered, "Good idea," and 30 minutes later, both Maria and Karl were again, fitfully asleep, while Tom and Bill began the deathwatch.

Saturday, July 20, 2014, 03:31 GMT

Because both Maria and Karl had taken sedatives, because their sleep had been disturbed by John's turn for the worse, because they had slept badly the night before, and because Bill had suggested they sleep late, they slept well past 2:00 GMT and were starting to stir when they heard Bill and Tom talking a little louder than usual. Maria was immediately wide-awake and said urgently, "It must be John."

They got up quickly, went to John's bed, but found he was still alive, then continued to the forward part of the cabin and Karl asked, "What's going on?"

Bill answered, with a very worried look on his face, "The external power supplies are going out, nearly ¾ a day earlier than I had expected and more than a day earlier than I had hoped. I guess the batteries in the Base are just too cold to put out as much power as I had hoped, or they were damaged during the quake." Though those possibilities were undoubtedly partially true, everyone knew why the batteries ran out early. Regardless of the reason, the chances of their surviving until the OTV arrived just dropped a notch or two.

Bill added, "The voltage is already down to less than 23 volts and it's dropping rapidly. I'll drain every microwatt out of the batteries and fuel cells I can before I make the switch over to the Traverse Vehicle's internal power — but they can't last more than an hour."

The dim lights of the emergency lighting were already getting noticeably dimmer and they decided to have a meal of vacuum packed food while they waited for the switchover.

Saturday, July 20, 2014, 04:23 GMT

At 04:23 GMT, the emergency lights went out and Bill immediately switched the power from external power to internal power. The emergency lights quickly returned to their original level and Bill said, "Well, the external sources are dead, we have 14¼ days of power left, give or take a little, depending on how cold we can make it in here. According to Houston, the rescue vehicle will be in orbit for the rendezvous in — let me see, I wrote that down somewhere — here it is, 17½ days, as of about 8-hundred on the 17th, or a few hours less than 3 days ago. If I did the arithmetic right in my head, the rescue vehicle should be in orbit in a little more than 14½ days — crap, that means we're 6 hours shy of the 14½ days we need. But, we have 8 hours of oxygen in the PLSSs and another hour in the emergency bottles, so we have maybe as much as 2 or 3 hours of positive margin — give or take 2 hours or so. What worries me is the 'take' part of that equation. So, it looks like we might still make it, but the cavalry had better get here in the nick of time."

Resigned to the unyielding and indifferent facts of the dire situation, Bill said, "Well, we're going to hit the sack. Wake us if you see anything strange on the console."

Saturday, July 20, 2014, 04:34 GMT

Alone again, but comparatively well rested, Maria and Karl began the dull routine of their night watch, which was made even more difficult because they knew John was dying.

As they were sitting in the bright, blue earthlight at the front of the vehicle, Maria said, "I feel so helpless and frustrated since there's nothing we can do for John, except watch him die. No one deserves to go this way, in pain for several days, despite the morphine, nearly half-a-million kilometers from family and home. At least he's not dying alone."

"Ja, you're right Liebling. Despite everything, John was one hell of an astronaut. It's too bad NASA put him in a position here at the Base where he felt useless. I'll bet if he had something constructive to do, he would not have gotten into it with Isabel and would have left you and Pam alone.

"Mensch, how I hate NASA for killing him — and Pam, Isabel, and Jim, too. This Base could have been so great, and now look at it and at us, too. If we don't get back, NASA will just cover this up, like it does all its failures, and pretend this was just an unforeseen act of nature."

Maria nodded and said, "That's what worries me, too. We just have to make it, if for no other reason, we have to make sure the US changes the way we explore space and take NASA out of the driver's seat."

Karl added bitterly, "This time the government had better make the responsible people pay for their crimes. If they had done that after Challenger, Columbia, or Atlantis, we might not be in this Scheisse."

Saddened, Maria replied, "Let's talk about something else, this is too depressing."

As their watch continued, John's condition kept getting worse, despite his being sedated with heavy doses of morphine. He was increasingly restless and frequently mumbled incoherently.

The long, cold night passed so slowly that each second seemed to be an eternity.

Saturday, July 20, 2014, 12:29 GMT

Bill and Tom woke up shortly after noon, had breakfast as Maria and Karl had a late lunch, and then all four talked during the entire afternoon, trying to keep their spirits up — and watched John, who was getting worse by the hour.

Reluctantly, after a light evening snack, Maria and Karl went to bed at about 18:00 GMT, so they would get a full 8 hours of sleep before their 02:00 GMT watch began.

Saturday, July 20, 2014, 20:12 GMT

A commotion woke both Maria and Karl up a couple of hours after they had fallen asleep. They both instinctively knew John had died. They quickly got out of bed and went the few steps to John's bed, where Tom and Bill were already waiting.

Bill said, "A minute ago, John moaned and we came running with the flashlights. He moaned again and sat straight up with his eyes wide open — they had a glazed or puzzled look to them. Then he mumbled something and just flopped back down, with his eyes still wide open. He was not breathing and had no pulse. That's when you got here. He's dead, the poor bastard. That makes a total of 23 NASA has killed since Apollo."

It took the moonquake $4\frac{1}{2}$ agonizing days to kill John.

Chapter 4-6
Paying the Last Respects

They took the blankets off John, took the IV needle out of his arm, took the urination device off him, emptied the urine bottle, which he had filled as his urinary tract muscles relaxed immediately after his death, and covered him with his sheet.

Bill said, "Let's go to the front and discuss what comes next." They all walked forward.

Maria said, "Drop the heat immediately as low as you can."

Bill replied, "I'll drop it to 5° and see how we can take it," and immediately turned the thermostat down to 5° C.

Maria said, "We can't leave him in here. I say we take him to Kitchen and put him with Isabel, Pam, and Jim."

Bill said, "We'll use a lot of power doing that — it will take 3 egresses and 2 ingresses, but I guess we don't have a choice. I can shut off essentially all of the monitoring systems in the Traverse Vehicle — that will help a little with the power. Any other suggestions?"

Karl answered, "We don't need to use the galley light any more, and the earthlight shining in the windows is more than bright enough to illuminate the front of the cabin, and even the back a little, so we can turn off all the emergency lights."

Bill agreed and said, "As soon as we're finished, I'll do that."

Tom added, "Since it's going to be 5° in here, I think we can turn off the refrigerator and freezer — they take a lot of power — and the food will stay cold anyway, even if the frozen foods thaws."

Bill went and turned off the refrigerator and freezer without further discussion.

Maria, who was already freezing, said, "When we take John to Kitchen, we can get Isabel, Pam, and Jim's clothes from Dorm to help keep us warm."

That prompted Karl to say, "Ja, I sure could use some long pants. Also, we should bring all the mattresses from Dorm. They make excellent blankets and, by putting extra ones under the existing mattresses, they will help insulate us from the cold floor."

Since no one could think of anything else, Karl said, "Bill, let's do it now."

Maria said sternly to Karl, "You're not going out again. Your ribs are killing you as it is. I'll go with Bill, and that's that."

Karl simply said, "Ja, ok, you're right."

Bill turned to Tom, "Call Houston and tell them about John while we get ready to take him to Kitchen."

Saturday, July 20, 2014, 21:19 GMT

An hour later, Maria and Bill were suited up and, after very careful suit checks, they were ready to take John to his resting place.

Bill egressed first. Then Karl and Tom placed John in the airlock and cycled it. Bill took him out and cycled the airlock, so Maria could egress.

Maria and Bill carried John's stiffening body — it was 4 days after sunset and the surface temperature was $-164°$ C — to the SW entrance of the dead Base, their path was illuminated by the very bright, blue light of the nearly full Earth that was standing $16°$ to the east of the zenith — an inviting island of life and safety in a jet-black sky.

Maria said, "John is freezing fast."

Bill added, "And beginning the freeze drying process, too."

Maria frowned, "What do you mean?"

"John is slowly losing his water to the vacuum. I guess in a few days, he'll be completed desiccated, freeze-dried, just the way they make instant coffee and preserve other things. Haven't you heard about people having their pets freeze dried after they are dead, so Fluffy or Rover can stand quietly in the corner forever? I would guess that Isabel, Pam, and Jim are already freeze-dried, or well on their way there. They'll all stay perfectly preserved, until somebody comes to take them back to Earth for a proper burial or cementation."

Maria was more than a little put off by what Bill had just told her and just uttered a soft, "Oh."

They reached the SW entrance, turned on their flashlights, went into West Utility Tunnel through the open doors of the airlock, proceeded to the open back door of Kitchen, entered, went through Hospital, and entered Kitchen proper.

They laid John on the table next to Jim, straightened his sheet, and just as Bill was turning to leave for Lab, Maria said, "Bill, we can't leave Pam under the freezer. We have to get her out and put her with the others."

Bill said, "It's too dangerous to try to move the freezer and we don't have time." But he looked into Maria's pleading eyes, hesitated a moment, and sighed, "Ok, you're right, but we have to be very, very careful."

They went to where Pam was crushed under the freezer. Bill very carefully took some debris and propped up the broken ceiling as best he could and Maria and he began, very gingerly, to remove the debris from the freezer. After a few minutes, it was cleared and, together, they tipped the freezer back to its upright position — exposing Pam, who was lying on her face and stomach.

As they shined their flashlights on her body, they saw her head had been badly crushed between the floor and the falling freezer and there was some damage to her upper body. Clearly she had died instantly from the extensive damage to her head. As a result, there was only a small pool of freeze-dried blood extending from her head along her left arm — the pool of blood seen by Karl when he first discovered the 3 bodies in Kitchen over 4 days earlier.

Maria cringed at the sight of Pam's sad condition, but she "screwed her courage to the sticking place" and helped Bill gently pick Pam's stiff body up, which was very light — because of the low lunar gravity and because she was already freeze-dried — and placed it on the table next to her fallen crewmates.

When Maria saw Jim's body, she said, holding back the tears, "Poor Jim, he's never going to see his new baby and the poor baby will grow up never knowing its father. How sad, how very, very sad."

Bill added, "Yeah, the poor bastard. What a turn of events — for all of them, and for us, too."

As Bill turned Pam over, Maria turned away to avoid seeing the crushed, distorted, and bloody face of her friend and left Kitchen as Bill covered Pam with part of John's sheet. Then he, too, left Kitchen and was too moved to say anything as Maria and he went the few steps to Lab.

Saturday, July 20, 2014, 22:01 GMT

Once in Lab, they shook off their sadness and turned to the dire work of their own survival. They quickly collected the 3 mattresses they had brought from Dorm 4 days earlier. Then they went to Dorm and collected all of Isabel, Pam, and Jim's clothes they could easily find and the 3 remaining mattresses in there.

They exited the Base with their bulky loads and collected the 2 mattresses they had used for stretchers to carry John and Tom to the Rovers on their way to the Traverse Vehicle 4 days earlier. They stumbled their way back to the Traverse Vehicle, having a difficult time carrying all they had collected.

When they reached the airlock, they stuffed as many of the mattresses as they could in the airlock and cycled it. When the external door again opened, Maria stepped in with a mattress and load of clothes and was soon inside. Bill quickly repeated the process and finally, the sad trip was finished.

Chapter 4-7
Surviving the Freezing Lunar Night

Saturday, July 20, 2014, 22:43 GMT

After they had stashed the clothes and mattresses in the empty bunks, they assembled at the console in the front of the cabin and continued their survival discussion. As they sat down, Bill shut off all the dim emergency lights and they sat in the bright, bluish light of the waxing gibbous, but nearly full Earth coming in the front window of the cabin.

As long as the dim emergency lights were on, their reddish light had given the survivor's faces a pleasant, ruddy hue. However, with only the pale blue earthlight illuminating their faces, they all had sickly, ghostly complexions, visions that did nothing to lift their spirits.

Maria said, "Since John is gone and the external power supplies are dead, there's no need for the watches. I suggest we go back to all sleeping at the same time." Everyone agreed.

Tom said, "Well, we can't all sleep in the back, so why don't Bill and I set up our bed here, up front."

Bill asked, "Anything else? — No, ok. Then I'm going to suggest we have a hot meal. The little bit of power we use, won't make any difference and I think it will do us all good. Everybody, go pick out your favorite meal and we'll celebrate life and survival and pay our last respects to Isabel, Pam, Jim, and John."

Everyone quickly picked out their last hot meal for sometime and Bill stuffed them in the microwave.

Several minutes later, they were eating the best food they had ever tasted in their lives. The food lifted their spirits a little and helped warm Maria — a little.

After eating, Karl put on Jim's long pants, which were far too big for him, and Maria, Bill, and Tom put on extra clothes.

Then they fixed their beds with all the available mattresses, with 2 mattresses on the bottom and 1 on top of all the blankets.

They said goodnight and crawled into their beds. Maria and Karl snuggled together against the cold, as presumably did Tom and Bill, though they certainly did not kiss each other and hold each other as tightly as did Maria and Karl.

It was 23:21 GMT on July 20, just a little over $10\frac{1}{2}$ days until lunar sunrise and the temperature outside was $-165°$ C.

It was also the last hour of the 45th anniversary of man's first landing on another celestial body — Apollo 11, July 20, 1969. NASA's triumph of getting the Lunar Base operational by that date had turned into another of NASA's deadly, but avoidable, disasters.

Sunday, July 21, 2014, to Wednesday, July 31, 2014

The next 10 days passed with agonizing slowness in the cold and dark. The temperature of the earth-lit, lunar surface dropped very slowly from -165 to $-170°$ C, and the Earth waxed to full on the 23rd, when it was 75 times brighter than the full Moon as seen from Earth, and then waned to third quarter, when it was still 25 times brighter than the full Moon.

Life in the Traverse Vehicle was like living in the eternal ices of Dante's Central Pit of Malebolge. They ate cold meals and drank cold water and juices. They took care of their bodily need, but could only periodically wash their hands and faces in the icy water. Icy water condensed on the cold walls and on every cold surface. Everything, bedding included, became damp and cold. The only warmth they had was what they generated in their mattress and blanket cocoons, and so they spent most of the time in those cocoons.

On the plus side, the swelling in Tom's broken leg continued to decrease and so did the pain. Karl's inflamed ribs got worse during the first couple of days and then they started to hurt less and less as time slowly marched on.

Maria was bothered most by the penetrating cold and by the 27th she developed a painful urinary tract infection, which was exacerbated by the small amounts of fluid they had to drink. It was so painful by the 28th that Tom called

Houston and asked for Dr. Maxwell. When he came on line, Maria described her symptoms and Dr. Maxwell said, "If you have Cipro or Augmentan, take a pill twice a day and drink as much fluid as possible. If you don't have those antibiotics, take whatever you have."

Maria found some Augmentan and started taking it and Karl, Tom, and Bill gave so much of their own liquids to Maria over the next few days, they became dehydrated.

To save power, they reported to Houston only every third day. Besides the power issue, how many times and how many ways could they say they were freezing, hungry for real food, thirsty, and exhausted?

Also, using the excuse that they had to save power, but in reality, because they wanted to avoid emotionally draining conversations with their loved ones, they asked NASA to limit the reports to technical issues and save their possibly, final goodbyes for the very end. It was tough enough having their lives hanging by 2 very tenuous threads — their questionable power reserves and the uncertain boil-off rate of the hydrogen in the Lander — and a somewhat thicker thread, the on-time arrival of the OTV, without having to go through emotional roller coaster rides every 3 days. Their families understood, for it was as hard on them as it was on the crew to try to keep up an optimistic front, knowing what the odds of survival were.

Houston reported on the progress of the launches to take fuel to the OTV that would rescue them 76 hours after lunar sunrise and explained how they were going to be rescued.

"Ok, first things first. The final engineering calculations show, given the fact that the payload will just be the 4 of you and 4 hard suits, the amount of hydrogen expected to be left in the Lander by the time of take off will require only 46% of the oxygen that will then be in the 2 LOX tanks. There is no way you can de-tank 56% of the LOX without power from the nuke. But you have to get rid of as much of the excess LOX as possible, or the Lander will not even achieve a minimum orbit and you will crash less than an hour after takeoff. So, we concur with Karl's suggestion that you punch a hole in one of the LOX tanks and let all the LOX run out. That will still leave an excess of 4% oxygen in the other tank, but that will be the best you can do."

Also, as Karl suggested, but never got around to calculate via the lever rule, Houston told them exactly where to sit on the Lander, in order to balance it, since only one tank would have oxygen in it.

"Second, it's still very unlikely that the Lander can burn into a standard elliptical transfer orbit with a 10-kilometer periselene and a 200-kilometer aposelene and then do a circularization burn at the first aposelene passage to get into the 200-kilometer altitude, circular rendezvous orbit. The engineers are 99% certain there will be enough hydrogen to get the Lander into a 10-kilometer altitude, circular orbit, 78% certain there will be enough to get it into the elliptical transfer orbit, but only 19% certain that it can achieve the 200-kilometer altitude, rendezvous orbit.

"Third, if the Lander only achieves a 10-kilometer altitude, circular orbit — which would be quasi-stable for only 3 or 4 orbits before the lunar gravity anomaly perturbations would cause the Lander to crash — it would be possible, but very difficult, for the rescue vehicle to burn into a 10-kilometer altitude, quasi-circular orbit and effect a rendezvous.

"Fourth, if the Lander burns longer than required to achieve the 10-kilometer altitude, circular orbit, but did not achieve the standard elliptical transfer orbit or did not circularize the orbit at 200 kilometers, then a rendezvous would be impossible to achieve before your oxygen ran out in 9 hours.

"Fifth, if the Lander can achieve a 20-kilometer altitude, circular orbit via a single, direct burn — and the engineers are 74% certain there will be enough hydrogen left to do that — the orbit will be stable long enough for the rescue vehicle to effect a rendezvous before your life support runs out. That is your only option.

"Sixth, we need to track the Lander for 2 full orbits, or 220 minutes, to know exactly what your orbit is, so we can compute how to adjust the rescue vehicle's insertion burn into the 20-kilometer altitude orbit of the Lander and effect a direct rendezvous, almost exactly at the end of the insertion burn.

"Given those data, the rescue scenario is as follows. You drive or walk to the Lander, starting 2 hours before liftoff and arrive at the Lander no later than 1 hour before liftoff. Turn on its communications-, command-, and avionics-subsystems. That gives us enough time to upload and verify the avionics computer load for the direct ascent burn to the 20-kilometer orbit. Since you can't communicate with us via your suit radios, we will know you are at the Lander when the Lander's subsystems come online. Punch a hole in the Number 2 LOX Tank and insure that all the LOX has flowed out of Tank 2. Get on the Lander, sit at the designated points, secure yourselves to the Lander structure, and wait for liftoff that is set for August 3 at 14:48:11 GMT. The end of the rescue vehicle's injection burn is at 19:23:14 GMT or 4 hours and 35 minutes after liftoff. If all goes well, the rendezvous will be achieved in the next 30 minutes. If you leave the Traverse Vehicle 2 hours before liftoff, you would have been on your PLSSs for just over 7¼ hours by the latest expected time of docking. That leaves 1¾ hours of contingency. Do you copy all of that?"

Bill said quietly to Maria, Karl, and Tom, "That all sounded good on paper, but there is clearly and absolutely no room for error and, at best, we have only 3 chances out of 4 of even making the 20-kilometer altitude rescue orbit. Do you all understand that?"

Maria, Karl, and Tom all understood exactly what had to happen and what their chances were of being rescued and they nodded. Bill told Houston in a louder voice, "Yes, we copy."

As soon as the com-session ended, Bill looked at each of his companions to see how they were reacting. He looked at Karl again and said, "Karl, I remember your comment when the Administrator wanted us to sacrifice John to save ourselves. Don't get any dumb ideas about walking out the airlock or anything like that. One less person on the Lander will not increase our chances more than a percent or two. Either there is enough hydrogen and we all make it or we all die. Do you understand?"

Defiantly, Karl challenged Bill, "How do you know that? Houston never said anything about calculating the percentages if only 3 of us were on the Lander."

Bill answered forcefully, "Karl, you're one hell of a physicist and selenophysicist — and you'd make a hell of a good engineer — but you're not a rocket scientist and you can't make the kind of first order physics calculations you're so good at when it comes to rockets. It's much more complicated than that. Even in the simplest cases, you have to use the rocket equation to get close to a meaningful answer, understand? My engineering has always involved rockets and I'm telling you it makes no real difference whether 3 or 4 of us are sitting on the Lander when it takes off. And, for your information, I do know the rocket equation and how to use it, especially when you and Maria are asleep. So, just forget what you're thinking."

Karl, who knew nothing about rockets, looked defeated and Maria, who looked totally perplexed, asked, "Karl, you weren't really thinking of kil—— of staying behind to save me, were you?"

Karl did not answer the love of his life, but his silence spoke louder than words.

After several seconds of that deafening silence, Maria said softly, with tears rolling slowly down her cheeks, "Karl, I love you so much, but I could never let you do that for me. If we are to die, we die together," and she could say no more.

Chapter 4-8
Sunrise — the Start of a New Lunar Day

Wednesday, July 31, 2014, 08:35 GMT

Finally, the day the freezing crew had been waiting for arrived — the day of lunar sunrise — the day they would start to get warm again. Sunrise was scheduled to start at 15:05:14 GMT and would take the Sun's ½° diameter disk an hour and 2 minutes to completely rise above the horizon.

The crew woke up just after 08:35 GMT and rustled around to keep warm and to get something to eat. Then they waited impatiently for the warming Sun.

Outside the freezing cabin, the surface temperature was −170° C and the Earth was a waning crescent, just a little over a day older than last quarter.

Karl went to the window to see if he could see any stars. To his delight, he saw a very bright star about 40° above the eastern horizon and exclaimed, "Look everybody, Venus is the morning star — and I can see several bright stars. Let's see, there's Capella in the Charioteer — Aldebaran in Taurus the Bull, Betelgeuse and Rigel in Orion the Hunter, and just above the southeastern horizon, there's Sirius in Canis Major, the Big Dog."

Suddenly Karl remembered the faint line of illumination along the sunrise horizon discovered by the unmanned Surveyor Lander missions in 1966, 1967, and 1968. He explained and said, "If we're lucky, we might be able to see the faint line of light along the eastern horizon starting a couple of hours before sunrise. Since the Moon has no atmosphere, no one could explain what caused it for years. Somebody finally figured it out during Apollo. It's caused by sunlight scattering off lunar dust grains that are electrostatically suspended a few meters above the surface." And sure enough, at about 13:23 GMT and despite the bright earthlight, Karl said, "Hey, I can just see the first hint of the glow on the horizon," and the others joined him to look at his prize.

Wednesday, July 31, 2014, 15:00 GMT

As the magic moment of sunrise approached, the frozen crew watched the glow along the eastern horizon get brighter and brighter and they counted down the minutes and then the seconds to the time when the sun's upper limb should appear above the mean horizon. As anticipated though, the Sun's limb did not appear on time — it first had to climb above the low hills of the Fra Mauro formation. At 15:38:37 GMT, Karl exclaimed, "Look, the solar chromosphere — that red arc — it's just peeking above the horizon and see there, to the left — there's a tiny solar prominence." The view of the chromosphere and prominence lasted just about 45 seconds, and then the brilliant solar photosphere, which was far too bright to look at directly, blasted into view.

Though it would take several minutes before enough of the solar disk was visible to spend any significant amount of heat, just seeing their faces lit by the first sliver of the rising Sun, after 2 weeks of near total darkness, brightened their spirits. They all cheered the Sun, hugged each other, and danced around and Maria and Karl gave each other several kisses and a long boisterous hug. Between kisses, Maria said jubilantly, "I know it's too early, but I feel like I'm getting warm already."

Fifteen minutes later, a quarter of the solar disk was visible and Maria said, "I can definitely feel the warmth of the sunlight now," and everyone shouted in agreement. They just stood there, basking in the bright sunlight — absorbing every bit of its life-giving energy and warmth they could.

After a few more minutes, the crew began to hear disconcerting pops and groans and, perplexed, Tom asked, "What is going on?"

Karl though for a moment and said, with a knowing smile, "The outer parts of the vehicle have been cold soaked at −170 for days. Right now, the Sun is shining directly on the front of the Traverse Vehicle, so the front of the hull is heating up very, very fast and is rapidly expanding thermally. But the sides are still close to −170. So, as the front expands with respect to the cold sides, the hull groans and pops."

By that time, the heat of the rising Sun began to noticeably increase the internal temperature of the cabin and Maria said, "Now I really do feel it, this icebox is getting warmer."

Finally, by 16:41 GMT, the Sun's lower limb was definitely clear of the horizon and sunrise was over. The cabin was truly warmer, though it would take several hours for everyone and everything inside the Traverse Vehicle to reach a comfortable temperature and even longer for everything to dry out.

Outside, the surface temperature was rapidly rising. In just thirty hours, the outside temperature would rise from −170° C to 0° C. By the time they left the Traverse Vehicle in 3 days to go to the Lander for launch, the surface temperature would be 59° C and the Traverse Vehicle would become unlivable, once the power gave out and the cooling failed. In the meantime, everyone was beginning to thaw out and to, once again, enjoy life a little bit — especially Maria, since the warmer she got, the less her urinary infection bothered her.

After an early, but cold supper, everyone went to bed at 19:00 GMT. They were going to get up by 04:00 GMT to listen to the trans-lunar injection burn of the rescue vehicle that was scheduled to start at 04:57:53 GMT the next morning.

Thursday, August 1, 2014, 04:00 GMT

Karl was the first to awaken at 04:00 GMT. He gave Maria a wake-up kiss and she responded sleepily, having slept better than she had in the 11 days since they had turned the cabin temperature down to 5° C after John's death. They snuggled a bit, while Maria became fully awake, and just enjoyed the warmth and dryness they had missed for so many endless days and nights.

Finally, they got out of bed, followed by Bill and then by Tom. Tom called Houston, which reported the OTV countdown was proceeding smoothly and then, to save power, they signed off for 35 minutes.

Thursday, August 1, 2014, 04:55 GMT

Tom hailed Houston again and all 4 listened intently to the terminal countdown. At T=0, they heard John Gruener, the Commander of the OTV, say, "Ignition — building up the thrust to 101%."

The rescue was underway and Maria, Karl, Tom, and Bill excitedly shouted, "Hurray," and the classic, "Go baby, go," and then they listened in silence as the burn proceeded and John periodically gave Houston updates on various parameters.

The 1st stage burn lasted 10 minutes and 44 seconds and when that time was up, they heard John say, "First stage MECO[1] — separation — 2nd stage ignition." The 2nd stage burn lasted 29 seconds and John said, "Second stage MECO, TLI has been achieved," followed by a number of data regarding the burn and the status of the OTV and the life support equipment.

Filled with relief, Maria, Karl, Tom, and Bill all clapped and hugged each other. Their rescue had successfully begun.

They quieted down when they heard John say, "Tell Maria, Karl, Tom, and Bill to put on their best-Sunday-go-to-meet'n-clothes, because we'll be there to pick them up in 62 hours."

Bill told Houston, "Tell John, we'll be waiting — just don't be late."

Tom signed off and Bill said, "Let's splurge and have a hot breakfast," their first hot meal in 11 long, cold days. Maria, Bill, and Tom had scrambled eggs, bacon, and coffee and Karl had pancakes with butter and honey, sausage, and a carbonated grape juice. Life just couldn't get any better.

Thursday, August 1, 2014, 06:00 GMT, through Friday, August 2, 2014, 10:00 GMT

The next 2 days passed rather quickly — in large part, because Maria, Karl, Tom, and Bill were finally warm again, and in part, because they listened to several of the periodic reports from the OTV on its way to the Moon.

Note: [1]Main Engine Cut Off

Maria's urinary infection, though better because of the warmth and antibiotics, would have to wait until she was back on Earth to be completely treated — but Dr. David Weaver, MD, the other astronaut in the 2 man rescue crew, would have the proper medication to combat her infection the minute she was on board the OTV.

Tom's leg was healed to the point where he was sure he could walk to the Lander, if they could not drive the Traverse Vehicle there, as Bill believed would be the case.

Karl's ribs were also mending and the inflammation was down to the point where, unless he strained himself, his ribs hardly bothered him.

By the evening of the first full day after sunrise, the cabin's temperature was agreeably warm and by the morning of the second full day, the temperature was 40° C, since Bill had turned off the Traverse Vehicle's cooling system to save power. It was just like a nice hot day in good old Tucson during midsummer. Maria loved it, but it was already a little too much of a good thing for her companions, especially Karl, and so everyone had dressed down to their underwear.

Maria had resisted dressing down somewhat longer than her companions. When Karl, who was the first to have taken off his clothes, except his briefs, suggested the others do the same, Maria resisted and said indignantly, but with the hint of a sly smile, "I'm not taking my clothes off with all you lecherous guys in here. Besides, I love the heat, so don't get your hopes up."

Later, when she finally had to take off her blouse and shorts, she whispered to Karl, "At least I have on a plain cotton bra and plain cotton panties and not the sexy ones I had on the day of the quake." Karl laughed at her modesty.

Somewhat later, it was getting too hot even for Maria, so Bill set the thermostat down to 35° C. Maria promptly put her shorts and blouse back on.

Friday, August 2, 2014, 10:03 GMT

At 10:03 GMT on the second morning after sunrise, Karl noticed with alarm that the voltage of the fuel cells had dropped below its standard 31 volts and was continuing to drop fast. He immediately told Bill, who swore, "Goddamn it, the fuel cells are giving out earlier than I had hoped — several hours early. We have 24 hours of power from the emergency batteries, but we'll be leaving the Traverse Vehicle at about 12-hundred, so we should just make it. But there will be no time or power to spare — at all. We're definitely not going to have any electrical power to start the diesel motor, so we'll have to walk to the Lander."

Half-an-hour later, at 10:34 GMT, the fuel cells gave out and the electrical system automatically switched over to the emergency batteries. Bill had been watching the gauges and said in a strained voice, "Well, that's it. We're going to have to stretch the power in those batteries out to the very last microwatt. They had better not give out early."

Finally, early that evening, a very nervous crew went to bed, worried about the critical events set for the next day.

Part Five
THE RESCUE

Chapter 5-1
The Day of the Rescue

Saturday, August 3, 2014, 05:23 GMT

Karl was the first to wake up, because it was still a little too warm in the cabin for him to sleep very well, but mainly because, like the rest of the crew, he was worried about the power situation, the hydrogen in the Lander, the ride to orbit on the open Lander, and the final rescue.

His getting out of bed disturbed Maria, who began to slowly wake up, and Karl said, "Es tut mir leid, Schatz[1], I didn't mean to wake you up."

Maria responded sleepily, "That's ok, I want to get up. I've been looking forward to this day for 18 days. Now that it's here, I want to live every minute of it, regardless of what happens."

When everyone was up, Karl asked Bill, "Is there enough power so we can have a hot breakfast?"

Bill answered emphatically, "No," but added, "As soon as we get in the OTV crew module, we can have all the hot food we want."

After breakfast, which they hardly touched, Bill said, "There's enough water left so each of us can take a sponge bath," which brightened everyone's spirit. Though none of them liked not being able to wash more than their hands and faces with icy water during the previous days, Maria had been the most concerned about her hygiene. She had repeatedly groused about looking so grubby and unkempt during that long time and especially because her once beautiful, long hair was dirty, greasy, and stringy.

The one nice thing was, since the surface temperature was 48° C and the hot water tank, by design, was exposed to the lunar surface via thermally controlled louvers at tempera-

---

Note: [1] I'm sorry, sweetheart

tures above 20° C, the heat from the lunar surface warmed the water. They had had room temperature water the day before and had 48° C hot water that morning. Maria, who was given the honors first, took a very welcome sponge bath in the lavatory and washed her hair as best she could, put it into a long ponytail, and put on fresh clothes. She looked and felt better than she had in over 2 weeks, despite the gnawing concerns she had.

Karl, Tom, and Bill, in turn, made their trip to the lavatory. Though their sponge baths were far better than nothing, each longed for a long, hot shower or bath, depending on his custom.

After cleaning up, they called Houston to find out both the latest on the rescue OTV, which was only about 13 hours from its lunar orbit insertion burn, and to get any last minute instruction about their liftoff, which was only 8½ hours off. Since essentially everything was cut and dried about their departure, most of what Houston said were reminders, but it helped calm the crew's raw nerves.

Saturday, August 3, 2014, 08:00 GMT

Finally, it was time to start their final preparation to leave. They very carefully started checking the 4 hard suits and 5 PLSSs, making absolutely sure each PLSS had 8 hours of life support oxygen plus 1 hour of reserve oxygen. As they were doing so, Karl asked, "What should we do with the 5th PLSS, take it with us as a spare?"

Tom responded, "That sounds like a good idea to me."

Maria said, "I don't see how we could change out a PLSS when we're seated and strapped to the Lander in zero-g. It's hard enough to do when we are standing on the lunar surface and can move around."

Bill added very quickly, "I agree with Maria. We leave the spare PLSS behind."

Maria asked, "Bill, can I take a little bag of personal things, or would the mass be too much?"

Bill asked cautiously, "How much do you want to take?"

Maria answered, "I just wanted to take the embroidered blouse my mother made for me and a couple of other pieces of clothing that mean a lot to me. Altogether, they can't even be half-a-kilogram."

Bill said, "Ok, that's no problem."

Maria began packing a small plastic bag with the clothes she had worn on that fateful day, 18 days earlier. Besides the blouse, she packed three other things from that day; the pair of silky, white, bikini panties, the matching bra, and the White Diamonds perfume. Maria was ready to go home.

Saturday, August 3, 2014, 09:43 GMT

When Bill was finished checking his suit, he went to the instrument panel to check on the power and said, "Crap, the voltage is 21 volts and dropping fast. The batteries will be dead in a few more seconds — they didn't quite make the 24 hours we needed."

Maria asked in anguish, "What do we do now?"

Bill recovered quickly from the initial shock and answered calmly, 'I'm sorry — I didn't mean to scare you. Even through the batteries will die . . . ," right then the air circulation fans stopped working and Bill corrected himself, ". . . have died, we still have an hour or so before the air in here gets unbreathable and it starts to get too hot. But we have to get suited up before that happens and forego eating lunch."

Karl said, "Who in hell could eat anything now anyway? Let's get suited up."

They suited up. Tom had a little trouble getting his splinted leg into the hard suit, though he finally succeeded — but he was careful not to let anyone know it hurt his leg to do so. They did the final checks of the suits, but left their helmets off and stayed off their PLSSs, waiting as long as possible before starting to use their precious 9 hours of oxygen, which had to last until 20:00 GMT — at a minimum.

Saturday, August 3, 2014, 10:39 GMT

As they were standing around, waiting nervously, Karl suddenly broke the silence and said, "I'm hungry. I'm going to get something to eat. It's going to be 10 hour before we can eat," and he went to the galley and found some cookies and grape juice to satisfy his hunger. Seeing the wisdom in Karl's actions, Maria, Bill, and Tom each got something to munch on, even though they were not hungry. But eating helped pass the time.

Saturday, August 3, 2014, 11:00 GMT

By 11:00 the air had started to get noticeably thick and hot, but Bill said, "We have to wait as long as possible. If we go on the PLSSs now, we may run out of oxygen before the OTV can rendezvous and dock with us and we can transfer to it, even if it docks on time."

But by 11:15 GMT, they could wait no longer; resigned, Bill said, "Ok, that's it. Put on you helmets and turn on your PLSSs. Note the time is 11:15. We have to go to the emergency oxygen at 19:15, which is about 10 minutes before the OTV finishes its LOI burn and 40 minutes before they expect to dock. That leaves us just 20 minutes to get on board and hence no margin. We have to stretch the 9 hours of oxygen out as long as possible, so stay calm so you don't use your oxygen up too fast. And, we'll walk slowly to the Lander and keep our breathing rates as low as possible. That might buy us 15 or 20 extra minutes. Ok, let's do it."

Chapter 5-2
The Walk

Saturday, August 3, 2014, 11:15 GMT

They put their helmets on and went on their PLSSs. Bill manually opened the emergency valve to let all the air out of the Traverse Vehicle. Then he manually opened both doors of the airlock. Maria, carrying her little plastic bag of clothes, went through the open airlock, followed by Karl, Tom, and finally, Bill, who carried a battery operated power drill, with which he was going to drill a bunch of holes in Tank 2, so its LOX could flow out.

The Sun was 34° above the eastern horizon and the surface temperature was 55° C, which their hard suits could easily handle.

They started off at a slow pace that would get them to the Lander in a little more than an hour without using up too much oxygen. Halfway there, Tom said, "I hate to say it, but I cannot go even this fast. My leg is beginning to hurt quite badly."

Bill said, "Ok, we've plenty of time, you 3 slow down and I'll go ahead and take care of the tank and switch everything on 1 hour before launch."

Karl, wanting to ensure Maria's rescue, said sharply, "Nein, take Maria with you. I'll help Tom." Maria started to protest, but Karl cut her off gently, saying, "Maria, go with Bill. I promise, we'll be there in plenty of time for the liftoff."

Reassured, Maria nodded.

Bill and Maria took off at their previous pace and Tom, with help from Karl, started walking at a slower pace Tom could handle.

Saturday, August 3, 2014, 13:31 GMT

Maria and Bill arrived at the Lander with 15 minutes to spare and Bill immediately went to work on Tank 2. Within a few minutes he had about twenty, 1-centimeter diameter holes drilled in the bottom of the tank and the LOX was streaming out and boiling away immediately in the hot lunar environment.

While Bill was working on the tank, Maria took the shade panels — their critical work done — away from the east side of the Lander and stacked them outside the landing pad crater's rim.

Finished with the tank, Bill unplugged the electrical connector and the LOX and HL hoses from the Lander, went to the control panel and switched the com-, command-, and avionics-subsystems on at 13:43 GMT, about 5 minutes early, and said to his crewmates, via his suit radio, "Ok, the LOX is drained and the Lander is activated. I hope Houston knows we're here." Then he asked Tom and Karl, who Maria and Bill could easily see less than a kilometer away, "How are you guys doing?"

Karl replied, "We should be there in 10 minutes or so."

They arrived at 13:56 GMT — 52 minutes before liftoff, which was more than enough time for them to climb on the Lander and strap themselves down.

Saturday, August 3, 2014, 13:59 GMT

Karl climbed up on the Lander first and then turned to help Maria up. Tom, whose leg caused a little difficulty, followed her, with additional help from Bill, who took up the rear.

They sat down — Maria and Karl side by side, with Tom and Bill sitting with their backs against Maria's and Karl's, respectively. They were about ¾ of the way between the center of the Lander and its edge nearest the empty oxygen tank; that way, the Lander would be a little off balance to the left when they launched and a little to the right at the end of the burn — but, on average, it would be in balance and well within the capability of the steering engines to keep the Lander on course.

They secured themselves to the Lander with bungee cords they had brought from the Traverse Vehicle. They were ready to ascend the Matterhorn.

At 14:18 GMT, Bill, who was looking at his watch, said, "Thirty minutes to go."

No one acknowledged Bill's statement — they all knew they would be dead within 1½ hours, if there was not enough hydrogen in the tanks for the Lander to reach any kind of orbit and just went on a ballistic trajectory, or they would be dead in 6 hours when they ran out of life support oxygen if the rendezvous failed.

Then Bill called out, "20 minutes — 10 minutes — 5 minutes — 3 minutes — 1 minute — 30 seconds — 10 seconds."

Orbiting 20 Kilometers
Above the Moon

Saturday, August 3, 2014, 14:48:11 GMT

As Bill said "Zero," they all felt — through the Lander's structure and their bottoms — the fuel pumps start up, the hydrogen and oxygen tank valves slam open, and the main and steering engines burst into life. The Lander slowly lifted off with a mild acceleration of 4.6 m/sec^2 and Bill, having carefully unhooked his bungee cords while Maria, Karl, and Tom were concentrating on his countdown, stood up and leapt off the Lander by the time it had risen 1.5 meters and had accelerated to a velocity of 3 m/sec.

Caught totally by surprise, Maria and Tom gasped in disbelief and horror and Karl yelled, "Bill, what in hell are you doing?"

Bill answered quickly, while still in his 4½-second jump to the rim of the North Landing Pad crater, "I lied. I'm increasing your chances to 100%.

By then, the Lander had risen nearly 45 meters and was traveling 16.5 m/sec and Bill was about to land on the crater's rim. The exhaust of the Lander's main engine, which expanded radially and cooled adiabatically to a very low temperature, hit Bill, pushed him gently a little beyond the crater's rim, and caused him to rotate slowly backwards — so when he hit the lunar surface, he landed on his butt. He tumbled and skidded a few more meters and came to a rest about 8 seconds after jumping off the Lander. Slightly disoriented, he got up and turned until he saw the Lander some 182 meters above him and moving at a velocity of 33 m/sec.

While Bill was landing, tumbling, and skidding, Maria had screamed, "No Bill, no, you're killing yourself."

As soon as he had the Lander in view, he replied calmly, "Yeah, I know. But I've had a good life with a great wife, my boys are grown, and you guys are young. Tom, you've got a little girl and Maria and Karl, you guys deserve a chance to get married and have kids. Name one after me, ok? And you 3 make sure NASA can never do this again. Tell Nancy I love her dearly and I hope she understands. I'm shutting off my suit radio now. Goodbye my friends, have a safe trip home," and Bill switched off his radio before Maria, Karl, or Tom could utter another word.

The Lander was 338 meters above the surface and traveling at 45 m/sec. Maria sobbed and Karl said softly, with tears in his eyes, "Leb wohl, mein Freund, leb wohl[1]," and then the 3 just sat on the accelerating Lander in stunned silence.

As Bill continued to watch, the Lander rose vertically for another 25 seconds and then, at an altitude of 2.4 kilometers and traveling at 120 m/sec, pitched over 57° and started traveling due west with an acceleration of 3.2 m/sec².

A minute and 50 seconds later, the Lander pitched over to nearly a full 90° and automatically adjusted its burn rate to accelerate at 3 m/sec². It was traveling nearly parallel to the surface at an altitude of 15.6 kilometers and was down range 17 kilometers. Bill was able to follow the bright, but rapidly fading star, shining by reflected sunlight, for another minute-and-a-half before it dimmed to obscurity nearly 60 kilometers down range and he said softly, "Goodbye my friends, I hope you make it," for Bill's simple calculation using the rocket equation had shown that his sacrifice would gain the Lander only 24 m/sec of velocity. Bill knew little about celestial mechanics, so he did not know if that was enough to save his friends. And he had not dared to ask Houston if that was enough to raise the probability of hitting the 20-kilometer rendezvous orbit to 100%, or Houston might have blown his secret. Had he asked that question, the answer would have been a disappointing 91%.

After his final goodbye to Maria, Karl, and Tom, Bill turned south and began his lonely, 6-kilometer trek back to

---

Note: [1]Live well, my friend, live well — the German phrase for a final goodbye the Base, walking slowly, enjoying the beauty of the Fra Mauro that had been his home for the past 3 months.

Saturday, August 3, 2014, 14:58:15 GMT

A few seconds more than 10 minutes after liftoff, the Lander was traveling at 1670.7 m/sec and the engine cut off. However, its crew had no way of knowing if they made it to their 20-kilometer altitude, circular, equatorial, rendezvous orbit or not. If they didn't, they would impact the Moon in less than 55 minutes, while they were in the dark on the Moon's nightside — and they would not even see their deaths coming.

But, since Karl believed what Bill had said about his sacrifice increasing the probability of their hitting the rendezvous orbit to 100%, Karl said, "Mensch, we made it. I wonder how much hydrogen is left in the tanks. It would be tragic if there were enough for all 4 of us and Bill's sacrifice was for nothing."

Though they would never know the answer, there was no hydrogen in the tanks and just over two kilograms in the nearly empty fuel lines to the engines. Had Bill not leapt off the Lander, its velocity would have been too low by 19 m/sec and all 4 would have died as the Lander impacted on the lunar nightside. Bill's desperate gamble had paid the rich dividend he had hoped for — with just 5 m/sec, or less than 1.6 seconds of burn time — to spare.

Saturday, August 3, 2014, 14:59 GMT

Less than a minute after the end of the burn, they were 540 kilometers — or nearly 18° — to the west of North Landing Pad and they had already passed over the crater Lansberg in the eastern most part of an enormous smooth volcanic plain, Oceanus Procellarum, somewhat before the end of the burn.

Though the view from 20 kilometers up and from the open Lander was spectacular, it was largely wasted on them. Because of the fear of not knowing if the rescue would succeed, coupled with the knowledge that Bill had sacrificed himself for them and that he might already be dead or, if not,

would soon die when his oxygen ran out, they were just
numb. But they did watch quietly as lunar surface features
passed beneath them at 1.67 km/per sec. At that altitude, the
horizon was 264 kilometers away and so they could see, at
any instance, 219,000 km^2 of the Moon's surface, which was
nevertheless only 0.6% of it. When something appeared on
the western horizon, they passed over it just 158 seconds
later.

Two minutes after burnout, they passed 264 kilometers
south of the prominent crater Kepler and Maria said, with little enthusiasm, "Look, you can just see Kepler silhouetted on
the horizon."

They were still traveling over Oceanus Procellarum 4½
minutes later, when they passed over the morning terminator
and 2½ minutes later, the Lander passed into the Moon shadow, where it would stay for the next 49.7 minutes.

Less than 9 minutes after they had passed into the lunar
night, they watched the cloud covered, bluish, crescent Earth
set. It was an awe-inspiring sight and Maria said, choking back
tears, as the Earth slid below the horizon, "Look how beautiful the Earth is. I hope we make it back, especially consider-
ing what Bill did for us."

With earthlight gone, they were in the total darkness of
the lunar nightside and they could finally see the stars in all
their glory. Karl said, with a little enthusiasm, "See the bright
red star there, that's Mars. It's near opposition and at its
brightest." Mars stood out prominently among the well-
known summer constellations, Scorpius, the Scorpion, and
Sagittarius, the Archer, in the heart of the ghostly Milky Way,
which drew Karl's attention as his eyes became totally dark-
adapted.

Upon seeing our home galaxy in all its glory, Karl
exclaimed in wonder that suppressed some of the concern
about their immediate future and Bill's doom, "Will you look
at the Milky Way. I've never seen it this beautiful." The view of
the Milky Way was so breathtaking that, despite their dire circumstances, they were all in awe of its beauty.

The 49.7 minutes of nighttime passed very quickly and
the Sun came leaping above the horizon, but just before the

upper limb of the Sun shot above the horizon, Karl said, "Look, you can see the inner, solar corona." Then the upper limb appeared, instantly blotting out the view of its own pearly white, faint, outer atmosphere.

They continued westward in their 110.2-minute orbit and, after passing over the evening terminator just 2½ minutes after sunrise, they viewed the heavily cratered lunar farside.

As they were passing over Mare Smythii, the Earth rose and they could again see the glorious, bluish, cloud-covered crescent, a beacon of hope in a jet-black sky, to which they would hopefully return in less than 3 days.

Their orbit carried them over the northern end of Mare Fecunditatis and then over the southern part of Mare Tranquillitatis and Tranquility Base, where Neil Armstrong and Buzz Aldrin had made man's first landing on the Moon 45 years and 14 days earlier.

They orbited over a bit of the frontside highlands, then back over the mare, and headed for Fra Mauro, which they had left a scant 115 minutes earlier.

When they were passing over the Fra Mauro Base — what had been man's first outpost on the Moon — they strained to see what had been their home, work place, and then prison. However, from their altitude, there was nothing they could see of the Base.

Then Karl's attention was drawn to the SW of the Base and he shouted, his excitement overwhelming his sorrow, "Unglaublich. Schau mal[1], there's a brand new fault scarp several 10's of kilometers to the SW of the Base. It must be 20 kilometers long. That's where the quake occurred. Look how close it is to the Base. No wonder it creamed us!"

Maria immediately found the new thrust fault scarp, the youngest major feature on the otherwise very slowly changing Moon, and she, too, responded with utter amazement.

Tom asked, "Where is it?" Since he was not used to seeing selenological or even geological features from altitude, he had difficulty finding the new feature, whose birth had killed

---

Note: [1]Unbelievable. Look

4 of their crewmates, was about to kill the 5th, and had caused them such hardships.

Karl answered hurriedly, "Look to the southeast. It's just about to go over the horizon." With that help, Tom found it, just before it went out of view — a scant 2 minutes after Karl first saw it.

Saturday, August 3, 2014, 16:48 GMT

They entered the second 110.2-minute orbit and began looking at the same features they had seen during the first orbit, but since their spirits were somewhat lifted, they noticed many details they had missed the first time.

Just before the Lander passed into its second nighttime pass, Bill entered the Traverse Vehicle through its open airlock. He found a flashlight and turned to leave, but he stopped and patted the back of the driver's seat — his seat — and said, "Well old girl, you saved us when everything else had gone to hell. I hope they put you in a lunar museum some day," and then he exited the Traverse Vehicle for the last time.

Bill walked around the west side of the mound covering the Base to the SW entrance they had used during their escape and return trips. He turned the flashlight on and entered the dark access tunnel, went through the open SW airlock, and went directly to Kitchen's back door. He entered and walked the few steps through Hospital and into Kitchen where the bodies of his fallen comrades awaited him.

Finding a kitchen chair, he sat down clumsily.

After a few moments, Bill said to the corpses, "I'm sorry I didn't fight NASA harder. I'm sorry you had to die the way you did, but I know Karl — and Maria, too — will see to it you didn't die in vain. I salute you all and all the astronauts who have died needlessly," and he paused again.

Lifting his face towards the unseen Earth so far, far away, he said, "Nancy, I wish I could hold you in my arms just once more and tell you how much I love you and what a perfect wife you are. But I can't and I know you'll understand why — you would do the same. Goodbye my love."

Bill reached around and turned off the flow of oxygen from his PLSS, exhaled deeply, and opened his faceplate.

Saturday, August 3, 2014, 17:00 GMT

They again entered the lunar night, saw sunrise and the beautiful earthrise again, passed over the eastern mare and, as they approached Fra Mauro for the second time, Maria and Karl were preparing to make the best observations of the new fault scarp they possibly could.

Saturday, August 3, 2014, 18:33 GMT

As the fault scarp came into view over the horizon, Maria and Karl began noting its characteristics, when all of a sudden — faintly over the suit radios, they all heard, "Fra Mauro crew, OTV here. Do you read? Fra Mauro crew, OTV here. Do you read?"

Karl shouted, "Damn right we read you. We've just entering our third orbit. What's your status?"

John Gruener answered, "Houston has a good fix on your orbit and they're uploading the corrections to our LOI burn that will put us about 1 kilometer behind you at the end of the burn. That will allow us to rendezvous with you very quickly — about 7 minutes later or at about 19:30 GMT — and we should dock a few minutes later. What is the status of your life support?"

Karl answered, "We each have about 40 minutes left on our PLSSs and 1 hour of emergency oxygen. So we'll be fine, if you get here by 19:30. But there are just 3 of us, Tom, Maria, and me." Karl choked a little as his eyes filled with tears, but continued, "We'll tell you about Bill when we're in the OTV, ok?"

John, understanding something had gone wrong and that Karl did not want to talk about it, simply replied, "Sure."

Saturday, August 3, 2014, 18:38 GMT

With only 40 minutes to go before the beginning of the OTV's critical LOI burn and the beginning of the rendezvous, all selenological observation came to an abrupt end, which they would have anyway, when the Lander again entered the Moon's shadow at 18:47 GMT.

Maria, Karl, and Tom listened intently to the brief communications the OTV was radioing to Houston and kept quiet.

At 19:06 GMT, John reported to Houston and the crew, "We have a hard radar lock on the Lander and the range and range-rate data are being accepted by the nav computer."

John said, "Fra Mauro, if you look almost directly behind you, you'll be looking right up our main engine bell and hence you might be able to see the burn going on inside the combustion chamber. Also, look for our running lights a little later in the burn. We'll be looking for yours."

Alarmed, Maria said, "I'm getting the 15 minute warning light, my PLSS is about to go dry."

Karl said, "Scheisse, mine is also on, I guess I didn't notice it earlier."

A few minutes later Tom said, "Mine is flickering on, too."

Saturday, August 3, 2014, 19:18:21 GMT

John gave the terminal count down to the LOI burn and when he hit zero at 19:18:21 GMT he said, "307 is in, we have ignition."

A couple of seconds later Maria shouted, "I see it. I see it. There they are," and the others quickly saw the pale light of the burning hydrogen in the combustion chamber of the rescue OTV's main engine.

Saturday, August 3, 2014, 19:19 GMT

Karl's oxygen warning light began pulsing bright red. His PLSS was out of oxygen. He clumsily shut the PLSS valve off and turned on the emergency oxygen supply on his chest. He had 1 hour's worth of oxygen.

A minute or two later, Maria made the switchover, followed shortly by Tom. The die was cast.

All they could do was to listen to John's reports to Houston. As they did, the tiny pale light of the engine flame became bigger and brighter. Just before John said, "Engine off, LOI is completed," at 19:23:14 GMT, Karl caught sight of the much fainter running lights of the OTV.

Just as Karl said to everyone on the radio, "I can see the running lights," the engine cut off and all that was left visible in the pitch-black of the lunar farside night were the OTV's running lights and the stars.

John said, "OTV range to Lander is 1037 meters and closing at 3 m/sec. We are doing the 180° pitch — and we have a visual on the Lander's running lights, as well as an excellent radar lock."

Three minutes later, John said, "Range 500 meters and closing at 3 m/sec," and after another 1 minute and 6 seconds, "Range 300 meters and closing at 3 m/sec," and again after another 1 minute and 6 seconds, "Range 100 meters and closing at 1 m/sec."

Two minutes later, just before 19:30 GMT, the OTV came to a standstill 5 meters from the Lander. John maneuvered the OTV into the correct position and started to nudge it forwards at 20 cm/sec.

The solid bump of the two vehicles docking together occurred at 19:37 GMT and Maria, Karl, and Tom let out great cries of relief.

Saturday, August 3, 2014, 19:38 GMT

Since the Lander was meant to carry cargo or the crew module and not people strapped to it, its docking fixture was at the side of its top platform. So there was no direct way to get to the docking port atop the OTV crew module. Thus, when Dr. David Weaver opened the docking port of the crew module and stood up in it, he had a line in his hand and radioed, "Catch this line and fasten it to the structure of the Lander. There are safety belts attached to it. One at a time, fasten yourselves to the line and pull yourselves to the open docking hatch," and then he threw the line, which Tom caught.

Tom and Karl quickly secured the line and Tom said, "Ladies first."

Without hesitation, Maria clipped the safety belt to her spacesuit, undid the bungee cords that had held her securely to the Lander since liftoff and went hand-over-hand along the line to the safety of the OTV's crew module.

Karl said, thinking of Tom's leg, "Tom, you go next."

Tom replied, "No, you should get in there with your sweetheart," and so he did, followed by Tom.

Once the 3 of them were safely inside, David disconnected the line, closed the hatch, and repressurized the crew module.

Finally it was over, they were safe — safe at last, 18 days, 12 hours, and 29 minutes after Karl had felt the first tremors of the approaching apocalypse.

EPILOG

The trans-earth injection burn, the 106-hour coast to the Earth's upper atmosphere, the aerobraking maneuver in the Earth's upper atmosphere, the rendezvous of the rescue vehicle with the Space Plane in LEO, and the latter's return to Cape Kennedy from LEO, all occurred routinely.

Once on the ground at the Cape, Maria, Karl, and Tom were immediately whisked to the NASA medical facilities, where they were examined and remained for three days. All three were found to be exhausted and had lost significant weight, but were otherwise in remarkably good condition. The remnants of Maria's urinary infection were quickly treated, Karl's ribs were x-rayed and found to be ok, and Tom's leg was x-rayed and examined. The physicians said Maria, Karl, and Bill had done a good, but not a perfect job of setting Tom's leg. When they asked him if he wanted his leg re-broken and re-set, Tom said emphatically, "No, I like the way my friends set it — no one will ever change what they did for me."

Well before they had landed at the Cape, their families had flown in from Houston. Once Maria, Karl, and Tom had been examined on the first day of their safe return to Earth, they had been reunited with their families.

While still in the hospital, the three were debriefed by NASA officials and several Senators and Congressmen.

Once out of the hospital, they flew to Washington, DC, where they were further debriefed at NASA Headquarters, testified before Congress, greeted by the President, and were extensively interviewed by the press, radio, and TV. Needless to say, all three, especially Karl, placed the blame for the catastrophe and the deaths of their crewmates squarely on NASA management for ignoring Bill's objections to having the Base be built tele-robotically and pushing aside the decades old warnings that too little was known about the seismic risk factor to proceed with the design of the Fra Mauro Base.

After leaving Washington, they flew to Houston for their final debriefings at JSC. While in Houston they attended and spoke at a memorial honoring their dead companions. Maria gave an especially moving tribute to Bill who had sacrificed himself so she, Karl, and Tom could live and carry on the fight to reform the space program.

While at JSC, Maria and Karl — knowing NASA was at its end — resigned from NASA and flew to Tucson, where their families had prepared everything for their wedding.

While in Tucson, they rejoined the staffs of the Lunar Research Institute and Lunar Exploration Inc. By doing so, they felt they would have the best chance of helping to push Congress into transitioning the American Space Program from one based on NASA's mismanagement and incompetence to one based on American enterprise and commercialism. They also felt by doing so, they would have their best chance to go back to the Moon and help set up the commercial Lunar Base that had been the penultimate goal of those twin science and engineering lunar exploration companies.

As Maria and Karl anticipated, and as had a large number of people who had been advocating the commercialization of the exploration of space for well over 2 decades, the mood in Congress, and of the American public, after the latest life-costing NASA mismanagement disaster, was clearly leading to the end of NASA.

Over the next year, Congress worked out and passed legislation to replace NASA with a purely administrative federal agency — modeled after the efficient Defense Advanced Research Programs Agency — and finally, 17 years after it had passed the *Commercial Space Act of 1998* — Congress put the exploration of space and its utilization for the benefit of humanity on a competitive, commercial basis. NASA facilities were sold or rented to commercial corporations or conglomerates and finally, 19 years after Dr. Binder had set up the Lunar Research Institute and Lunar Exploration Inc. to promote the commercial exploration of the Moon and to set up a commercial Lunar Base, those twin companies were finally able to begin to fulfill their charters.

THE BEGINNING OF A NEW ERA

APPENDIX 1
SELECTED SCIENTIFIC PAPERS ON MOONQUAKES, THE SEISMIC RISK FACTOR, AND LUNAR RESOURCES

Binder, A.B., Post-Imbrium Global Lunar Tectonism: Evidence for an Initially Totally Molten Moon, *The Moon and the Planets,* Vol. 25, pp. 117–133, 1982.

Binder, A.B., Lunar Resources: What is Known and Expected, *Engineering and Space Construction, and Operations in Space,* Aerospace Div/ASCE, Albuquerque, pp. 48–54, 1988.

Binder, A.B. and H.C. Gunga, Young Thrust-Fault Scarps in the Highlands: Evidence for an Initially Totally molten Moon, *Icarus,* Vol. 63, pp. 421–441, 1985.

Binder, A.B. and M.A. Lange, On the Thermal History, Thermal State, and Related Tectonism of a Moon of Fission Origin, *Journal of Geophysical Research,* Vol. 85, pp. 3194–3208, 1980.

Binder, A.B. and J. Oberst, High Stress Shallow Moonquakes: Evidence for an Initially Totally molten Moon, *Earth and Planetary Science Letters,* Vol. 74, pp. 149–154, 1985.

Heiken, G.H., D.T. Vaniman, and B.M. French, eds., *Lunar Sourcebook,* Cambridge University Press, NY, 1991.

Lammlein, D.R. et al., Lunar Seismicity, Structure, and Tectonics, *Reviews of Geophysics and Space Physics,* Vol. 12, pp. 1–21, 1974.

Nakamura, Y., HFT Events: Shallow Moonquakes?, *Physics of the Earth and Planetary Interiors,* Vol. 14, pp. 217–223, 1977.

Nakamura, Y., A_1 Moonquakes: Source Distribution and Mechanism, *Proceedings of the 9th Lunar and Planetary Science Conference*, pp. 3589–3607, 1978.

Nakamura, Y., Shallow Moonquakes: How They Compare with Earthquakes, *Proceedings of the 11th Lunar and Planetary Science Conference*, pp. 1847–1853, 1980.

Nakamura, Y. et al., High-Frequency Lunar Teleseismic Events, *Proceedings of the 5th Lunar Science Conference*, pp. 2883–2895, 1974.

Nakamura, Y. et al., Shallow Moonquakes: Depth, Distribution, and Implications as to the Present State of the Lunar Interior, *Proceedings of the 10th Lunar and Planetary Science Conference*, pp. 2299–2309, 1979.

APPENDIX 2
CANDIDATE LUNAR BASE SITES
ALONG THE EQUATOR AND
AT THE NORTH AND SOUTH POLES

Mare Orientale, near 83° W longitude, would allow the exploration of the northern parts of the Mare Orientale Basis, its ejecta blanket, and Mare Orientale itself.

Hevelius, near 68° W longitude, would allow the exploration of a small part of the giant lava plain, Oceanus Procellarum, the lava floored crater Grimalde, as well as Mare Orientale Basin ejecta and highlands materials.

Reiner, near 50° W longitude, would allow the exploration of part of Oceanus Procellarum and the volcanoes and differentiated volcanic units of the Marius Hills volcanic complex.

Fra Mauro, near 16° W longitude — 120 kilometers NNE of the Apollo 14 landing site, would allow the exploration of Mare Imbrium Basin ejecta at Fra Mauro and that in the ancient crater Ptolemaeus; the Imbrium Basin structure expressed in the Carpathian Mountains; the 1 billion-year-old crater Copernicus, as well as the craters Reinhold and Lansberg; the Davy and Herschel crater chains that might be diatreme volcanoes; the mare volcanic units in Mare Imbrium, Mare Cognitum, Mare Nubium, Sinus Aestuum, and eastern Oceanus Procellarum; the Hortensius volcanic domes; part of the central highlands; and several other units.

Sinus Medii, near 0° E longitude, would allow the exploration of the Imbrium Basin eject in Ptolemaeus; the Davy and Herschel crater chains; part of the central highlands; the volcanic units of Sinus Medii, Sinus Aestuum, Mare Vaporum; the Hyginus Rill and volcanic complex; the Ariadaeus Rill; and the southern ramparts of the Apennine Mountains.

Mare Tranquillitatis, near 25° E longitude — 50 kilometers SEE of the Apollo 11 landing site, would allow the exploration of Mare Tranquillitatis; the central highlands and those north of Mare Nectaris; the northern part of Mare Nectaris; the young crater Theophilus; and the Ariadaeus Rill.

Censorinus, near 35° E longitude, would allow the exploration of Mare Tranquillitatis; the northwestern part of Mare Fecunditatis; the highlands north of Mare Nectaris; the northern part of Mare Nectaris; and the Cauchy rill, fault, and volcanic complex.

Mare Spumans, near 62° E longitude, would allow the exploration of the southern part of Mare Crisium and its southern ejecta units and basin structure; the northern part of Mare Fecunditatis, Mare Spumans, and Mare Undarum; the young crater Langrenus; and the westernmost part of the far-side highlands.

Mare Smythii, near 81° E longitude, would allow the exploration of Mare Smythii, Mare Marginis, Mare Undarum, and the westernmost part of the farside highlands.

North and South Poles, would allow the exploration of the polar hydrogen deposits, which are presumed to be water ice deposits and which were discovered and mapped by Lunar Prospector in the permanently shadowed craters of the Polar Regions. Also, since both Polar Regions consist of highland materials, they offer excellent sites to study some of the ancient crustal units.

APPENDIX 3
KNOWN LUNAR RESOURCES
Binder, 1988; Heiken et al., 1991

Essentially all lunar materials are made up, at the 98 to 99% level, of 7 elements. These 7 elements are the major resources available for future use in developing a lunar colony and industrial complex that will greatly affect the Earth's economy and wealth. The abundances of these 7 elements, in decreasing average abundances, in the lunar regolith (soil) are:

> Oxygen, 41 to 45%
> Silicon, 18 to 22%
> Aluminum, 5 to 15%
> Iron, 3 to 15%
> Calcium, 7 to 11%
> Magnesium, 2 to 8%
> Titanium, 0 to 6%

Of these, iron (Fe), magnesium (Mg), and titanium (Ti) are most abundant in the mare volcanic units, and aluminum (Al) and calcium (Ca) are most abundant in the highland units. The abundances of oxygen (O) and silicon (Si) in lunar materials are quite uniform in all lunar material.

In addition, there are 12 minor elements — elements whose abundances are generally between 0.1 and 1% in lunar materials — that are sufficiently abundant to be of economic value in lunar industry. They are in decreasing order of abundance:

> Sodium (Na)
> Potassium (K)
> Phosphorous (P)
> Sulfur (S)
> Manganese (Mn)
> Chromium (Cr)
> Nickel (Ni)
> Vanadium (V)
> Zirconium (Zr)
> Yttrium (Y)
> Barium (Ba)
> Strontium (Sr)

Seven elements (Na, K, P, Zr, Y, Ba, and Sr) are concentrated in KREEP [a minor and trace-element-rich material characterized by — and named after — high concentrations of potassium (K), the rare earth elements (REE) and phosphorous (P)]. Four elements (S, Mn, Cr, and V) are concentrated in mare basalt materials. And Ni is most abundant in ancient highland regoliths.

As mapped by the Lunar Prospector Spacecraft, hydrogen (H) is concentrated in permanently shadowed craters in the both lunar polar regions. If the hydrogen is in the form of water ice, the amount of ice is a few billion metric tons, or enough to fill a small lake about 10 kilometers (6 miles) in diameter and 30 meters (100 ft) deep.

FRA MAURO LUNAR BASE CREW BIOGRAPHIES
(Enhanced versions of the official NASA biographies)

Roberts, John Harrison, Colonel USAF (retired)
Pilot Astronaut
Responsibilities: Base Commander
Age: 48 years old, born on February 23, 1965, in Kerrville, Texas, USA
Height: 1.75 m (5' 9")
Mass: 71 kg (156 lbs)
Hair: Blonde, short, wavy
Eyes: Blue
One of the best, if not the best, NASA Pilot Astronauts; medium build; very handsome; strong personality; moderate sense of humor; reliable; devoted father; very well groomed and dressed; vain; socially very active, especially with the ladies, i.e., a womanizer
Languages: English
Status: Married, two daughters

Gray, Pamela Ann, MS and RN
Nutritionist and Physical Trainer
Responsibilities: Nutritional studies and physical fitness training
Age: 35 years old, born on May 30, 1977, in Cedar Rapids, Iowa, USA
Height: 1.63 m (5' 4")
Mass: 58 kg (128 lbs)
Hair: Dark blonde, shoulder length, wavy
Eyes: Blue-green
Medium build; cute; kind, caring, jovial personality; has homey sense of humor and finds many thing funny; motherly; conscientious; neatly groomed and dressed; friend and confidant to almost everyone; a great cook and enjoys seeing to it that crew eats well
Languages: English
Status: Married, three sons and one daughter

Gutierrez, Maria Selena, PhD
Selenologist and Selenopetrologist
Responsibilities: Lunar science — structural, stratigraphic, and morphological studies of tectonic and volcanic features and craters; highland rock petrology
Age: 28 years old, born on November 16, 1984, in Tucson, Arizona, USA
Height: 1.60 m (5' 3")
Mass: 51 kg (112 lbs)
Hair: Very dark brown, long, straight
Eyes: Dark brown
Slight build; soft, beautiful Hispanic features; strong, but somewhat quiet, loving, sweet, and happy personality; has a pleasant sense of humor and likes to tease the people close to her; stands her ground in any situation; determined; careful; courageous; enjoys her femininity and likes to look attractive and appealing; enjoys being with the girls
Languages: Spanish, English, and some German
Status: Single

Huff, William (Bill) Peter, BE
Base Engineer
Responsibilities: Maintain Base, nuclear power plant, Rovers and Traverse Vehicle, primary driver of Traverse Vehicle
Age: 50 years old, born on December 14, 1962, in Shelbyville, Indiana, USA
Height: 1.71 m (5' 7")
Mass: 65 kg (143 lbs)
Hair: Dark brown, short, straight
Eyes: Blue-green
Led the design and development phases of the Lunar Base; medium build; pleasant looking; casual in appearance and dress; easy going and friendly; has a well developed sense of humor; meticulous in work, but casual in personal life; makes friends easily and is at ease in social situations; minimizes risk before going forwards
Languages: English
Status: Married, three sons

Meyer, Karl Frederick, PhD
Selenophysist and Selenopetrologist
Responsibilities: Lunar science — seismology; selenomagnetic, and gravity studies; heat flow measurements; mare basalt petrology
Age: 29 years old, born on April 20, 1983, in Herrieden, Bavaria, Germany
Height: 1.70 m (5' 7")
Mass: 62 kg (137 lbs)
Hair: Dark blond, short, straight
Eyes: Blue
Medium build; nice looking, but not handsome; cares little about clothes and appearance; strong personality; chooses his battles and speaks his mind without worrying about consequences; typical German lack of a sense of humor; persistent; thorough; dedicated; chooses his own path; cares little for social activities; takes any calculated risk
Languages: German, English, and some Spanish
Status: Single

Rodriguez, Isabel Luisa, MD
Medical Doctor and Psychologist
Responsibilities: Crew's mental and physical health and physiological studies of human adaptation to living on the Moon
Age: 42 years old, born on June 17, 1970, in Buenos Aires, Argentina
Height: 1.73 m (5' 8")
Mass: 61 kg (134 lbs)
Hair: Black, shoulder length, straight
Eyes: Brown
Medium build; handsome, classic female Spanish features; strong, professional, slightly reserved personality; has a very reserved sense of humor; has strong opinions; meticulous in her work and personal life; well groomed and dresses fashionably; socially conservative, does not mix with crowd, has selected friendships
Languages: Spanish, English, and French
Status: Married, one son and one daughter

Williams, James (Jim) Eugene, MS
Industrial Engineer
Responsibilities: Lunar resource utilization experimentation and development
Age: 46 years old, born on August 29, 1966, in Edmonton, Alberta, Canada
Height: 1.78 m (5' 10")
Mass: 70 kg (154 lbs)
Hair: Light brown, medium, wavy
Eyes: brown
Medium build; nice looking; has neat appearance in dress; has "take it easy" attitude, but is dedicated and careful worker; has strong sense of humor and finds almost anything funny; essentially fearless, but does not push it to the point of endangering his crewmates; likes to flirt with women, but is loyal to his wife and family; friendly and socially at ease at all times
Languages: English
Status: Married, one son and one daughter

Wong, Tom, BS
Communication and Computer Engineer
Responsibilities: Base computers and all Base communications equipment
Age: 30 years old, born on November 3, 1982, in San Francisco, California, USA
Height: 1.60 m (5' 3")
Mass: 53 kg (117 lbs)
Hair: Black, short, straight
Eyes: Black
Slight build; nice looking with strong oriental features; quiet and very polite, somewhat shy and reserved; extremely competent and meticulous; tends to keep to himself and to his work; does not mix with others, has strong friendships with special, trusted friends
Languages: English and Chinese
Status: Married, one daughter

APPENDIX 5
GLOSSARY

Aerobraking. A method to slow vehicles that are coming back from LLO or high Earth orbit, by using the Earth's upper atmosphere.

GMT. Greenwich Mean Time which is the same as Universal Time (UT).

HLV. Heavy Lift Vehicle. A reusable Shuttle-like vehicle to lift heavy loads to LEO.

JSC. Johnson Space Center located southeast of Houston, TX

KREEP. See definition on the bottom of page 305 and 306

Lunar Lander (Lander). A vehicle that shuttles cargo and crew between the Moon's surface and a Moon orbit.

LEI. Lunar Exploration Inc.

LEO. Low Earth Orbit

LLO. Low Lunar Orbit

LOI. Lunar Orbit Injection

LRI. Lunar Research Institute

LH. Liquid Hydrogen

MECO. Main Engine Cut Off

MET. Mission Elapsed Time

NASA. National Aeronautical and Space Administration

LOX. Liquid Oxygen

OTV. Reusable Orbit-to-Orbit Transfer Vehicle for transporting crew between LEO and LLO.

PLSS. Portable Life Support System

SEI. Space Exploration Initiative

Tug. Nuclear-Electric Tug or just plain Tug.

TEI. Trans-Earth Injection

TLI. Trans-Lunar Injection

   Alan Binder, PhD, is a space scientist with over 43 years of experience as a lunar and planetary scientist, a spacecraft design and systems engineer, and a lunar base and manned Mars mission designer. He has worked in both the American and European space programs and was a Principal Investigator on the Lander Camera Team of the 1976 Viking Mars Lander Missions. He was the Principal Investigator of the Lunar Prospector mission and was responsible for all of its phases — mission definition, spacecraft design, construction, testing, and mission operations. The Lunar Prospector orbital mapping mission provided the first complete, global maps of the compositions of the Moon's surface and its gravity and magnetic fields — as well as discovering and mapping the polar hydrogen deposits that are believed to be water ice. He is also the author of *Lunar Prospector: Against All Odds*, his account of Lunar Prospector from its beginning in late 1988, as a private effort, to its successful conclusion, as a NASA supported mission, in July 1999. He lives in Tucson with his wife Rebecca and is the Director of the Lunar Research Institute and the CEO of Lunar Exploration Inc.

–000/00:57 MET through –000/00:15 MET:
The Athena II Launch

At –000/00:57 MET, there were just 22 seconds to lift off. I reminded everyone that I wanted it quiet in Mission Ops — all of it — both inside the Glass Room and outside of it. There was to be no shouting, jumping around, and celebrating the launch — we were there to do a serious job and we had to concentrate on it and not act like a bunch of high school kids, as did the Mars Pathfinder Mission Ops Team when Mars Pathfinder successfully landed on Mars in July.

Then, as we watched the image of the Athena II on the TV screen, bathed in the glare of the launch-pad lights, the voice on the TV began calling out the final 10 seconds: 10-9-8-7-6-5-4-3-2-1-0.

Exactly on time, at T = 0, I saw a small bright light appear at the bottom of the Athena II — we had ignition; that was it — there was no more waiting, no more delays, we were irrevocably committed to launch. Once that 1st Stage Castor 120 started to burn, there was no going back and I was relieved. Good, bad, or indifferent, Lunar Prospector had started its journey to the Moon and there was nothing I could do to change the course of its fate for the next hour. Automatically, it would either get launched onto its proper translunar trajectory, or end up in the Atlantic, or burn up in the Earth's atmosphere after a failed TLI burn, or have such a bad launch that there was no way we could get it to the Moon — all that was out of my hands for a little more than an hour.

All that went through my mind at that instant of ignition. Then, in a fraction of a second, the small bright light grew to an ever increasingly brighter and larger exhaust plume as the Athena II lifted off Pad 46 and my thoughts turned to the acoustical waves that were assaulting my spacecraft. The noise that was being generated by the burning Castor 120, enhanced by its being reflected off the launch pad and back up the Athena II to the spacecraft, was so intense for the first few seconds of the launch that it could have damaged the science instruments and the delicate solar cells of the solar panels. Remembering that some of the delicate APS filters had been torn apart during our acoustic testing, I hoped — and expected — that they, and everything else on the spacecraft, would withstand their first acoustical assault of the launch.

Simultaneous with the initial acoustical assault on Lunar Prospector, the infamous pipe organ effect had also started its work of violently shaking the Athena II and Lunar Prospector — starting at 50 Hz. Though the amplitude of the pipe organ effect was large at the beginning of the burn, the amplitude decreased as the 1st Stage burn continued. Also, its effect was lessened because of the damping effects of the some 20 meters of rocket (the 2nd and 3rd Stages, the Orbit Adjustment Module or OAM, and the TLI Stage) between the top of the screaming 1st Stage Castor 120 and Lunar Prospector. I had little concern about the pipe organ vibrations during the 1st Stage burn, even though, as the burn continued, its frequency slowly increased towards its maximum of 60 Hz at the end of the 1st Stage burn, i.e., up towards the 65 to 70 Hz where the spacecraft did have some major resonances — but if we had done our work correctly, it would pose no problem.

In addition to the initial acoustical assault and the continuing pipe organ vibrations, the winds and the resistance of the Earth's atmosphere also buffeted the Athena II and Lunar Prospector as the rocket struggled to plow its way through the thick lower atmosphere. As the rocket's speed increased, the atmospheric buffeting increased until a crescendo was reached some 74 seconds after lift-off — when the Athena II passed through the sound barrier. As it did, the acoustical level, for the second time, reached an intensity that was great enough, for a few seconds, to damage the spacecraft. Finally, after passing through the sound barrier, the noise and atmospheric buffeting rapidly abated as the Athena II climbed out of the Earth's atmosphere, but the howling gasses inside the Castor 120 continued to shake the spacecraft. Finally, 89 seconds after lift-off, the 1st Stage burn came to its end and I hoped the spacecraft had survived the noise, the buffeting, and the howling of the 1st Stage burn. Also, during that 1½ minute, Athena Launch Control kept informing us, and the world, that the launch trajectory was near perfect!

As the 1st Stage burn trailed off, a sensor detected the end of the burn and sent a critical signal to ignite the Castor 120, 2nd Stage of the Athena II rocket. 2nd Stage ignition occurred while still attached to the 1st Stage. That "Fire in the Hole" ignition had never been done before and, while insuring that the Athena II was under positive attitude control during the transition between the 1st Stage and the 2nd Stage burns, it did pose some danger, since if the exhaust vents between the stages did not blast open at ignition, the back pressure of the igniting 2nd Stage could damage the engine bell and steering mechanism of the 2nd Stage.

Nevertheless, Athena Launch Control called out 1st Stage burnout and 2nd Stage ignition and we could plainly see on the TV screen that the bright exhaust plume (that was all one could see in the dark of the night) of the Athena II, suddenly and very briefly expanded as the exhaust of the burning 2nd Stage splashed off the top of the then dying and separated 1st Stage.

Unlike the 1st Stage burn, where the noise of lift-off, the breaking of the sound barrier, and the buffeting of the atmosphere presented dangers for the spacecraft, the only danger after 2nd Stage ignition was caused by the howling of the hot gasses inside the Castor 120, i.e., the pipe organ effect was at it again. However, unlike the 1st Stage burn, where there were 20 meters of rocket between the top of the burning stage and Lunar Prospector, Lunar Prospector was only 10 meters from the fiercely burning and howling Castor 120, 2nd Stage, so the howling was much more intense at the level of the spacecraft and certainly intense enough so that if there were an error in the design of Lunar Prospector, the consequences could have been serious. Regardless, the 2nd Stage burn began to die-out ninety-two seconds after 2nd Stage ignition or just three minutes and 1 second into the flight. As was the case for the 1st Stage burn, Launch Control kept reporting that we had a good launch trajectory — so far, so good.

After 2nd Stage burnout, the Athena II (minus the 1st Stage) coasted upwards for fifty-seven seconds, during which the shroud was to separate. Remembering that the shroud had failed to separate on the first LLV1 test launch and that the electrical connectors between the shroud and the adapter had had to be fixed by the launch preparation crew just two weeks before launch, I awaited shroud separation with some concern — for if it did not separate, the Lunar Prospector Mission would have, in effect, ended less than four minutes into its launch — the Athena II could not have even reached the parking orbit carrying along the heavy shroud, and even if it could have done so, the TLI Stage, and Lunar Prospector would have been destroyed as they tried to ram through the shroud at TLI Stage ignition. However, 52 seconds into the coast or 3 minutes and 53 seconds after launch, the shroud successfully separated and Launch Control announced the success of that critical event.

Five seconds later, at 3 minutes and 58 seconds into the flight, the two minute and 34 second burn of the Orbus solid fuel rocket 3rd Stage was to have begun. However, when that time came, no one at Athena Launch Control said a word about 3rd Stage ignition, so I thought it had failed to ignite! I immediately asked Kim what the status of the 3rd Stage burn was. It took two or three queries before Kim confirmed that the 3rd Stage was burning as planned — that was a relief! After the violent burns of the 1st and 2nd Stages, the 3rd Stage burn was relatively mild and posed no threat to the spacecraft. The worst of the launch was over. Finally, the Orbus burn came to its end and, throughout the $6\frac{1}{2}$-minute launch, everyone had remained pretty quiet in the Mission Ops, as I had requested.

Immediately after the 3rd Stage burnout, the 7-minute burn of the OAM liquid fuel engines began. That very low thrust burn was made to correct all the errors in the trajectory caused by the relatively crude burns of the first three, solid fuel stages of the Athena II rocket and when the OAM burn was finished, the OAM, the TLI Stage, and Lunar Prospector would start their 42-minute coast in Earth parking orbit, a coast that would bring the stack over the NW coast of Australia to the exact point in time and space where the critical TLI burn was supposed to occur. About 45 seconds after the OAM began its corrective burn, it and the payload went over the horizon with respect to the tracking station and we had LOS (Loss Of Signal) at –000/00:49 MET, as planned. The next time we would hear from Lunar Prospector, it would be at turn-on, assuming it did turn on and assuming TDRS did pick it up.

Thus, we had a little over $\frac{3}{4}$ of an hour during which we would be in radio silence. I said to my Mission Ops Team and my Support Teams outside the Glass Room, that we had time to go to the bathroom, get a coke and a candy bar or whatever and get prepared for the post-TLI burn activities — our job was about to begin. I was at the head of the pack going downstairs to relieve and refresh ourselves and I went back to the Glass Room in a few short minutes — ready for the main event.

After sitting down at my console, I checked all my screens. The way the Oasis system worked, I could have as many graphs or data tables, each being about 8 cm or so in dimensions, active on my computer screen as I wanted and I could have any number of graphs or data tables activated and stored as little icons — to be called up at a moment's notice. Given the size of my computer screen, I could get 10 or so of the most important graphs on my screen and several others iconized all over the place.

The graphics I absolutely needed to be able to monitor the health of the spacecraft were the battery voltage and current, the load current, the solar array current and temperature, the tank pressure and the temperatures of the 3 tanks (all on one graphic), the temperature of the 6 engines on two different graphs (one from 0 to 150° C to monitor their normal temperatures and the second from 0 to 1300° C to measure their temperatures during the burns), one of two status tables that indicated which subsystems were turned on, and which were turned off, and a command table which told me the status of a command when I sent one.

The data on those graphics were also color coded: green meaning the data were within the normal operational range of the subsystem or it was turned on; yellow meaning the data were getting close to the upper or lower limits of the operational range; and red meaning the data were higher or lower than the operation limits of that subsystem or it was turned off.

The normal status table had the subsystem identified with dark letters, while the status words, On and Off, were in green or red, respectively. However, our SIM training had shown me that if the subsystem identifiers were also color coded, I would not waste precious time reading the table when the spacecraft was first turned on. In a special table — the "Acquisition Status Table" — all the engineering subsystems were written in green, since they were supposed to be turned on during the automatic spacecraft turn-on sequence initiated by the TLI timer and all the science instruments were written in red, since they were supposed to be off until I turned them on. Hence, all I had to do was to quickly glance at the Acquisition Status Table and see if every subsystem that was written in green had a green status word next to it and that each subsystem that was written in red had a red status word next to it — without actually reading any of the words. The Acquisition Status Table would be the first thing I would look at when we started getting data from the spacecraft.

Similarly, Dan was checking his numerous graphs, Paul had his uplink command screen up, and John had a little of everything on his computer screen. We were ready for turn-on.